READER'S DIGEST CONDENSED BOOKS

READER'S DIGEST CONDENSED BOOKS

VOLUME 5 • 1973

THE READER'S DIGEST ASSOCIATION
PLEASANTVILLE, NEW YORK

The original editions of the books in this volume are published and copyrighted as follows:

All Creatures Great and Small, published at $7.95 by St. Martin's Press, Inc.,
© 1972 by James Herriot

The Salamander, published at $7.95 by William Morrow & Company, Inc.,
© 1973 by Compania Financiera Perlina S.A.

A Thousand Summers, published at $6.95 by Doubleday & Company, Inc.,
© 1973 by T.F.T. Corporation

Shipwreck: The Strange Fate of the Morro Castle, published at $7.95 by Stein and Day, Incorporated, © 1972 by Stein and Day, Incorporated

FIRST EDITION
96
 Library of Congress Catalog Card Number: 50-12721

PRINTED IN THE UNITED STATES OF AMERICA

CONTENTS

All Creatures Great and Small
The warm and joyful memoirs of an animal doctor
a condensation of the book by
James Herriot
illustrated by Don Stivers

"*All Creatures Great and Small* may well be the happiest book of the year."

—*The New York Times Book Review*

"There is a dedication here, not only to animals, not only to people, but to life itself."

—Baton Rouge *Advocate*

A born storyteller with a zestful love for life, James Herriot writes of his experiences as a rural veterinary doctor in the days before antibiotics, when stamina, skill and the gift of humanity were what counted most. His operating room might be a muck-filled stable, a sunny meadow or a simple Yorkshire cottage; his patients animals of the field or household pets. In his chosen environment and profession he finds satisfaction, joy and romance.

1

THEY didn't say anything about this in the books, I thought, as the snow blew in through the gaping doorway and settled on my naked back.

I lay face down on the cobbled floor in a pool of nameless muck, my arm deep inside the straining cow, my feet scrabbling for a toehold between the stones. I was stripped to the waist—it was still considered vaguely sissy to wear a calving overall in 1938—and the snow mingled with the dirt and dried blood on my body. I could see nothing outside the circle of flickering light thrown by the smoky oil lamp which the farmer held over me.

No, there wasn't a word in the books about searching for your instruments in the shadows; about trying to keep clean in a half bucket of tepid water; about the cobbles digging into your chest. Nor about the slow numbing of the arms, the creeping paralysis of the muscles as the fingers tried to work against the cow's powerful expulsive efforts. There was no mention anywhere of the gradual exhaustion and the little far-off voice of panic.

My mind went back to that picture in the obstetrics book. A cow standing in the middle of a gleaming floor with a sleek veterinary surgeon in a spotless overall. He was relaxed and smiling, the farmer and his helpers were smiling, even the cow was smiling. That man had just finished an excellent lunch and had stepped next door to do a bit of calving for the sheer pleasure of it, as a kind of dessert. He hadn't crawled shivering from his bed at two in the morning and bumped over twelve miles of frozen snow to a lonely mountain farm. He hadn't climbed half a mile of white hillside to the doorless stone barn where his patient lay.

I tried to wriggle my arm an extra inch inside the cow. The calf's head was back and I was painfully pushing a thin looped rope toward its lower jaw. The pressure on my arm from the cow's straining became almost unbearable, but if I didn't snare that jaw soon I would never get the calf out in one piece. I groaned, set my teeth and reached forward again. There is always a time at a bad calving when you begin to wonder if you will ever win the battle. I had reached this stage. For nearly two hours, pushing a noose around that little jaw had been my major goal in life. And I had tried everything else before that.

It had been a miserable session all through. The farmer, Mr. Dinsdale, was a long, sad, silent man who always seemed to be expecting the worst. He had a long, sad, silent son with him and the two of them had watched my efforts with deepening gloom. But worst of all had been Uncle. When I had first entered the hillside barn I had been surprised to see a little bright-eyed old man settling down comfortably on a bale of straw. He was filling his pipe and clearly looking forward to the entertainment.

"Now then, young man," he cried in the twang of Yorkshire's West Riding. "I'm Mr. Dinsdale's brother. From Listondale."

I nodded. "How do you do? My name is Herriot."

The old man looked me over piercingly. "My vet is Mr. Broomfield. Expect you'll have heard of him. Wonderful man, he is, especially at calving. Never seen 'im beat."

"I'm afraid I don't know Mr. Broomfield," I said as I peeled my shirt over my head. "But I haven't been here very long."

Uncle was aghast. "You don't know him! Well, you're the only one as doesn't." He shot a glance at my goose-pimpled torso. "Strips like a boxer does Mr. Broomfield. Never seen such muscles."

A wave of weakness coursed over me. I felt suddenly leaden-footed and inadequate. As I began to lay out my ropes and instruments on a clean towel the old man spoke again.

"And how long have you been qualified, may I ask?"

"Oh, about seven months."

"Seven months!" Uncle smiled indulgently, tamping down his tobacco. "Well, there's nowt like experience, I always says."

I tipped some antiseptic into the bucket, lathered my arms and knelt to make my exploration. Within seconds I would know whether I would be out of here in fifteen minutes or whether I had hours of hard labor ahead of me.

I was going to be unlucky this time; it was a nasty presentation. Head back and no room at all; more like being inside an undeveloped heifer than a second calver. And she was bone-dry. She had been running out on the high fields and had started to calve a week before her time; that was why they had had to bring her into this half-ruined barn.

"Head back, eh?" Uncle's penetrating voice cut through the silence. "You won't have much trouble, then. Mr. Broomfield turns the calf right round and brings it out back legs first."

I had heard this sort of nonsense before. A short time in practice had taught me that all farmers were experts with other farmers' livestock. And another phenomenon I had observed was that their advice was usually regarded as more valuable than the vet's. Like now, for instance; Uncle was an accepted sage.

I gasped as I felt my way around. "I'm afraid it's impossible to turn a calf completely in this small space."

The Dinsdales narrowed their eyes. Clearly they thought I was hedging.

And now, hours later, defeat was just around the corner. I was just about whacked. The Dinsdales watched me in morose silence and Uncle kept up a nonstop stream of comment. He hadn't had such a happy night for years. As I lay there, eyes closed, face stiff with dirt, mouth hanging open, he leaned forward on his straw bale. "You're about beat, young man," he said with deep satisfaction. "Well, I've never seen Mr. Broomfield beat, but he's had a lot of experience. What's more, he's strong. That's one man you couldn't tire."

Rage flooded through me like a draft of strong spirit. The right thing to do, of course, would be to get up, tip the bucket of cold bloody water over Uncle's head, run down the hill and drive away; away from Yorkshire, from Uncle, from this cow.

Instead I clenched my teeth, braced my legs and pushed with everything I had; and with a sensation of disbelief I felt my noose slide into the calf's mouth. Gingerly, muttering a prayer, I pulled and felt the slipknot tighten. At last I had hold of that jaw.

"Now hold this rope, Mr. Dinsdale, and just keep a gentle tension on it. I'm going to push the calf back, and if you pull steadily at the same time, the head ought to come round."

"What if the rope comes off?" asked Uncle hopefully.

I didn't answer. I put my hand in against the calf's shoulder and began to push against the cow's contractions. "Now a steady pull, Mr. Dinsdale, without jerking." And to myself, Oh God, don't let it slip off.

I felt the small body move. The head was coming around. I could feel the neck straighten against my arm. I let go the shoulder, grabbed the little muzzle and guided the head till it was resting where it should be, on the forelimbs. Quickly I extended the noose till it reached behind the ears. "Now pull on the head as she strains."

"Nay, you should pull on the legs now," cried Uncle.

"Pull on the bloody headrope, I tell you!" I bellowed, and felt immediately better as Uncle retired, offended, to his bale.

In a moment the little animal lay motionless on the cobbles, eyes glassy and unseeing, tongue blue and grossly swollen.

"Bound to be dead," grunted Uncle, returning to the attack.

I cleared the mucus from the mouth, blew hard down the throat and began artificial respiration. The calf gave a gasp and the eyelids flickered. Then it started to inhale and one leg jerked.

Uncle scratched his head in disbelief. "By gaw, it's alive. I'd have thowt it'd sure to be dead after you'd messed about all that time." A lot of the fire had gone out of him.

"I know what this little fellow wants," I said, and pulled the calf up to its mother's head. The cow was stretched out on her side, her eyes closed; she looked past caring about anything. Then she felt the little body against her face and there was a transformation; her eyes opened wide and her muzzle began a snuffling exploration of the new object. Her interest grew with every sniff and she struggled onto her chest with a deep rumbling noise and began to lick him methodically. Nature provides the perfect stimulant massage for a time like this, and the little creature arched his back as the coarse tongue dragged along his skin. Within a minute he was shaking his head and trying to sit up.

I grinned. This was the bit I liked. The little miracle. It was something that would never grow stale no matter how often I saw it. I cleaned as much of the caked filth from my body as I could, but most of it would have to wait for the hot bath at home. Pulling my shirt over my head, I felt as though I had been beaten for a long time with a thick stick. Every muscle ached. My mouth was dried out, my lips almost sticking together.

A long, sad Dinsdale hovered near me. "How about a drink?"

I could feel my grimy face cracking into an incredulous smile. A vision of hot tea well laced with whisky swam before me. "That's very kind of you, Mr. Dinsdale. I'd love a drink."

"Nay," said Mr. Dinsdale steadily. "I meant for the cow."

I began to babble. "Oh yes, certainly, by all means give her a drink. She must be very thirsty. It'll do her good."

I gathered my tackle and stumbled out into the wind. Uncle's voice, strident and undefeated, followed me down the slope.

"Mr. Broomfield doesn't believe in giving a drink after calving. Says it chills the stomach."

Oh well, everything had worked out just great. If only vetting just consisted of treating sick animals. But it didn't. There were so many other things.

IT WAS hot in the rickety little bus the day I first saw the Yorkshire Dales. The July sun beat on the windows and I shifted uncomfortably in my best suit. It was a foolish outfit for this weather, but a few miles ahead a prospective employer was waiting for me and I had to make a good impression.

There was a lot hanging on this interview; a newly qualified veterinary surgeon in this year of 1937 emerged from college, after a hard five years' slog, faced by a world indifferent to his enthusiasm and bursting knowledge. Agriculture was depressed by a decade of government neglect, and the draft horse, which had been the mainstay of the profession, was fast disappearing. So many of my friends were unemployed or working as laborers in the shipyards that when the letter came from Darrowby I had grabbed at the lifeline unbelievingly. Mr. Siegfried Farnon M.R.C.V.S. would like to see me on Friday afternoon; I was to come to tea and if we were mutually suited I could stay on as assistant.

The driver crashed his gears again as he went into another steep bend. We had been climbing steadily now for the last fifteen miles or so, moving closer to the blue swell of the Pennines. I had never been in this part of England before, but its name, Yorkshire, had always raised a picture of a county as stodgy and unromantic as its pudding; I was prepared for a total lack of charm. But as the bus groaned its way higher I began to wonder. The formless heights were resolving into heathery hills that they call fells in this country. Fences and hedges gave way to dry stone walls, countless miles of them, bordering the roads, enclosing fields and solid gray stone farmhouses, and tracing their patterns high on the green uplands.

But as I neared my destination, horror stories from college kept forcing their way into my mind; tales of assistants who were starved and worked into the ground. I rubbed my sweating palms on my knees and tried to concentrate on the man I was going to meet. Siegfried Farnon. Strange name for a vet in the Yorkshire Dales. Probably a German who had done his training in this country. The image of a hulking, cold-eyed, bristle-skulled Teuton kept obtruding. I cursed my fevered imagination.

I realized suddenly that the bus was clattering along a narrow street. Above an unpretentious grocer shop I read DARROWBY CO-OPERATIVE SOCIETY. We had arrived.

I got out and stood beside my battered suitcase, looking about me. Darrowby didn't get much space in the guidebook, but when it was mentioned it was described as a gray little town on the river Darrow with a cobbled marketplace and little of interest except its two ancient bridges. But when you looked at it, its setting was beautiful on the pebbly river where the houses clustered thickly and straggled unevenly along the lower slopes of Herne Fell. Everywhere in Darrowby, in the streets, through the windows of the houses, you could see the fell rearing its calm green bulk more than two thousand feet above the rooftops.

There was a clarity in the air and a sense of space that made me feel I had shed something on the plain, twenty miles behind. The confinement of the city, the grime, the smoke—already they seemed to be falling away from me.

Trengate was a quiet street leading off the square and I had my first sight of Skeldale House. I knew it was the right place before I was near enough to read S. FARNON M.R.C.V.S. on the old-fashioned brass plate hanging askew on the iron railings. I knew by the ivy which climbed untidily over the mellow brick to the topmost windows. It was what the letter had said—the only house with ivy. I felt breathless, as though I had been running. If I got the job, this was where I would find out about myself. There were many things to prove.

I liked the look of the old Georgian house with its fine white-painted doorway and wide graceful windows. The paint was flaking and the mortar looked crumbly between the bricks, but there was a changeless elegance about the place.

I rang the doorbell and instantly the afternoon peace was shattered by a distant baying like a wolf pack in full cry. The upper half of the door was of glass and, as I peered through, a river of dogs poured around the corner of a long passage and dashed itself with frenzied yells against the door. If I hadn't been used to animals I would have turned and run for my life. After a minute I realized that my first rough count of about fourteen was exaggerated. There were, in fact, five: a huge fawn greyhound, a cocker spaniel, a Scottie, a whippet and a tiny short-legged hunt terrier. I was thinking of ringing the bell again when I saw a large woman in the passage. She rapped out a single word and the noise stopped as if by magic. When she opened the door the ravening pack was slinking around her feet, wagging their tucked-in tails. I had never seen such a servile crew.

"Good afternoon," I said with my best smile. "My name is Herriot. James Herriot."

The woman nodded and looked at me with grim benevolence, but evidently the name struck no spark.

"Mr. Farnon is expecting me. He asked me to come today."

"Mr. Herriot?" she said thoughtfully. "Surgery is from six to seven o'clock. If you wanted to bring a dog in—"

"No, no," I said, hanging on to my smile. "I'm applying for the position of assistant. Mr. Farnon said to come for tea."

"Assistant? Well, now, that's nice." The lines in her face softened a little. "I'm Mrs. Hall. I keep house for Mr. Farnon. He said nothing to me about you, but never mind, come in and have a cup of tea. He shouldn't be long." I followed her down tiled passages and was beginning to wonder how far back the house extended when she showed me into a sunlit room.

It had been built in the grand manner, high-ceilinged and airy, with a massive fireplace flanked by arched alcoves. One end was taken up by a French window which gave on a long walled garden. I could see unkempt lawns, a rockery and many fruit trees. Above and beyond were the green hills with their climbing walls.

Ordinary-looking furniture stood around on a very worn carpet. Hunting prints hung on the walls, and books were scattered everywhere. A pewter pint pot occupied a prominent place at one end of the mantelpiece. It was an interesting pot. Checks and bank notes had been stuffed into it till they bulged out of the top and overflowed onto the hearth beneath. I was studying this with astonishment when Mrs. Hall came in with a tea tray.

"I suppose Mr. Farnon is out on a case," I said.

"No, he's gone through to Brawton to visit his mother. I can't really say when he'll be back." She left me with my tea and the dogs, who arranged themselves in various chairs from which they regarded me with friendly boredom.

A feeling of letdown gripped me; I had screwed myself up for an interview and I was left dangling. This was all very odd. Why should anyone write for an assistant, fix a time to meet him and then go to see his mother? Another thing—if I was engaged, I was to live in this house, yet the housekeeper had never heard of me.

My musings were interrupted by the doorbell ringing, and the dogs, as if touched by a live wire, leaped screaming into the air. There was no sign of Mrs. Hall so I went out to the front door, where the dogs were putting everything into their fierce act.

"Shut up!" I shouted and the din switched off. I opened the door and looked into a round eager face. Its owner, a plump man in rubber boots, leaned confidently against the railings.

"Hello, 'ello, Mr. Farnon in?"

"Not at the moment. Can I help you?"

"Aye, tell 'im Bert Sharpe has a cow wot wants borin' out."

"Boring out?"

"That's right, she's nobbut going on three cylinders."

"Three cylinders?"

"Aye, and if we don't do summat she'll go wrang in 'er ewer, won't she?"

"Very probably."

"Don't want felon, do we?"

"Certainly not."

"Okay, you'll tell 'im, then. Ta-ta."

I returned thoughtfully to the sitting room. This was disconcerting. I had listened to my first case history without understanding a word of it.

I had hardly sat down when the bell rang again. This time I unleashed a frightening yell which froze the dogs in midair; they took the point and returned, abashed, to their chairs.

Outside the front door a lovely red-haired girl was standing. She smiled. "Good afternoon," she said in a loud well-bred voice. "I am Diana Brompton. Mr. Farnon is expecting me for tea."

I gulped. "He's asked *you* to tea?"

The smile became fixed. "Yes, that is correct," she said, spelling the words out carefully. "He asked me to tea."

"I'm afraid he isn't home. I can't say when he will be."

The smile was plucked away. "Oh," she said, and she got a lot into the word. "At any rate, perhaps I could come in."

"Oh, certainly, do come in. I'm sorry," I babbled, suddenly conscious that I had been staring openmouthed at her.

She brushed past me down the passage and disappeared into the sitting room. Clearly she knew her way about. I tiptoed past the door and broke into a gallop which took me along another thirty yards of twisting passage to a huge stone-flagged kitchen.

"Mrs. Hall, there's a young lady, a Miss Brompton. She's come to tea, too." I had to fight an impulse to pluck at her sleeve.

Mrs. Hall didn't seem surprised. "You go and talk to her and I'll bring a few more cakes," she said.

"But what the heck am I going to talk to her *about?* How long is Mr. Farnon going to be?"

"Oh, just chat for a bit. I shouldn't think he'll be long."

When I opened the door the girl turned quickly with the makings of another big smile until she saw it was only me. "Perhaps you'd join me in a cup of tea while you wait," I said.

She gave me a quick glance which raked me from my rumpled hair to my scuffed old shoes. Then she shrugged her shoulders and turned away. A heavy silence blanketed the room. I poured a cup of tea and held it out to her. She ignored me and lit a cigarette. This was going to be tough, but I could only try.

I cleared my throat and spoke lightly. "I've only just arrived myself. I hope to be the new assistant."

She didn't trouble to look at me. She just said, "Oh."

"Lovely part of the world, this," I said.

"Yes."

"I've never been in Yorkshire before, but I like what I've seen."

"Oh."

"Have you known Mr. Farnon very long?"

"Yes."

"I believe he's quite young—about thirty?"

"Yes."

"Wonderful weather. . . ." I kept at it with courage and tenacity for about five minutes, but finally Miss Brompton, instead of answering, took the cigarette from her mouth and gave me a long blank stare. I shrank into silence.

After that she sat staring out of the French window, pulling deeply at her cigarette. As far as she was concerned I just wasn't there. So I was able to observe her at will and she was interesting. I had never met a living piece of a society magazine before. Cool linen dress, expensive-looking cardigan, elegant legs, and the glorious red hair falling on her shoulders. And yet here was a fascinating thought. She was sitting there positively hungering for a hulking German vet. This Farnon must have something.

The tableau was finally broken up when she jumped to her feet, hurled her cigarette savagely into the fireplace and marched from the room.

Wearily I got out of my chair and shuffled through the French window into the garden. My head ached. I flopped down in the deep grass and rested my back against a towering acacia tree. Where the devil was Farnon? Had somebody played a horrible practical joke on me? I felt suddenly cold. I had spent my last few pounds getting here. If there was some mistake, I was in trouble.

But, looking around me, I began to feel better. The sunshine beat back from the high old walls, bees droned among the bright masses of flowers, a gentle breeze stirred the magnificent wisteria which almost covered the back of the house. There was peace here.

I leaned my head against the bark and closed my eyes. I could see Herr Farnon, looking as I had imagined him, standing over me. "Wass is dis you haff done?" he spluttered, his jowls quivering with rage. "You kom to my house under false pretenses, you insult Fräulein Brompton, you trink my tea, you eat my food. Vat else you do, *hein?* You steal my spoons? You talk about assistant but I vant no assistant. Is best I telephone the police." Herr Farnon seized the phone. Even in my dream I wondered how the man could use such a completely corny accent. "Hello, hello," he said.

And I opened my eyes. Somebody was saying "Hello," but it wasn't Herr Farnon. A tall thin man was leaning against the wall, his hands in his pockets. Something seemed to be amusing him. As I struggled to my feet he held out his hand. "Sorry you've had to wait. I'm Siegfried Farnon."

He was just about the most English-looking man I had ever seen. Long, humorous, strong-jawed face. Untidy sandy hair. Old tweed jacket and shapeless flannel trousers. I shook my head to get my eyes fully open and tufts of grass fell from my hair. "There was a Miss Brompton here," I blurted out. "She came to tea. I explained you had been called away."

"Mm, yes—never mind that. But I do apologize for being out when you arrived. I have a shocking memory and I just forgot."

It was the most English voice, too.

Farnon gave me a long searching look, then he grinned. "Let's go inside. I want to show you round the place."

"THIS," he said, with a secret gleam in his eye as though he were about to unveil the mysteries of Aladdin's cave, "is the dispensary."

The dispensary was an important place in the days before penicillin and the sulfonamides. Rows of gleaming Winchester bottles lined the white walls from floor to ceiling. I savored the familiar names: SWEET SPIRITS OF NITRE, TINCTURE OF CAMPHOR, CHLORODYNE, FORMALIN, SAL AMMONIAC, SUGAR OF LEAD, LINIMENTUM, PERCHLORIDE OF MERCURY, RED BLISTER. The lines of labels were comforting. Here I was an initiate among old friends. I had painfully accumulated their lore. I knew their origins, actions and uses, and their maddeningly varied dosage. The examiner's voice: "And what is the dose for the horse? And the sheep? And the dog?" These shelves held the vet's entire armory against disease, and on a bench under the window I could see the instruments for compounding them—the graduated vessels and beakers, the mortars and pestles. And underneath, in an open cupboard, the medicine bottles, corks of all sizes, pillboxes, powder papers.

As we moved around, Farnon's manner became more and more animated. His eyes glittered and he talked rapidly. "Look, Herriot, have you seen this trick?"

He placed a few crystals of resublimated iodine on a glass dish and added a drop of turpentine. Nothing happened for a second, then a dense cloud of purple smoke rolled heavily to the ceiling. He bellowed with laughter at my startled face. "Like witchcraft, isn't it? I use it for wounds in horses' feet. The chemical reaction drives the iodine deep into the tissues."

"It does?"

"Well, I don't know, but that's the theory, and anyway, you must admit it looks wonderful. Impresses the toughest client."

Some of the bottles on the shelves fell short of the ethical standards I had learned in college. Like the one labeled COLIC DRENCH and another with the legend UNIVERSAL CATTLE MEDICINE in ornate script—*A sovereign Remedy for coughs, chills, scours, pneumonia, milk fever, garget and all forms of indigestion.* At the bottom of the label, in flaring black capitals, was the assurance, NEVER FAILS TO GIVE RELIEF.

Farnon had something to say about most of the drugs. Each one had its place in his five years' experience of practice; they all had their fascination, their individual mystique. Many of the bottles were beautifully shaped, with Latin names cut deep into their sides; names familiar to physicians for centuries. The two of us stood gazing at the gleaming rows without any idea that it was nearly all useless and that soon the old drugs would be hustled into oblivion by the headlong rush of new discoveries.

"This is where we keep the instruments." Farnon showed me into another little room. The small-animal equipment lay on green baize shelves, very neat and impressively clean. The large-animal instruments mostly hung from hooks on the walls. Many of the instruments, too, were soon to be museum pieces.

We finished up in the operating room, with its bare white walls, high table, oxygen and ether anesthetic outfit, and a small sterilizer. Farnon smoothed the table with his palm. "Not much small-animal work in this district. But I'm trying to encourage it. It makes a pleasant change from lying on your belly in a cowhouse. A lot of the old hands won't look at a dog or a cat, but the profession has got to change its ideas."

He went over to a cupboard in the corner and opened the door.

I could see the glass shelves with scalpels, artery forceps, suture needles, bottles of catgut in spirit. An auroscope. An ophthalmoscope. "Well, what do you think of it all?"

"Great," I replied. "I'm really impressed." Then, as we walked back to the sitting room, I told him about Bert Sharpe. "Something about boring out a cow which was going on three cylinders and her ewer and felon—I didn't get it."

Farnon laughed. "He wants a Hudson's operation done on a blocked teat. Ewer is the udder and felon the local term for mastitis. We'd better get out there. I have another visit on the way—I'll show you a bit of the district."

Outside, Farnon motioned me toward a battered Hillman. I shot a startled glance at the treadless tires, the rusty bodywork, the almost opaque windshield with its network of fine cracks. What I didn't notice was that the passenger seat was not fixed to the floor. I dropped into it and went over backward, landing with my head on the rear seat and my feet against the roof. Farnon helped me up, apologizing with great charm, and we set off.

Once clear of the marketplace, the road dipped quite suddenly and we could see all of the Dale stretching away from us in the evening sunshine. The outlines of the great hills were softened in the gentle light, and a broken streak of silver showed where the river Darrow wandered on the valley floor. Farnon was an unorthodox driver. Apparently captivated by the scene, he drove slowly down the hill, elbows resting on the wheel, his chin cupped in his hands. At the bottom of the hill he came out of his reverie and spurted to seventy miles an hour. The old car rocked crazily along the narrow road and my movable seat slewed from side to side as I jammed my feet against the floorboards. Then he slammed on the brakes, pointed out some pedigree Shorthorns and jolted away again. That was the bit that worried me. All his attention was on the countryside around and behind him.

We left the road at last, made our way along a gated lane and drew up in a farmyard. "Lame horse here," Farnon said. A strapping Clydesdale gelding was brought out and we watched attentively as the farmer trotted him up and down.

"Which leg do you make it?" my colleague asked. "Near fore? I think it must be. Like to examine it?"

I put my hand on the foot, feeling how much hotter it was than the other. I tapped the wall of the hoof with a hammer. The horse flinched, raised the foot and held it trembling for a second before replacing it carefully on the ground. "Looks like pus in the foot to me."

"I'll bet you're right," Farnon said. "They call it gravel around here, by the way. What do you suggest we do about it?"

"Open up the sole and evacuate the pus."

"Right." He held out a hoof knife. "I'll watch your technique."

With the uncomfortable feeling that I was on trial, I tucked the foot between my knees. I knew what I had to do—find the dark mark on the sole where the infection had entered and follow it down till I reached the pus. I scraped away the caked dirt and found not one but several marks. After more tapping to find the painful area I selected a likely spot and started to cut.

The horn seemed as hard as marble and only the thinnest shaving came away with each twist of the knife. The horse appeared to appreciate having his sore foot lifted off the ground and gratefully leaned his full weight on my back. He hadn't been so comfortable all day. I groaned and dug him in the ribs with my elbow, but he went right on leaning.

I swore quietly. The mark I was cutting into was growing fainter, then disappeared. I started on another. With my back breaking and the sweat trickling into my eyes, I knew that if this one petered out, too, I would have to let the foot go and take a rest. And with Farnon's eye on me I didn't want to do that.

Agonizingly, I hacked away. My knees began an uncontrollable trembling. The horse rested happily, his fifteen hundredweight cradled by this thoughtful human. I was wondering how it would look if I finally fell flat on my face, when, under the knife blade, I saw a thin spurt of pus.

"There it goes," the farmer grunted. "He'll get relief now."

I enlarged the drainage hole and dropped the foot. It took me a long time to straighten up.

"Well done, Herriot." Farnon took the knife from me. "It just isn't funny when the horn is as hard as that."

He gave the horse a shot of tetanus antitoxin, then said, "I wonder if you'd hold up the foot for a second while I disinfect the cavity." I gripped the foot between my knees as Farnon filled the hole with iodine crystals and added some turpentine. I watched, fascinated, as the billowing purple curtain spread.

I could locate the farmer only by his spluttering noises. Then the smoke began to clear and a pair of round startled eyes came into view. "By gaw, Mr. Farnon, I wondered what the 'ell had happened for a minute," the farmer said between coughs. He looked at the blackened hole in the hoof and spoke reverently. "It's wonderful what science can do nowadays."

Mr. Sharpe was our next visit. He led us into the byre and Farnon gestured toward the cow. "See what you make of it."

I squatted down and palpated the teat, feeling the mass of thickened tissue halfway up. It would have to be broken down by a Hudson's instrument, and I began to work the thin metal spiral up the teat. One second later I was sitting gasping in the dung channel, with the neat imprint of a cloven hoof on my shirtfront just over the solar plexus.

It was embarrassing, but there was nothing I could do but sit there fighting for breath, my mouth opening and shutting, like a stranded fish.

Mr. Sharpe held his hand over his mouth, his innate politeness at war with his natural amusement at seeing the vet come to grief. "I'm sorry, young man. This is a very friendly cow. She allus likes to shake hands." Overcome by his wit, he rested his forehead on the cow and went into a paroxysm of mirth.

I took my time to recover. Then, with Mr. Sharpe holding the nose and Farnon the tail, I managed to get the instrument in and clear the obstruction; but though the precautions cramped the cow's style a little, she still got in several telling blows on my arms and legs. When it was over the farmer grasped the teat and sent a long white jet frothing on the floor. "Capital! She's going on four cylinders now!"

"WE'LL GO HOME a different way," Farnon said. "Over the Brenkstone Pass and down Sildale. I'd like you to see it."

We climbed a steep winding road, with the hillside falling sheer to a dark ravine where a rocky stream rushed headlong to gentler country below. On the top, we got out of the car. A wild panorama of tumbling fells and peaks rolled away and lost itself in the crimson and gold ribbons of the western sky. Just to the east a black mountain overhung us, menacing in its naked bulk. Huge squarecut boulders littered the lower slopes. I whistled softly. This was different from the friendly hill country I had seen on the way to Darrowby.

Farnon turned toward me. "Yes, one of the wildest spots in England. A fearsome place in winter."

I pulled the clean air deeply into my lungs. A curlew cried faintly and I could just hear the roar of the torrent a thousand feet below.

It was dark when we got into the car and started the long descent into Sildale. We came to a silent village and Farnon applied his brakes violently. I tobogganed effortlessly across the floor on my mobile seat and collided with the windshield. My head made a ringing sound against the glass, but Farnon didn't seem to notice. "There's a grand little pub here. Let's go in."

The pub was something new to me. It was, simply, a large kitchen, square and stone-flagged. An enormous fireplace and an old black cooking range took up one end. A kettle stood on the hearth and a single large log hissed and crackled, filling the room with its resinous scent. About a dozen men sat on the high-backed benches which lined the walls. In front of them, rows of pint mugs rested on the oak tables fissured and twisted with age.

There was a silence as we went in. Then somebody said politely, "Now then, Mr. Farnon," and this brought some friendly grunts and nods from the company. They were mostly farmers taking their pleasure without fuss. Most were burned red by the sun and some of the younger ones were tieless, muscular necks and chests showing through the open shirtfronts. Soft murmurs and clicks rose from a peaceful domino game in the corner.

Farnon guided me to a seat, ordered two beers and turned to face me. "Well, you can have this job if you want it. Four quid a week and full board. Okay?"

The suddenness struck me silent. I was in. And four pounds a week! Four pounds a week was affluence.

"Thank you," I said, trying hard not to look triumphant. "I accept."

2

THE past five years of training had been leading up to one moment and it hadn't arrived yet. I had been in Darrowby for three days and still hadn't been to a visit on my own. I had gone around with Farnon and had met more of the clients. But for a man who seemed careless, forgetful and a few other things, he was frustratingly cautious about launching his new assistant. And working under his supervision was like being back at college with the professor's eye on me. I felt strongly that my professional career would not start until I, James Herriot, went out and attended a sick animal unaided and unobserved.

The time came—it was not in fact as long as it seemed—when Farnon went off to Brawton to see his mother again. A devoted son, I thought wonderingly. And he had said he would be back late, so the old lady must keep unusual hours. Never mind—I was in charge. I sat in an armchair, looking through the French window at the shadows thrown by the evening sun across the shaggy lawn, and wondered what my first call would be. Probably an anticlimax—like a pig with constipation. And maybe that would be no bad thing—to start with something I could easily put right. The telephone exploded these comfortable musings.

"Is that Mr. Farnon?" The voice had a harsh edge to it.

"No. I'm sorry, he's out. This is his assistant."

"When will he be back?"

"Not till late, I'm afraid. Can I do anything for you?"

"I am Mr. Soames, Lord Hulton's farm manager. I have a valuable hunting horse with colic. Do you know anything about colic?"

My hackles rose. "I should. I am a veterinary surgeon."

There was a long pause and the voice barked, "I reckon you'll have to do. In any case, I know what the horse wants. Bring some arecoline. And don't be all night getting here."

My face felt hot as I heard the receiver bang down. So my first case wasn't going to be a formality. Colics were tricky things and I had an aggressive know-all called Soames thrown in. On the eight-mile journey, pages from that great classic, Caulton Reeks's *The Common Colics of the Horse*, hovered in front of me, phantomlike, as I drove the tiny Austin of almost forgotten vintage which had been allotted to me.

This would probably be a mild impaction or a bit of spasm. Might have had a change of food or too much rich grass. A quick shot of arecoline, maybe some chlorodyne to relieve the discomfort, and all would be well. There was nothing to it, really.

I was elaborating this happy picture as I drove into a spotless graveled yard surrounded on three sides by box stalls. A man was standing there—a thickset figure, trim in checked cap and jacket, well-cut breeches and shiny leggings. As I got out of the car the man slowly and deliberately turned his back on me and stood motionless, hands in pockets. When I tired of looking at his back I spoke. "Mr. Soames?"

Very slowly the man turned. His small fiery eyes took in the worn raincoat, my youth, my air of inexperience.

"Yes, I am Mr. Soames." He stressed the "Mr." His gaze was directed into the sky. "I am a very great friend of Mr. Farnon."

"My name is Herriot."

Soames didn't appear to have heard. "Clever man, Mr. Farnon."

"I understand you have a horse with colic." I wished my voice didn't sound so high and unsteady.

Soames jerked his head toward one of the boxes. "In there. One of his lordship's best hunters. In need of expert assistance." Emphasis on the "expert."

I opened the door and went inside. And I stopped as though I had walked into a wall. It was a very large box, bedded with peat moss. A bay horse, staggering around and around, had worn a deep path in the peat. He was lathered in sweat from nose to tail, his nostrils dilated, his eyes staring blankly in front of him. His head rolled about at every step, and through his clenched teeth gobbets of foam dripped to the floor. A rank steam rose from his body as though he had been galloping. My mouth went dry. "How long has he been like this?"

"Had a bit of bellyache this morning. I've been giving him black drafts all day, or at least this fellow has—if he hasn't made a mess of it like he does everything."

I saw that there was somebody standing in the shadows in the corner of the box; a large fat man with a halter in his hand.

"Oh, I got the drafts down him, Mr. Soames. But they haven't done 'im no good." The big man looked scared.

"If I'd done the job myself he'd have been better by now."

"It would take more than a black draft to help him," I said. "This is no ordinary colic."

"What the hell is it, then?"

"Well, I can't say till I've examined him, but severe continuous pain like that could mean a torsion—a twisted bowel."

"Twisted bowel, my foot! He hasn't passed anything all day and he wants something to shift him. Have you got the arecoline?"

"If this is a torsion, arecoline would be the worst thing you could give him. He's in agony now, but that would drive him mad. It acts by contracting the muscles of the intestines."

"Don't give me a bloody lecture," snarled Soames. "Are you going to start doing something for the horse or aren't you?"

"Slip on that halter, would you?" I asked the man.

With the halter on, the horse was brought to a stop. He stood there, trembling and groaning, as I passed a hand between ribs and elbows, feeling for the pulse. It was as bad as it could be—a racing thready beat. The mucous membrane under the eyelid was a dark brick red. The thermometer read a hundred and three.

"May I have hot water, soap and a towel, please, Mr. Soames?"

"You've done nothing yet and you want to have a wash?"

"I want to make a rectal examination. I need water, please."

Soames swung around on the big man. "Come on, don't stand

there. Get him his water and we'll maybe get something done."

When the water came I soaped my arm and gently began to examine the horse. My hand could feel plainly the displacement of the small intestine on the left side and a tense tympanitic mass. As I touched it the animal shuddered and groaned again. My heart pounded. What was I to do? What could I say?

Soames was stamping in and out of the box as the pain-maddened animal writhed and twisted. "Hold him!" he bellowed at the horseman.

I took a deep breath. "I'm convinced this horse has a torsion."

"All right, then, but do something, will you?"

"There's nothing anybody can do. There is no cure for this. The important thing is to put him out of his pain, and quickly."

"No cure? Rubbish! Just what are you getting at?"

I took a hold on myself. "I suggest you let me shoot him now, straightaway. I have a humane killer in the car."

"What do you mean?" Soames's mouth fell open. "Are you stark-raving mad? Do you know what that horse is worth?"

"It makes no difference what he's worth, Mr. Soames. He has been going through hell all day and he's dying. You should have called me out long ago. He might live a few hours more, but the end would be the same. And he's in dreadful continuous pain."

Soames sank his head in his hands. "Oh God, why did this have to happen? His lordship is on holiday or I'd call him to make you see some sense. I tell you, your boss would have that horse put right in half an hour. Look here, can't we wait for Mr. Farnon to have a look at him?"

Something in me leaped at the idea. Give a shot of morphine and get away out of it. Leave the responsibility to somebody else. Then I looked again at the horse, stumbling around and around in a despairing attempt to leave his agony behind. He raised his lolling head and gave a little whinny. It was a desolate, uncomprehending, frantic sound and it was enough for me.

I strode quickly and got the killer from the car. "Steady his head," I said to the big man and placed the muzzle between the glazing eyes. There was a sharp crack. The horse thudded on the peat. Soames was staring at the body in disbelief. "Mr. Farnon will carry out a postmortem in the morning. I'd like Lord Hulton to have my diagnosis confirmed," I said, and went out to my car.

Soames, furious, pushed his head in the window. "I'll let Mr. Farnon know what kind of an assistant he's landed himself with. You'll be proved wrong and I'm going to sue you."

I decided to wait up for my boss, and I sat there trying to rid myself of the feeling that I'd blasted my career before it had started. Yet, no matter how often I went over it, the conclusion was always the same. It was one a.m. before Farnon got back. His evening with his mother had stimulated him. He was flushed and smelled pleasantly of gin. I was surprised to see that he was wearing evening dress, and though the dinner jacket was of old-fashioned cut and hung in loose folds on his bony frame, he still managed to look like an ambassador.

He listened in silence as I told him about the horse. He was about to comment when the phone rang. "Oh, it's you, Mr. Soames." He nodded at me and settled down in his chair. He was a long time saying "Yes" and "No" and "I see," then he sat up decisively and began to speak.

"Thank you for ringing, Mr. Soames, and it seems as though Mr. Herriot did the only possible thing in the circumstances. No, I cannot agree. One of our duties is to prevent suffering. Well, I'm sorry you feel like that, but I consider Mr. Herriot to be a highly capable veterinary surgeon. I'd have done the same thing. Good night, Mr. Soames. I'll see you in the morning."

I felt overwhelmed with gratitude.

Farnon reached for a bottle of whisky. He slopped some into two tumblers and pushed one at me. Leaning back in his armchair, he looked up with a smile. "Well, you certainly got chucked in at the deep end, my boy. Your first case! And Soames, too."

"Do you know him very well?"

"I know him for a nasty piece of work. He'd put anybody off their stroke. Rumor has it he's been feathering his nest for years at his lordship's expense. He'll slip up one day."

The neat whisky burned a fiery path to my stomach, but I needed it. "I wouldn't like too many sessions like tonight's, but I don't suppose veterinary practice is like that all the time."

"Well, not quite," Farnon replied. "But it's a funny profession, ours, you know. It offers unparalleled opportunities for making a chump of yourself, even if you're a positive genius. Animals are unpredictable things, so our whole life is unpredictable. It's a long tale of little triumphs and disasters and you've got to really like it to stick it. Tonight it was Soames, tomorrow it'll be something else. One thing, you never get bored. Here, have some more whisky."

We talked on and on, until the dark bulk of the acacia tree began to emerge from the gray light beyond the French window. A blackbird tried a few tentative pipes and Farnon yawned, jerked the knot out of his tie and looked at his watch. "Five o'clock. Who would have thought it? Well, we did have to celebrate your first case. It was a right one, wasn't it?"

Two and a half hours' sleep was a meager ration, but I made a point of being downstairs, shaved and scrubbed, by eight. Mrs. Hall, impassively placing scrambled eggs before me, told me that my employer had left some time ago to do the PM on Lord Hulton's horse. I wondered if he had bothered to go to bed at all.

I was busy with the last of the toast when he burst into the room, in excellent spirits. "Anything left in that coffeepot?" He crashed down on a protesting chair. "Well, you've nothing to worry about. The PM showed a classic torsion. Several loops of bowel involved—black and tympanitic. I'm glad you put the poor beggar down straightaway."

"Did you see my friend Soames?"

"Oh, he was there. I pointed out that he had delayed far too long in sending for us and that Lord Hulton wasn't going to be pleased when he heard how his horse had suffered. I left him chewing over that."

The news did a lot to lighten my outlook. I went over to the desk and got the daybook. "Here are this morning's calls. What would you like me to do?"

Farnon picked out a round of visits and handed me a scribbled list. "A few nice trouble-free cases for you," he said. "Oh, there's one other thing. My young brother is hitching from Edinburgh today. He's at the veterinary college there and the term finished yesterday. When he gets within striking distance he'll probably give us a ring. I wonder if you'd pick him up?"

"Certainly. Glad to."

"His name is Tristan, by the way."

"Tristan?"

"Yes. Oh, I should have told you. You must have wondered about my own queer name. Music ruled my father's life—mainly Wagner. We got it morning, noon and night. And then to be stuck with a name like Siegfried!"

It was late afternoon before the call came. The voice was uncannily familiar. "This is Tristan Farnon."

"Gosh, you sound just like your brother."

A pleasant laugh answered. "So everybody says."

I went to give him a lift. However his voice may have sounded, the small boyish-faced figure sitting on a rucksack could hardly have looked less like his brother except for the charm of the smile that greeted me.

"Had much walking to do?" I asked.

"Oh, a fair bit, but I needed the exercise. We had a roughish end-of-term party last night." He settled himself in the seat beside me as though it were a luxurious armchair, pulled out a packet of Woodbines and lit one with tender concentration.

"You'll have just finished exams?" I said.

"Yes, pathology and parasitology."

I almost asked if he had passed, but I stopped myself in time. There was no shortage of conversation, though, and I felt a growing conviction that I was in the presence of a quicker and livelier mind than my own. It seemed no time at all before we pulled up outside Skeldale House.

Siegfried was out and it was early evening when he returned. He came in through the French window, gave me a friendly greeting and threw himself into an armchair. He had begun to talk about one of his cases when Tristan walked into the room.

The atmosphere changed as though somebody had clicked a switch. Siegfried's smile became sardonic. He gave his brother a long appraising look, grunted "Hello," then reached up and began to run his finger along the books in the alcove beside his chair. He seemed absorbed in this for a few minutes and I could feel the tension building up. Tristan's face had gone deadpan, but his eyes were wary.

Siegfried finally took down a book and leafed through it. Without looking up he said quietly, "Well, how did the exams go?"

Tristan took a deep breath. "Parasitology's all right."

Siegfried appeared to have found something interesting in his book. He took his time over it, then stood up and began looking for another. With his back to his brother, he spoke again in the same soft voice. "How about pathology?"

Tristan was on the edge of his chair now, as if ready to make a run for it. "Didn't get it," he said tonelessly.

There was no reaction from Siegfried. He kept up the patient search, occasionally glancing at a volume, then replacing it carefully. At last he dropped back in his chair and looked at Tristan. "So you failed pathology," he said conversationally.

I was surprised to hear myself babbling with an edge of hysteria in my voice. "Well now that's pretty good you know. It puts him in the final year and he can sit pathology at Christmas so he won't lose any time. It's a tough subject."

Siegfried turned a cold eye on me. There was a silence which was broken by a totally unexpected bellow as he rounded on his brother. "I think it's a damned disgrace! What the hell have you been doing all this term? Boozing, chasing women, spending my money, anything but working. And now you've got the nerve to walk in here and tell me you've failed pathology." His face was darkly flushed and his eyes glared. "You're bone idle!" he yelled. "I've had enough. I'm sick of you. You're sacked, do you hear me? Sacked once and for all. So get out of here—I don't want to see you around anymore. Go on, get out!"

Tristan, preserving an air of injured dignity, withdrew.

Writhing with embarrassment, I looked at Siegfried. His face had gone blotchy; he drummed his fingers on the arm of the chair. I was aghast at having witnessed this breakup and I was grateful when Siegfried noticed my presence and sent me out on a call.

It was dusk when I drove back into the yard, and I saw Tristan standing by the door.

I felt as though I were intruding on the poor fellow. "Sorry about the way things turned out," I blurted.

The tip of his cigarette glowed as he took a long pull. "No, no, that's all right. Could have been a lot worse, you know."

"But what are you going to do? Where are you going to sleep?"

"I can see you don't understand." I saw the gleam of very white teeth as Tristan smiled. "Don't worry, I'm sleeping here. I'll see you at breakfast. Siegfried's always sacking me and he always forgets. The only tricky bit this time was getting him to swallow that bit about the parasitology."

I stared at the shadowy form. There was a rustling as the rooks stirred in the tall trees. "The parasitology?"

"If you think back, all I said was that it was all right."

"Then you mean . . . ?"

Tristan laughed softly and thumped my shoulder. "I failed it, too. Don't worry, I'll pass them both at Christmas."

I SPENT a lot of time in the next few weeks wondering where Tristan fitted into the setup at Skeldale House. Was he supposed to be seeing practice, having a holiday, working or what? But it soon became clear that he was a factotum who dispensed and delivered medicines, washed the cars, answered the phone and even, in an emergency, went to a case. At least, that was how Siegfried saw him, and he had a repertory of tricks aimed at keeping Tristan on his toes. Like returning unexpectedly or bursting into a room in the hope of catching him doing nothing.

Tristan interpreted his role rather differently from his brother and did, in fact, devote a considerable amount of his acute intelligence to the cause of doing as little as possible. When he was left behind to dispense while we were out on our rounds, he followed an unvarying procedure. He half filled a sixteen-ounce bottle with

water, added a few drams of chlorodyne and a little ipecac, pushed the cork in and took it through to the sitting room to his favorite chair. It was a wonderful chair for his purpose—old-fashioned and high-backed, with wings to support the head. There he would settle down with his *Daily Mirror* and his Woodbines. If Siegfried rushed in on him he grabbed the bottle and started to shake it madly, inspecting the contents at intervals. Then he went through to the dispensary, filled up the bottle and labeled it. It was a sound workable system, but it had one big snag. He never knew whether it was Siegfried or not when the door opened, and often I walked in and found him staring up with startled, sleep-blurred eyes while he agitated his bottle. Siegfried's victories, in fact, were few. Tristan's gift for quick comeback, after what looked like devastating defeat, was prodigious.

Most evenings found him sitting on a high stool at the bar counter of the Drovers' Arms, conversing effortlessly with the barmaid. At other times he would be out with one of the young nurses from the local hospital, which he seemed to regard as an agency to provide him with female company. All in all, he managed to lead a fairly full life.

SATURDAY night, ten thirty p.m., and I was writing up my visits when the phone rang. I swore and lifted the receiver.

"Hello. Herriot speaking."

"It's you, is it?" a voice growled. "Ah want Farnon."

"I'm sorry, Mr. Farnon is out. Can I help you?"

"I 'ope so, but I'd raither 'ave your boss. This is Sims."

(Oh no, not Sims on a Saturday night. Miles up in the hills.)

"Yes, Mr. Sims, and what is the trouble?"

"Ah'll tell you, my gurt big show 'oss has cut 'isself badly on the hind leg, just above the hock. I want him stitched."

(Glory be! Above the hock! What a place to have to stitch a horse. This is going to be a real picnic.)

"How big is the wound, Mr. Sims?"

"It's a gurt big thing about a foot long and bleedin' like 'ell. And this 'oss is as wick as an eel. Ah can't get near 'im."

(Damn you, Mr. Sims, and damn your gurt 'oss.)

"Well, I'll be along straightaway. Try to have some men handy just in case we have to throw him."

"Throw 'im? You'd never throw this 'oss. Anyways, Mr. Farnon wouldn't want a lot of men to help 'im."

(Oh lovely, lovely. This is going to be one for the diary.)

"Very well. I'm leaving now, Mr. Sims."

"My road's washed out. You'll 'ave to walk the last mile and a half. Get a move on and don't keep me waiting all night."

(This is just a bit much.)

"Look here, Mr. Sims, I don't like your tone. I said I would leave now and I will get there just as soon as I can."

"You don't like ma tone, eh? Well, ah don't like useless young apprentices. You know nowt about t'damn job, anyways."

(That finally does it.)

"Now just listen to me, Sims. If it wasn't for the horse I'd refuse to come out at all. Who do you think you are, anyway? If you ever try to speak to me like that again—"

"Now, now, Jim, get a grip on yourself. That temper of yours, you know. You'll burst a blood vessel."

"Tristan! Where the hell are you?"

"The phone booth outside the Drovers'. Thought I'd give you a ring."

"I'll murder you one of these days if you don't stop this game. It's the third time this week."

"Ah, but Jim, this was by far the best. When you started drawing yourself up to your full height—it nearly killed me. If you could have heard yourself." He trailed off into helpless laughter.

Every day at Skeldale House began with the phone ringing around seven o'clock, after the farmers had had the first look at their stock. Our only phone then was downstairs in the long tiled passage, and Siegfried had delegated to Tristan the job of taking these early calls. The Monday after "Sims" had called me from the Drovers' Arms, I huddled under my blankets and listened to the ringing. It went on and on. There was no sound from Tristan's room and I waited for the next move in the daily drama. It came with a door crashing back on its hinges and the sound of Siegfried bounding down the stairs three at a time. I could picture him shivering in the drafty passage, his bare feet freezing on the tiles as he listened to some animal's symptoms. I heard the mad pounding of feet on the stairs as he made a dash for his brother's room, and the yell of rage. Tristan, trying to snatch the extra few seconds, was caught between the sheets. "Why didn't you answer the phone? Don't tell me you're deaf as well as idle! Come on, out of it, out, out!"

This morning, as usual when he was caught in bed, Tristan scored a point by being halfway through his breakfast before his brother had dressed and come down. I watched Siegfried's face as he walked in and saw Tristan happily munching his toast, his *Daily Mirror* balanced against the coffeepot. It was as if Siegfried had a sudden acute toothache.

I felt the strain badly when the brothers were at variance, and I escaped to collect my things for the morning rounds. Down the narrow passage, with its familiar exciting smell of ether and carbolic, and out into the high-walled garden which led to the yard where the cars were kept. It was the same every morning, but to me there was always the feeling of surprise when I stepped out into the sunshine—the scent of the flowers and the clear air which held a breath of the moorland; it was difficult to take it all in. Life was full for me. There were so many things to find out and a lot I had to prove to myself. The days were quick and challenging. But I never hurried through the garden. I'd look back before going out through the door into the yard, and it was like suddenly coming across a picture in an old book—the empty wild garden with fruit trees everywhere and flowers blazing in untidy profusion, the tall silent house beyond. I could never quite believe it was there and that I was a part of it.

The feeling of the past was heightened in the yard. It was square and cobbled and the grass grew in thick tufts between the stones. Buildings took up two sides: the two garages, which had once been coach houses; a stable and saddle room, a box stall and a pigsty. Behind the garage doors hanging crazily on their hinges was the Austin. Often it wouldn't start. But this morning, surprisingly, the engine coughed at once into life.

As I drove around the corner of the back lane I had the feeling every morning that this was where things really got started. The problems and pressures of my job were waiting for me out there, and at the moment I seemed to have plenty.

I had arrived in the Dales, I felt, at a bad time. The farmers, after a generation of neglect, had seen the coming of a prophet, the wonderful new vet, Mr. Farnon. He appeared like a comet, trailing his new ideas in his wake. He was able, energetic and charming and they received him as a maiden would a lover. And now, at the height of the honeymoon, I had to push my way into the act, and I just wasn't wanted. Tristan's impersonation of Sims had touched a raw nerve.

I was beginning to get used to their questions: "Where's Mr. Farnon?" "Is he ill or something?" "I expected Mr. Farnon." It was uphill work examining an animal when its owner was chafing in the background, wishing that I was somebody else. But I had to admit they were fair. When I got my jacket off and really worked at the job, they would thaw a little. And "Come in and have a bit o' dinner" was an invitation I heard nearly every day. Sometimes I could accept, and I ate some memorable meals with them. Often, too, they would slip eggs or butter into the car as I was leaving. Hospitality was traditional in the Dales, and knowing that a core of friendliness lay under an often unsmiling surface helped. I liked these people. They had a toughness and a philosophical attitude which was new to me. Misfortunes which would make the city dweller want to bang his head against a wall were shrugged off with, "Aye, well, these things happen."

It looked like being another hot day and I wound down the Austin's windows as far as they would go. I was on my way to do a tuberculin test; the national scheme was beginning to make its first impact in the Dales, and the more progressive farmers were asking for survey tests. And this was no ordinary herd. Mr. Copfield's Galloway cattle were famous. "The toughest lot in this practice," Siegfried had told me. "Eighty-five of them and none has ever been tied up. They live out on the fells, they calve and rear their calves outside. They're practically wild animals."

"What do you do with them when they're sick?" I had asked.

"Well, you have to depend on Frank and George—the Copfield sons. They've been reared with those cattle since they were babies—started tackling the little calves as soon as they could walk, then worked up to the big ones."

Frank and George were not as I expected. The durable men who helped me in my daily jobs tended to be dark and lean, with stringy muscles. The Copfields were good-looking young men about my age, golden-haired and smooth-skinned, but their wrestlers' arms and spread of shoulder were formidable.

The cattle had been herded into the buildings, and they just about filled a long passage down the side of the fold yard. I looked at the black untamed animals and they looked back at me, their reddish eyes glinting through the rough fringe of hair which fell over their faces. They kept up a menacing bad-tempered swishing with their tails. It wasn't going to be easy to get an intradermal injection into every one of them. I turned to Frank.

"Can you catch these beggars?" I asked.

"We'll give it a good try," he replied, throwing a halter over his shoulder. He and his brother lit cigarettes before climbing into the passage where the biggest beasts were packed. I soon found that the tales of Galloway cattle weren't exaggerated. If I approached them from the front they came at me with their great hairy heads, and if I went behind them they kicked me as a matter of course. But the brothers amazed me. One of them would drop a halter on a beast, get his fingers into its nose and then be carried away as the animal took off like a rocket. They were thrown about like dolls, but they never let go; the thing that fascinated me was that through all the contortions the cigarettes dangled undisturbed.

The affair was conducted in the spirit of a game, with encouraging shouts like "Sniggle 'im, George" or "Thou 'as 'im, Frank." In moments of stress they cursed softly and without heat.

They both stopped work and laughed with sincere appreciation when one cow slashed me in the face with her muck-sodden tail; and another little turn which was well received was when I was filling my syringe with both arms raised and a bullock, backing in alarm from Frank's halter, crashed its craggy behind into my midriff. The wind shot out of me in a sharp hiccup, then the animal decided to turn around in the narrow passage and squashed me like a fly against the railings, rendering me popeyed.

The smallest calves, though, were the most difficult. The shaggy little creatures kicked, bucked, ran through our legs and even hurtled straight up the walls. Often the brothers had to throw themselves on top of them and bear them to the ground before I could inject them, and when they felt the needle they bawled deafeningly; outside, the anxious mothers bellowed back in chorus.

It was midday when I reeled out of the buildings. I seemed to have been a month in there, in the suffocating heat, the continuous din, the fusillade of muck. Frank and George produced a bucket of water and a scrubbing brush and gave me a rough cleanup. But a mile from the farm I drove off the road and dropped down on the cool fellside. Throwing wide my arms, I wriggled my shoulders and my sweat-soaked shirt into the tough grass and let the sweet breeze play over me. My ribs ached and so did my legs, from a dozen kicks. I knew I didn't smell so good either. With the sun on my face, I closed my eyes and grinned at the ridiculous thought that I had been conducting a diagnostic investigation for tuberculosis back there. A strange way to carry out a scientific procedure; a strange way, in fact, to earn a living.

But then I might have been in an office with windows tight shut against petrol fumes and traffic noise, desk light shining on columns of figures, my bowler hat hanging on the wall. Lazily I watched a cloud shadow riding over the face of the green hill across the valley. No, no . . . I wasn't complaining.

I HARDLY noticed the passage of the weeks as I rattled along the moorland roads on my daily rounds; but the district was beginning to take shape, the people to emerge as separate personalities. Most days I had a puncture. The tires were through to the canvas on all wheels; it surprised me that they took me anywhere at all. But it was a fine summer, and mending a puncture was no penance on those high unfenced roads with the wheeling curlews for company. And I found other excuses to get out and sit on the crisp grass and look out over the airy roof of Yorkshire. It was like taking time out of life. Time to get things into perspective. Everything was so different: this countryside after years of city streets, the release from exams and study, the job with its daily challenge. And then there was my boss.

Siegfried Farnon charged around the practice with fierce energy from dawn till dark and I often wondered what drove him on. It wasn't money, because he treated it with scant respect. When the bills were paid, the cash went into the pint pot on the mantelpiece and he grabbed handfuls when he wanted it. I never saw him take out a wallet, but his pockets bulged with loose silver and balled-up notes. When he pulled out a thermometer they flew around him in a cloud.

He dashed off the list of calls each morning with such speed that I was quite often sent to the wrong farm or to do the wrong thing. When I told him of my embarrassment he would laugh heartily. Then one day he got caught himself. I had just taken a call from a Mr. Heaton of Bronsett about doing a PM on a dead sheep.

"I'd like you to come with me, James," Siegfried said. "I believe they teach you blokes a pretty hot postmortem procedure. I want to see you in action."

In Bronsett, Siegfried swung the car left into a gated lane.

"Where are you going?" I said. "Heatons' is the other way."

"But you said Seatons'."

"No, I assure you—"

"Look, James. I was right by you when you were talking to the man. I distinctly heard you say the name."

I opened my mouth to argue further, but the car was hurtling down the lane and Siegfried's jaw was jutting. I decided to let him find out for himself. We arrived at the farmhouse with a screaming of brakes. Siegfried was out and rummaging in the trunk before the car had stopped shuddering. "Hell!" he shouted. "No postmortem knife. Never mind, I'll borrow something from the house."

He beamed at the farmer's wife who answered the door. "Good morning, Mrs. Seaton, have you a carving knife?"

The good lady raised her eyebrows. "What was that you said?"

"A carving knife, Mrs. Seaton, and a good sharp one, please."

"You want a carving knife?"

"Yes, a carving knife!" Siegfried's scanty store of patience was beginning to run out. "And I wonder if you'd mind hurrying. I haven't much time."

The bewildered woman withdrew and I could hear whispering and muttering. Children's heads peeped out to get a quick look at Siegfried stamping irritably on the step. After some delay one of the daughters timidly held out a long dangerous-looking knife.

Siegfried snatched it and ran his thumb up and down the edge. "This is no damn good!" he shouted in exasperation. "Don't you understand I want something really sharp? Fetch me a steel."

The girl fled back into the kitchen. It was some minutes before another young girl was pushed around the door. She gave Siegfried the steel at arm's length and dashed back to safety.

Siegfried prided himself on his skill at sharpening a knife. As he stropped the knife on the steel, he warmed to his work and finally burst into song. When he had completed the job he peered inside the door. "Where is your husband?" he called.

There was no reply so he strode in, waving the gleaming blade. Mrs. Seaton and her daughters cowered in the corner, staring at Siegfried with frightened eyes. He made a sweeping gesture at them with the knife. "Well, come on, I can get started now!"

"Started what?" the mother whispered, clutching her family.

"To PM this sheep. You have a dead sheep, haven't you?"

Explanations and apologies followed.

Later Siegfried remonstrated gravely with me for sending him to the wrong farm. "You'll have to be more careful in future, James," he said. "Creates a very bad impression, that sort of thing."

ANOTHER THING about life with my boss which interested me was the regular traffic of women through Skeldale House. They were all upper class, mostly beautiful and they had one thing in common—eagerness. They came for drinks, for tea, for dinner, but the real reason was to gaze at Siegfried like parched travelers in the desert sighting an oasis. When their eyes passed over me without interest to fasten themselves hungrily on my colleague, I wasn't envious, but I was puzzled. I used to study him furtively, trying to fathom the secret of his appeal. There was something attractive in the long bony face and humorous blue eyes, that I could see, but a lot of the time he was so haggard and sunken-cheeked that he looked positively ill.

I often saw Diana Brompton there and every time had to fight down an impulse to dive under the sofa. She didn't seem like the brassy beauty of my first afternoon as she looked up meltingly at Siegfried, giggling like a schoolgirl. I used to grow cold at the thought that he might pick her out of the mob and marry her. It worried me a lot because I knew I would have to leave just when I was beginning to enjoy everything about Darrowby.

But Siegfried showed no sign of marrying any of them and as time went on I got used to it and stopped worrying. Time took care of other things, too.

3

I LOOKED again at the slip of paper where I had written my visits. "Dean, 3, Thompson's Yard. Old dog ill."

There were a lot of these "yards" in Darrowby. They were, in fact, tiny streets, uneven rows of little houses with no two alike, looking into each other's windows across eight feet of cobbles.

Number three, Thompson's Yard, looked as though it wouldn't be able to hold out much longer. The flakes of paint quivered on the rotten wood of the door as I knocked; above, the outer wall bulged dangerously on either side of a long crack in the masonry.

A small white-haired man answered. His face, pinched and lined, was enlivened by a pair of cheerful eyes; he wore a much-darned woolen cardigan, patched trousers and a pair of slippers.

"I've come to see your dog," I said, and the old man smiled.

"Oh, I'm glad you've come, sir. I'm getting a bit worried about the old chap. My missus used to think the world of him."

The grim evidence of poverty was everywhere in the house—in the fireless hearth, the dank musty smell. On the table the old man's solitary dinner was laid: a fragment of bacon, a few fried potatoes and a cup of tea. Life on the old-age pension.

In the corner, on a blanket, lay my patient, a crossbred Labrador. He lay quietly and looked at me without hostility.

"Getting on a bit, isn't he, Mr. Dean?"

"Aye, he is that. Nearly fourteen, but he's been like a pup galloping about until these last few weeks. Wonderful dog for his age, is old Bob, and he's never offered to bite anybody in his life. He's my only friend now—I hope you'll soon be able to put him right."

I looked at the dog with growing uneasiness. The abdomen was grossly distended and I could read the telltale symptoms of pain—the catch in the respirations, the anxious preoccupied expression in the eyes.

When his master spoke, the tail thumped twice on the blankets and a momentary interest showed in the white old eyes; but it quickly disappeared and the blank inward look returned.

I passed my hand carefully over the dog's abdomen. Ascites was pronounced and the dropsical fluid had gathered till the pressure was intense. "Come on, old chap," I said. "Let's see if we can roll you over." The dog whimpered but made no resistance as I eased him slowly onto his other side; the cause of the trouble was now only too easy to find. Through the thin muscle of the flank I could feel a hard corrugated mass—carcinoma, enormous and completely inoperable. I stroked the old dog's head as I tried to collect my thoughts. This wasn't going to be easy.

"Is he going to be ill for long?" the old man asked, and again came the thump, thump of the tail at the sound of the loved voice.

"Mr. Dean, I'm afraid this is something very serious. You see this large swelling. It is caused by an internal growth."

"You mean . . . cancer?" the little man said faintly.

"I'm afraid so, and it has progressed too far for anything to be done. I wish there were something I could do, but there isn't."

The old man's lips trembled. "Then he's going to die?"

I swallowed hard. "We really can't just leave him to die, can we? He's in distress now and it will soon be an awful lot worse. Don't you think it would be kindest to put him to sleep? After all, he's had good long innings." I always aimed at a brisk approach, but the old clichés had an empty ring.

The old man slowly knelt down by the dog. He did not speak, but ran his hand again and again over the gray old muzzle and the ears, while the tail thump-thumped on the floor. After a long time he struggled to his feet and gulped once or twice. Without looking at me he said huskily, "All right, will you do it now?"

I filled the syringe and said the things I always said. "You needn't worry, this is absolutely painless. Just an overdose of an anesthetic. It is really an easy way out for the old fellow."

The dog did not move as the needle was inserted, and, as the barbiturate began to flow into the vein, the anxious expression left his face and the muscles began to relax. By the time the injection was finished the breathing had stopped.

"Is that it?" the old man whispered.

"Yes, that's it," I said. "He is out of his pain now."

The old man stood motionless except for the clasping and unclasping of his hands. When he turned to face me his eyes were bright. "That's right, we couldn't let him suffer, and I'm grateful to you. And now, what do I owe you for your services, sir?"

"Oh, that's all right, Mr. Dean," I said quickly. "It's nothing—nothing at all. I was passing right by here—it was no trouble."

The old man was astonished. "But you can't do that for nothing."

"Now please say no more about it, Mr. Dean. As I told you, I was passing right by your door."

As I walked to my car I heard a shout behind me. The old man was shuffling toward me. His cheeks were streaked and wet, but he was smiling.

"You've been very kind, sir. I've got something for you." He held out a small brown object and I looked at it. It was tattered but just recognizable as a precious relic of a bygone celebration.

"Go on, it's for you," said the old man. "Have a cigar."

IT WAS unfortunate that Siegfried ever had the idea of delegating the bookkeeping to Tristan, because Skeldale House had been passing through a period of peace and I found it soothing.

For nearly a fortnight there had been hardly an angry word. Autumn had come with a sharpness in the air, and at nights the log fire burned bright in the big room. It was always a good time when the work of the day was through and the three of us lay back in the shabby armchairs and stretched our feet out to the blaze. Tristan was occupied with the *Daily Telegraph* crossword, which he did every night. Siegfried was reading. I was dozing, because it embarrassed me to be drawn into the crossword; Tristan could have the whole thing worked out while I wrestled with the first clue. The carpet around our feet was hidden by the dogs, all five of them, draped over each other in heavy-breathing layers and adding to the atmosphere of camaraderie and content.

Then Siegfried spoke. "Market day tomorrow and the bills have just gone out. They'll be queuing up to give us their money so I want you, Tristan, to devote the entire day to taking it from them. James and I are going to be busy, so you'll be in sole charge. All you have to do is take their cash, give them a receipt and enter their names in the receipt book. Now do you think you can manage that without making a hash of it?"

I winced. It was a discordant note and it struck deep.

"I think I might just about cope," Tristan replied haughtily.

But next day it was easy to see that the assignment was right up Tristan's street. Stationed behind the desk, he took in the money in handfuls, and all the time he talked. But he did not talk at random; each character got a personal approach. At teatime he was cock-a-hoop, presenting Siegfried with a column of neat figures accurately totaled at the bottom. "Thank you, Tristan, very efficient." All was sweetness.

At the end of the day I was putting the Austin in the garage when Tristan came panting into the yard from the garden. "Jim, I've lost the receipt book!"

"Always pulling my leg." I laughed. "Give it a rest!"

"I'm not joking, Jim, believe me. I really have lost it."

"You can't have," I said. "It's bound to turn up."

"It'll never turn up." Tristan did a bit of pacing on the cobbles. "I've ransacked the house. It's gone, I tell you."

"But you've put all the names down in the ledger, haven't you?"

"That's just it. I haven't. I was going to do it tonight."

"So that means that all the farmers who have been handing you money today are going to get the same bill next month?"

"Looks like it. I can only remember two or three names."

I sat down heavily on the stone trough. "These Yorkshire lads don't like parting with their brass once, but when you ask them to do it twice—oh, brother! How about Siegfried? Have you told him yet?"

A spasm crossed Tristan's face. "No, he's just come in. I'm going to do it now." He squared his shoulders and strode off.

I decided not to follow him to the house. I didn't feel strong enough for the scene which was bound to follow. Instead I took off for the Drovers' Arms.

THE receipt book was never found, and a month later all the bills were sent out again, timed, as usual, to arrive on market-day morning. By midmorning of that day I had finished my rounds. I didn't go into the house, because I could see through the window that one waiting room was crammed with farmers, all wearing the same offended self-righteous expression.

I stole away to the marketplace. Whenever I had time I enjoyed moving among the stalls which crowded the ancient square. You could buy fruit, fish, secondhand books, cheeses, clothes, in fact nearly everything; but the china stall was my favorite. It was run by a Jewish gentleman from Leeds with a hypnotic selling technique. I never got tired of watching him. He was in his best form today, and I was standing there deeply content when I saw a burly figure in a checked cap waving wildly at me from the edge of the crowd. He had his hand inside his jacket and I knew what he was feeling for. I didn't hesitate, but dodged quickly behind a stall laden with pig troughs. I had gone only a few steps before another farmer hailed me purposefully. He was brandishing an envelope. I saw only one way of escape. I plunged through the doorway of the Drovers' Arms and into the manager's office, out of sight of the bar, which was full of farmers. I was safe; this was one place where I was always welcome.

The manager looked up from his desk, but he did not smile. "Look here," he said sharply. "I brought my dog in to see you some time ago. In due course I received an account from you." I cringed inwardly. "I paid by return. I was extremely surprised this morning to find that another account had been rendered. I have here a receipt signed by—"

I couldn't stand any more. "I'm very sorry, Mr. Brooke, but there's been a mistake. I'll put it right. Please accept our apologies."

This became a familiar refrain over the next few days, but it was Siegfried who had the most unfortunate experience. It was in the bar of his favorite pub, the Black Swan. He was approached by Billy Breckenridge, a jocular little man, one of Darrowby's worthies. "Hey, remember that three and six I paid at your surgery? I've had another bill for it."

Siegfried made a polished apology and bought him a drink.

The pity of it was that Siegfried, who seldom remembered anything, didn't remember this. A month later in the Swan, Billy wasn't so jocular. "Hey, I've had that bill again."

Siegfried did his best, but his charm bounced off the little man. He was offended. "I can see you don't believe I paid. I had a receipt from your brother, but I've lost it." He brushed aside Siegfried's protestations. "No, no, there's only one way to settle this. I say I've paid the three and six, you say I haven't. All right, I'll toss you for it."

Miserably, Siegfried demurred, but Billy was adamant. He produced a penny and with great dignity balanced it on his thumbnail. "Okay, you call."

"Heads," muttered Siegfried and heads it was. Still dignified, the little man handed three and six to Siegfried. "Perhaps we may consider the matter closed." He walked out of the bar.

Now there are all kinds of bad memories, but Siegfried's was of the inspired type. He somehow forgot to make a note of this last transaction, and at the end of the month Billy Breckenridge received a fourth request for the amount which he had already paid twice. It was about then that Siegfried changed his pub and started going to the Cross Keys.

As autumn wore into winter and the high tops were streaked with the first snows, the discomforts of practice in the Dales began to make themselves felt. Driving for hours with frozen feet, climbing to the high barns in biting winds. The interminable stripping off in drafty buildings and the washing of hands and chest in buckets of icy water, using scrubbing soap and often a piece of sacking for a towel.

I really found out the meaning of chapped hands. When there was a rush of work, my hands were never quite dry and the little red fissures crept up almost to my elbows.

This was when small-animal work came as a blessed relief. To step out of the rough hard routine; to walk into a warm drawing room instead of a cowhouse and tackle something less formidable than a horse or a bull. And among all those comfortable drawing rooms there was none so beguiling as Mrs. Pumphrey's.

Mrs. Pumphrey was an elderly widow. Her late husband, a beer baron whose breweries and pubs were scattered widely over the broad bosom of Yorkshire, had left her a vast fortune and a beautiful house on the outskirts of Darrowby. Here she lived with a large staff of servants, a gardener, a chauffeur and Tricki Woo. Tricki Woo was a Pekingese and the apple of his mistress' eye.

Standing now in the magnificent doorway, I could almost see the deep armchair drawn close to the leaping flames, the tray of biscuits, the bottle of excellent sherry. Because of the sherry, I was always careful to time my visits for just before lunch.

A maid answered my ring, beaming on me as an honored guest. Mrs. Pumphrey, in the high-backed chair by the fire, put down her book with a cry of delight. "Tricki! Tricki! Here is your uncle Herriot." I had been made an uncle very early and, sensing the advantages of the relationship, had made no objection.

Tricki, as always, bounded from his cushion, leaped onto the back of a sofa and put his paws on my shoulders. He then licked my face thoroughly before retiring, exhausted. He was soon exhausted because he was given roughly twice the amount of food needed for a dog of his size. And it was the wrong kind of food.

"Oh, Mr. Herriot," Mrs. Pumphrey said. "I'm so glad you've come. Tricki has gone flop-bott again."

This ailment, not to be found in any textbook, was her way of describing the symptoms of Tricki's impacted anal glands. When the glands filled up he showed discomfort by sitting down suddenly in midwalk and his mistress would rush to the phone in great agitation.

The cure for flop-bott was to hoist the little dog onto a table and, by pressure on the anus with a pad of cotton wool, evacuate the glands. It baffled me that the Peke was always so pleased to see me. Any dog who could still like a man who grabbed him and squeezed his bottom hard every time they met had to have an incredibly forgiving nature. But Tricki never showed any resentment; in fact he was an outstandingly equable little animal, bursting with intelligence, and I was genuinely attached to him. It was a pleasure to be his personal physician.

Lifting my patient from the table, I noticed the increased weight, the padding of extra flesh. "You're overfeeding him again, Mrs. Pumphrey. Didn't I tell you to cut out cake and give him more protein?"

"But Mr. Herriot," she wailed. "He's so tired of chicken."

I shrugged; it was hopeless. I allowed the maid to lead me to the palatial bathroom where my private guest towel was laid out next to the slab of expensive soap. I returned to the drawing room. The maid filled my sherry glass and I settled down by the fire to listen to Mrs. Pumphrey. It couldn't be called a conversation because she did all the talking, but I always found it rewarding.

Mrs. Pumphrey was likable, gave widely to charities and would help anybody in trouble. She was intelligent and amusing and had a lot of waffling charm; but most people have a blind spot and hers was Tricki Woo. The tales she told about her darling ranged far into the realms of fantasy, and I waited eagerly for the day's installment while the subject of it all snored on my lap. The maid struck fresh life into the fire and refilled my glass. The wind hurled a handful of sleet against the window. This, I thought, was the life. Mrs. Pumphrey went on.

"And did I tell you, Mr. Herriot, Tricki had another good win yesterday? You know, I'm sure he must study the racing columns, he's such a tremendous judge of form. Well, he told me to back Canny Lad in the three o'clock at Redcar yesterday and, as usual, it won. He put on a shilling each way and got back nine shillings."

These bets were always placed in the name of Tricki Woo. Losing a regular flow of shillings to a dog must have been a heavy cross for the local bookies to bear. I was thinking with compassion of these unfortunate men when Mrs. Pumphrey did one of her abrupt changes of subject.

"I had such a fright last week. I was sure I'd have to call you. Poor little Tricki. He went completely crackerdog!"

I mentally lined this up with flop-bott among the new canine diseases and asked for more information.

"The gardener was throwing rings for him—you know he does this for half an hour every day." I had witnessed this spectacle several times. Hodgkin, a dour old Yorkshireman who looked as though he hated all dogs and Tricki in particular, had to go out on the lawn every day and throw little rubber rings which Tricki would bound after and bring back.

Mrs. Pumphrey went on. "Well, Tricki does adore it so. But suddenly, without warning, he went crackerdog. He forgot all about his rings and began to run around in circles, barking and yelping in such a strange way. Then he fell over on

his side and lay like a dead little thing. Do you know, Mr. Herriot, I really thought he was dead? And what hurt me most was that Hodgkin began to *laugh.* In twenty-four years I've never even seen him smile, and yet, when he looked down at that still form, he broke into a queer high-pitched cackle. It was horrid. I was just going to rush to the telephone when Tricki got up and walked away—perfectly normal!"

Hysteria, I thought, brought on by wrong feeding and over-excitement. I fixed Mrs. Pumphrey with a severe glare. "Now look, this is just what I was talking about. If you persist in feeding him all that fancy rubbish you'll ruin his health. You really must get him onto a sensible dog diet. Two small meals a day at most, of meat and biscuit. And nothing in between."

Mrs. Pumphrey shrank into her chair, a picture of abject guilt. "Oh, please don't speak to me like that. I do try to give him the right things, but when he begs I can't refuse him."

I was unrelenting. "It's up to you. If you go on as you are doing, Tricki will go crackerdog more and more often."

I left the cozy haven with reluctance, pausing on the graveled drive to look back at Mrs. Pumphrey waving and Tricki, as always, standing against the window, his widemouthed face apparently in the middle of a hearty laugh.

Driving home I mused on the advantages of being Tricki's uncle. When he went to the seaside he sent me boxes of oak-smoked kippers; when the tomatoes ripened in his greenhouse he sent a pound or two every week. Tins of tobacco arrived regularly, with photographs carrying a loving inscription.

But it was not until the Christmas hamper arrived from Fortnum & Mason's that it came to me, suddenly, that I had been guilty of a grave error. Hitherto, I had rung up and thanked Mrs. Pumphrey and she had been rather cool, pointing out that it was Tricki who had sent the things. This time I set myself to compose a letter to Tricki. Avoiding Siegfried's sardonic eye, I thanked my doggy nephew for all his generosity. I expressed my sincere hopes that the festive fare of Christmas had not upset his delicate digestion and suggested that, if so, he should have recourse to the black powder his uncle always prescribed. A vague feeling of professional shame was easily swamped by floating visions of kippers, tomatoes and hampers. I addressed the envelope to Master Tricki Pumphrey, Barlby Grange, and slipped it into the postbox.

On my next visit Mrs. Pumphrey drew me to one side. "Mr. Herriot," she whispered. "Tricki adored your charming letter and he will keep it always, but he was very put out about one thing—you addressed it to Master Tricki, and he does insist upon Mister. He was quite beside himself at first, but when he saw it was from you he soon recovered his good temper. I can't think why he should have these little prejudices. Perhaps it is because he is an only dog. . . ."

Entering Skeldale House was like returning to a colder world. Siegfried bumped into me in the passage. "Ah, who have we here? Why I do believe it's dear Uncle Herriot. And what have you been doing, Uncle? Slaving away at Barlby Grange. Poor fellow. Is it worth it, working yourself to the bone for another hamper?"

4

THE BEST thing Christmas brought to Skeldale House was a distinct improvement in the atmosphere. Tristan, whose arrangements with the college authorities had baffled me for months—he was never there—had casually slipped back to Edinburgh and, apparently without doing any work, passed both exams.

One morning soon after that cheerful event he and I were in the dispensary mixing up the day's medicines when Siegfried came in. He seemed positively to glow with inner satisfaction.

"I've got a bit of good news," he announced.

I screwed a cork into a bottle. "Well, don't keep us in suspense. Let's have it."

Siegfried looked from one of us to the other and smiled benevolently. I smiled, too. I could see that this was going to be one of the happy mornings.

"You remember that awful shambles when Tristan took charge of the bills?"

Tristan ground furiously away at the nux vomica, but Siegfried laid a friendly hand on his shoulder. "No, don't worry." He was almost smirking. "From now on, the job will be done by an expert." He cleared his throat. "We're going to have a secretary."

As we stared blankly at him he went on. "Yes, I picked her myself and I consider she's perfect."

"Well, what's she like?" I asked.

"It's difficult to describe her. But just think—what do we want here? We don't want some flighty young thing hanging about the place. We don't want a pretty little blonde making eyes—"

"We don't?" Tristan interrupted, plainly puzzled.

"No, we don't!" Siegfried rounded on him. "Just when we'd got her trained to our ways she'd be running off to get married."

Tristan looked unconvinced, which seemed to exasperate his brother. Siegfried's face reddened. "And there's another thing. How could we have an attractive young girl in here with somebody like you in the house? You'd never leave her alone."

Tristan was nettled. "How about you?"

"I'm talking about you, not me!" Siegfried roared.

I closed my eyes. The peace hadn't lasted long. I decided to cut in. "All right, tell us about the secretary."

"Well, she's in her fifties, and she has retired after thirty years as company secretary with Green and Moulton in Bradford. They say she is a model of efficiency and that's what we want in this practice—efficiency. It's just a stroke of luck for us that she decided to come and live in Darrowby. Anyway, you'll meet her in a few minutes—she's coming at ten o'clock."

When the doorbell rang, Siegfried raced to answer it. "Gentlemen, I want you to meet Miss Harbottle," he said in triumph.

She was a big high-bosomed woman with a round healthy face and gold-rimmed spectacles. A mass of curls peeped from under her hat; they looked as if they might be dyed and they didn't go with her severe clothes. It occurred to me that we wouldn't have to worry about her rushing off to get married. It wasn't that she was ugly, but she had an air of effortless command that would send any man running for his life.

I shook hands and was astonished at the power of Miss Harbottle's grip. We looked into each other's eyes and had a friendly trial of strength for a second. Triss was entirely unprepared, and a look of alarm spread over his face as his hand was engulfed; he was released only when his knees started to buckle.

She began a tour of the office while Siegfried hovered behind her, rubbing his hands like a shopwalker with his favorite customer. She paused at the desk, heaped high with papers and stray boxes of pills and tubes of udder ointment. Stirring distastefully among the mess, she extracted our ledger. "What's this?"

Siegfried trotted forward. "We enter the visits into it from our daybook, which is here somewhere." He scrabbled about on the desk. "Ah, here it is."

She studied the two books with amazement. "You gentlemen will have to learn to write. There are three different hands here, but this one is by far the worst. Quite dreadful. Whose is it?"

"That's mine, actually," said Siegfried, shuffling his feet.

"It won't do, you know, Mr. Farnon."

Siegfried put his hands behind his back and hung his head.

"I expect you keep your stationery in here." She pulled open a drawer. It appeared to be filled entirely with ancient seed packets. Peas and beans rolled gently from the top of the heap. The next drawer was crammed tightly with soiled calving ropes. They didn't smell so good, but Miss Harbottle was not easily deterred and tugged hopefully at the third drawer. It came open with a musical clinking and she looked down on a dusty row of empty ale bottles.

She straightened up slowly and spoke patiently. "And where, may I ask, is your cashbox?"

"Well, we just stuff it in there, you know." Siegfried pointed to the pint pot on the corner of the mantelpiece.

Miss Harbottle looked at the pot with horror. "You just stuff it in, and you go out and leave that money there day after day?"

"Never seems to come to any harm," Siegfried replied.

"And how about your petty cash?"

Siegfried gave an uneasy giggle. "All in there, you know."

Miss Harbottle's ruddy face had lost some of its color. "*Really*, Mr. Farnon. I don't know how you have gone on like this. I simply do not know. However, there is obviously nothing complicated about your business. I'll put things right very quickly."

"Fine, Miss Harbottle, fine. Monday morning then?"

"Nine o'clock sharp, Mr. Farnon."

After she had gone there was a silence. Tristan was smiling thoughtfully. I felt uncertain. "A demon of efficiency, maybe," I said, "but isn't she a bit tough?"

"Tough?" Siegfried gave a loud, rather cracked laugh. "Not a bit of it. You leave her to me. I can handle her."

THERE was little furniture in the dining room, but the noble lines and the very size of the place lent grace to the long sideboard and the modest mahogany table where Tristan and I sat at breakfast. The single large window was patterned with frost, and in the street outside the footsteps of the passersby crunched in the crisp snow. I looked up from my boiled egg as a car drew up. There was a stamping in the porch, the outer door banged shut and Siegfried burst into the room. He made for the fire and hung over it. He was muffled almost to the eyes in greatcoat and scarf, but what you could see of his face was purplish blue.

"A milk fever up at old Heseltine's. One of the high buildings. God, it was cold up there. I could hardly breathe."

As he pulled off his gloves and shook his numbed fingers he darted sidelong glances at his brother. Tristan's chair was nearest the fire and he was enjoying his breakfast as he enjoyed everything, slapping the butter happily onto his toast and whistling as he applied the marmalade. You could almost see the waves of comfort and contentment coming from him.

Siegfried dragged himself unwillingly from the fire and dropped into a chair. "I'll just have a cup of coffee, James. Heseltine was very kind—asked me to sit down and have breakfast with him. He gave me a lovely slice of home-fed bacon—what a flavor!" He put down his cup with a clatter. "You know, there's no reason why we should have to buy bacon. There's a perfectly good pigsty in the yard. All our kitchen waste could go toward feeding a pig. We'd probably do it quite cheaply."

He rounded on Tristan, who had just lit a Woodbine and was shaking out his *Mirror* with the air of ineffable pleasure which was peculiar to him. "And it would be a useful job for you. You're not producing much. A bit of stockkeeping would do you good."

Tristan put down his paper as though the charm had gone out of it. "I feed your mare." He didn't enjoy looking after Siegfried's new hunter, because every time he turned her out to water in the yard she would take a playful kick at him in passing.

"It doesn't take all day. It won't kill you to take on the pigs."

"Pigs?" Tristan looked startled. "I thought you said pig."

"I've been thinking. If I buy a litter of weaners we can sell the others and keep one for ourselves. Won't cost a thing."

"Not with free labor, certainly."

"Labor? Labor? You don't know what it means! Look at you lying there puffing your head off on those bloody cigarettes!"

WHEN Siegfried got an idea he didn't muck about. Within forty-eight hours ten little pigs had taken up residence in the sty.

Right from the start Tristan found them fascinating. He spent a lot of time in the yard, sometimes feeding or cleaning out, but more often resting his elbows on the door watching his charges. It was their characters he was interested in. "Jim! Come over here and look at these little beggars." He laughed excitedly. "I've just given them their swill and it's a bit hot. Just look at them!"

The tiny animals were seizing the food, dropping it and walking suspiciously around it. Then they would creep up, touch the hot potatoes with their muzzles and leap back in alarm. There was none of the usual gobbling rush; just a puzzled grunting.

But no animal converts food more quickly into flesh than a pig. As the weeks passed the little pink creatures changed with alarming speed into ten solid no-nonsense porkers, and their characters deteriorated. They lost all their charm. Mealtimes stopped being fun and became a daily contest: broad greedy snouts forcing into the bucket Tristan carried to them, sharp feet grinding his toes, heavy bodies thrusting against his legs. And I couldn't help smiling when I remembered the lighthearted game it used to be. There was no laughter now. Tristan finally took to brandishing a heavy stick at the pigs before he dared to go into the sty. Once inside, his only hope of staying on his feet was to clear a little space by beating on the backs.

It was on a market day when the pigs had almost reached bacon weight that I came upon Tristan sprawled in his favorite chair. But there was something unusual about him; he wasn't asleep, no medicine bottle, no Woodbines, no *Daily Mirror.* His arms hung limply over the sides of the chair, his eyes were half closed and sweat glistened on his forehead. "Jim," he whispered. "I've had the most hellish afternoon I've ever had in my life."

I was alarmed at his appearance. "What's happened?"

"The pigs," he croaked. "They escaped today."

"Escaped! How the devil could they do that?"

Tristan tugged at his hair. "It was when I was feeding the mare. I gave her her hay and thought I might as well feed the pigs at the same time. You know what they've been like lately—well, today they went berserk. Soon as I opened the door they charged out in a solid block. Sent me up in the air, bucket and all, then ran over the top of me." He shuddered. "I'll tell you this, Jim, when I was lying there on the cobbles, covered with swill and that lot trampling on me, I thought it was all over. But they didn't savage me. They just belted out through the yard door at a full gallop."

"The yard door was open, then?"

"Too true. I would just choose this one day to leave it open." He sat up and wrung his hands. "Well, you know, I thought it was all right at first. You see, they slowed down when they got into the lane. Didn't seem to know where to go next. I was sure I could head them back in. But just then one of them caught sight of itself in Robson's shopwindow."

He gave a remarkable impression of a pig staring at its reflection, then leaping back with a startled grunt. "That did it. The animal panicked and shot off into the marketplace at about fifty miles an hour, with the rest after it."

I gasped. Ten large pigs loose among market-day crowds!

"Oh, you should have seen it." Tristan fell back wearily into his chair. "Women and kids screaming. The stall holders, police and everybody else cursing me. There was a terrific traffic jam, too—miles of cars tooting like hell while the policeman on duty concentrated on browbeating me." He wiped his forehead. "You know that fast-talking merchant on the china stall—well, he was balancing a cup on his palm and in full cry when one of the pigs got its forefeet on his stall and stared him straight in the face. He stopped as if he'd been shot. Any other time it would have been funny, but I thought the perishing animal was going to wreck the place—until it changed its mind and made off."

"What's the position now?" I asked. "Have you got them back?"

Tristan leaned back and closed his eyes. "With the help of almost the entire male population of the district I've got nine of them back. The tenth was last seen heading north at a good pace. God knows where it is now. Oh, I didn't tell you—one of them got into the post office. Spent quite some time in there." He put his hands over his face. "I'll be in the hands of the law after this lot, Jim."

"Oh, no, Triss. I don't suppose there's been any serious damage done."

Tristan replied with a groan. "There's something else. When I finally got the pigs back in their sty I was on the verge of collapse. I was leaning against the wall gasping for breath when I saw the mare had gone. Yes, gone. I'd run straight out after the pigs and forgot to close her box. I don't know where she is." He lit a trembling Woodbine. "This is the end, Jim. Siegfried will have no mercy this time."

As he spoke, the door flew open and his brother rushed in. "What the hell is going on?" he roared. "I've just been speaking to the vicar and he says my mare is in his garden eating his wallflowers. He's hopping mad and I don't blame him. Don't just lie there, get over to the vicarage this instant and bring her back!"

Tristan did not stir. He lay inert. His lips moved feebly. "No," he said.

"*What?*" Siegfried shouted incredulously. "Go get that mare!"

"No," replied Tristan. I felt a chill of horror. This sort of mutiny was unprecedented.

"If you want your mare get her yourself." His voice was quiet. He had the air of a man to whom the future is of no account.

Even Siegfried could see that this was one time when Tristan had had enough. He got the mare himself.

Nothing more was said about the incident, but the pigs were moved hurriedly to the bacon factory and were never replaced. The stockkeeping project was at an end.

I FLIPPED idly through the morning mail. The usual stack of bills, circulars, advertisements for new drugs. I had almost reached the bottom of the pile when I came on something different—an expensive-looking envelope in heavy deckle-edged paper. I pulled out a gilt-bordered card, which I scanned and quickly slipped into my pocket.

I could feel my face redden as Siegfried looked up at me. "What are you looking so guilty about, James?"

"Go on, then," I said sheepishly, pulling out the card and handing it to him. "Have a good laugh. You'd find out, anyway."

"'Tricki requests the pleasure of Uncle Herriot's company on Friday February fifth. Drinks and dancing,'" Siegfried read aloud. "You know, that must be one of the most generous Pekingeses in England. Sending you hampers isn't enough—he has to ask you to his home for a party."

"All right, all right, I know. But what am I supposed to do?"

"Do? What you do is to sit down right away and get a letter off saying thank you very much, you'll be there on February the fifth. Mrs. Pumphrey's parties are famous. Mountains of exotic food, rivers of champagne. Don't miss it, whatever you do."

"I don't fancy it. Will there be a lot of people there?"

Siegfried struck himself on the forehead with his open hand. "Of course! Did you think it would be just you and Tricki? The cream of the county will be there in full regalia, and there will be no more honored guest than Uncle Herriot. Why? Because Mrs. Pumphrey invited the others, but Tricki invited you."

"Okay, okay," I groaned. "I haven't got a proper suit."

"My dear chap, don't mess about. Accept. Then go into Brawton and hire a suit. The debs will be tramping over each other to dance with you." He rose and put a hand on my shoulder. "And for Pete's sake, reply to Tricki himself or you're sunk."

I HAD a lot of mixed feelings on the night of February 5 when the maid led me into the hall. Mrs. Pumphrey was at the entrance to the ballroom receiving her guests, and beyond I could see an elegant throng standing around with drinks. I straightened the tie on my hired outfit, took a deep breath and waited.

Mrs. Pumphrey was smiling sweetly as she shook hands with the couple in front of me, but when she saw me her face became radiant. "Oh, Mr. Herriot, how nice of you. Tricki was so delighted to know you were coming. He'll be simply furious if I don't take you right in to see him." She led me across the hall.

Tricki was curled up in an armchair beside a bright fire. When he saw me he jumped on the back of the chair and tried to lick my face. Just then I caught sight of two large bowls on the carpet. One contained about a pound of chopped chicken, the other a mass of crumbled cake.

"Mrs. Pumphrey!" I thundered, pointing at the bowls.

"Oh, do forgive me," she wailed. "It's just a special treat because he's alone tonight. And it's so *cold.*"

"I'll forgive you," I said sternly, "if you remove the cake."

Fluttering like a little girl, she did so, then at once became brisk. "Now you must come and meet some of my friends."

I'd have preferred to stay with Tricki in front of his fire, but I was propelled into the ballroom, where light blazed down from three cut-glass chandeliers and was reflected dazzlingly from the many-mirrored walls. I squirmed as I heard myself introduced to her guests as "Tricki's dear kind uncle." But they were either people of superb self-control or familiar with their hostess' blind spot, because the information was received with complete gravity.

Along one wall a five-piece orchestra was tuning up. White-jacketed waiters bore heavily loaded trays; Mrs. Pumphrey stopped one of them. "François, some champagne for Mr. Herriot. I want you to look after him. See that his glass is kept full."

"Certainly, madame." He bowed and moved away.

I buried my face in the ice-cold champagne, and when I looked up again there was François holding out a tray of smoked salmon.

It was like that all evening. François seemed always to be at my elbow with something delicious to eat or drink. It was the first time I had had the opportunity of drinking champagne by the pint and it was a rewarding experience. I was quickly aware of a glorious lightness, a heightening of the perceptions. I stopped being overawed by this new world and began to enjoy it. I danced with everybody in sight—sleek young beauties, elderly dowagers and twice with a giggling Mrs. Pumphrey.

Or I just talked. I amazed myself by my lightning wit. And once I caught sight of myself in a mirror—a distinguished figure, glass in hand, the hired suit hanging on me with quiet grace. It took my breath away. Eating, drinking, talking, dancing, the evening winged past. When it was time to go and I was shaking hands with Mrs. Pumphrey in the hall, François appeared again with a bowl of hot soup. He seemed to be worried lest I grow faint on the journey home. I said good night to Tricki and went back to Skeldale House, carrying a memory of luxury and light.

I got into bed and lay on my back looking up into the darkness. Snatches of music still tinkled about in my head and I was beginning to swim back to the ballroom when the phone rang.

"Atkinson of Beck Cottage," a voice said. "I 'ave a sow what can't get pigged. She's been on all night. Will you come?"

It was two a.m. A farrowing on top of all that champagne and smoked salmon—and at Beck Cottage, one of the most primitive small holdings in the district. It wasn't fair. Sleepily I took off my pajamas and reached for the stiff worn corduroys I used for work. I groped my way down the long garden to the garage. In the darkness of the yard I closed my eyes and the great chandeliers blazed again, the mirrors flashed and the music played.

Beck Cottage lay in a hollow and in the winter the place was a sea of mud. I left my car and squelched through the blackness into the byre, where a light showed dimly. The warm sweet bovine smell met me as I peered toward a figure standing at the far end. Stumbling over the broken floor and mounds of manure—Mr. Atkinson didn't believe in mucking out too often—I arrived at a pen where a pig was lying on her side, very still except for the trembling of her flanks. As I watched she began straining.

Mr. Atkinson received me without enthusiasm. He stood hunched against a wall, holding a bicycle lamp with a fast-failing battery.

"Is this all the light we've got?" I asked.

"Aye." He looked from the lamp to me with a "What more does he want?" expression.

I trained the feeble beam on my patient. "Young, isn't she?"

"Aye, nobbut a gilt. Fust litter."

"Something stuck there, I reckon," I said. "Will you bring me a bucket of hot water, some soap and a towel, please?"

"Haven't got no 'ot water. Fire's out."

"Okay, bring me whatever you've got."

The farmer clattered away down the byre, taking the light with him, and with the darkness there was the music again. It was a Strauss waltz and I was dancing with Lady Frenswick, young and very fair, and she laughed as I swung her around.

Mr. Atkinson dumped a bucket of water beside me. I dipped a finger in. Ice-cold. And I'd have to watch my arms on the jagged rim of that ancient bucket. Quickly stripping off jacket and shirt, I sucked in my breath as a villainous draft blew through a crack onto my back.

"Soap, please," I said through clenched teeth.

"In t'bucket."

I pulled out an object as hard and unyielding as marble. I discarded the idea of asking for another piece. Instead I tracked out through the mud to my car, goose pimples rearing on my chest, and fished around for a jar of antiseptic lubricating cream.

Back in the pen, I smeared the cream on my arm and lay on my side by the pig. My fingers touched something and I forgot my discomfort; it was a tiny tail. Almost a transverse presentation, biggish piglet stuck like a cork in a bottle. Using one finger, I worked the hind legs back until I could grasp them and draw the piglet out. "This one was the trouble. He's dead, I'm afraid—but there could be some live ones still inside."

Almost at arm's length I found another piglet, and I was feeling at the face when a set of minute but very sharp teeth sank into my finger. I yelped and looked up at the farmer from my stony bed. "This one's alive, anyway. I'll soon have him out."

But the piglet had other ideas. He showed no desire to leave his warm haven, and every time I got hold of his slippery little foot he jerked it away. After a minute or two of this game I felt a cramping in my arm. I relaxed and lay back, my head resting on the cobbles. I closed my eyes and instantly I was back in the ballroom, holding out an immense glass to François. I shook myself. This wouldn't do. Falling asleep on the job. I reached again for the piglet and this time hauled him into the world. Once arrived, he tottered around philosophically to his mother's udder. There was no obstruction now and soon a second pink wriggler was deposited in the straw; then quite quickly another and another. "Coming off the assembly line now, all right," I said. Mr. Atkinson grunted. The light from the bicycle lamp had almost given out when the last of eight was born.

"Well, that's the lot." I felt suddenly chilled; I couldn't say how long I had been standing there looking at the wonder that never grew stale; the little pigs struggling onto their legs and making their way unguided to the long double row of teats; the mother with her first family easing herself over to them.

I swilled myself down with the cold water. "Have you a towel?" I gasped, and Mr. Atkinson handed me a meal sack, its edges stiff with old manure. The last bubbles of champagne left me, drifted up through the gaps in the roof and burst sadly in the darkness.

I dragged my shirt over my gritty back, sensing a return to my own world. I had a last look in the pen before I left. The row of little pigs sucked busily; the gilt shifted her position and grunted with deep content.

Yes, I was back and it was all right. I drove through the mud and up the hill, where I had to get out to open a gate. The wind, with the cold clean smell of frosty grass in it, caught at my face and I stood there thinking of the night which was ending now. My mind went back to an old gentleman who had talked to us in school about careers. He had said, "If you decide to become a veterinary surgeon you will never grow rich, but you will have a life of endless interest and variety."

I laughed aloud. The old chap certainly wasn't kidding. That was it—variety.

As I checked my list of calls the next morning I sensed a decline in what was becoming Miss Harbottle's ominous power. She had demanded that our visits be properly entered and priced in her book. She attempted to improve our penmanship and to keep our hands from dipping freely into the cashbox. She even tried to intimidate Siegfried himself. But this morning Siegfried didn't look so much like a schoolboy as he faced Miss Harbottle. For one thing, he hadn't marched straight in and stood in front of her desk, which routinely had been giving her the strategic position of power. Instead he had veered off to stand with his back to the window. This way she had to turn her head slightly to face him, and besides, he had the light at his back. He thrust his hands into his pockets and leaned back against the window frame. His face was illumined by his saintliest smile.

"I just wanted a word with you, Miss Harbottle. First, about your petty cashbox. I think you were quite right to institute it, but I think you would be the first to agree that the main function of a cashbox is to have cash in it." He gave a light laugh. "Now last night I had a few dogs in the surgery and the owners wanted to pay on the spot. I had no change and went for some to your box—

it was quite empty. It didn't look good, Miss Harbottle. I really must ask you to keep some cash in your cashbox."

Miss Harbottle's eyes widened incredulously. "But Mr. Farnon, you removed the entire contents to go to the hunt ball at—"

Siegfried held up a hand. "Please hear me out. There is another very small thing I want to bring to your attention. It is now the tenth day of the month and the accounts have not gone out."

"But Mr. Farnon—"

"Just one moment, Miss Harbottle. It is a known fact that farmers pay their bills more readily if they receive them on the first of the month. And there is another factor." The smile turned grave. "Have you ever stopped to work out how much interest the practice is losing on all the money lying out there because you are late in sending out the accounts?"

"Mr. Farnon—"

"Believe me, Miss Harbottle, it grieves me to have to speak like this." He spread out his hands in a gesture of charming frankness. "But the fact is, I can't afford to lose money in this way. So if you will just apply yourself to this little matter I'm sure all will be well."

"And how can I send the accounts when you refuse to write the—"

"In conclusion, Miss Harbottle, let me say this. I have been very satisfied with your progress, and I am sure that with time you will tighten up on those little points I have just mentioned." A roguishness crept into his smile. Miss Harbottle's strong fingers closed tightly around a heavy ebony ruler.

"Efficiency," he said. "That's what we must have—efficiency."

As I CAME into the operating room I saw that Siegfried had a patient on the table. He was thoughtfully stroking the head of an elderly and rather woebegone Border terrier.

"James," he said. "I want you to take this dog to Grier."

"Grier?"

"Vet at Brawton. He was treating the case before the owner moved into our district. Stones in the bladder. It needs an immediate operation and I think I'd better let Grier do it. He's a touchy, cantankerous old Scot and I don't want to step on his toes." He lifted the terrier from the table and handed him to me. "The sooner you get there the better. You can see the op and bring the dog back here afterward. But watch yourself. Don't rub Grier the wrong way or he'll take it out of you somehow."

At my first sight of Angus Grier I thought of whisky. Something had to be responsible for the fleshy, mottled cheeks and the pattern of purple veins which chased each other over his prominent nose. He wore a permanently insulted expression.

He didn't waste any charm on me; a nod and a grunt and he grabbed the dog from my arms. The operation was uneventful and as Grier inserted the last stitch he looked up at me. "You'll no' want to take the dog back till he's out of the anesthetic. I've got a case to visit—you can come with me to pass the time."

We didn't have what you could call a conversation in the car. It was a monologue—complaints of the sissiness of students nowadays, and of wrongs suffered at the hands of wicked clients and greedy colleagues. We drew up in a particularly dirty farmyard and Grier turned to me. "I've got a cow tae cleanse here."

"Right," I said. "Fine." I settled down in my seat and took out my pipe. Grier paused. "Are you no' coming to give me a hand?"

I couldn't understand him. Cleansing of cows is simply the removal of retained afterbirth and is a one-man job.

"Well, there isn't much I can do, is there?" I said. "And my boots and coat are in my car. I'd get messed up for nothing."

I knew immediately that I'd said the wrong thing. He gave me a malevolent glance, and halfway across the yard he stopped and stood for a moment in thought. Then he came back to the car. "I've got something here you can put on. Come in with me—you'll be able to pass me a pessary when I want one."

It sounded nutty to me, but I got out and went around to the back, where Grier was fishing out a large wooden box.

"Here's a calving outfit I got a bit ago. I haven't used it much because I found it a mite heavy, but it'll keep ye grand and clean."

It was a suit of thick, black, shining rubber. I lifted out the jacket; it bristled with zip fasteners and press studs and felt as heavy as lead. The trousers were even weightier. The whole thing was a most imposing creation, obviously designed by somebody who had never seen a cow calved. Anybody wearing it would be pretty well immobilized.

I began to take off my jacket—it was crazy, but I didn't want to offend the man. Grier, heaving and straining, helped me get into the suit. First the gleaming trousers were pulled on and zipped up fore and aft; then it was the turn of the jacket, a wonderful piece of work, fitting tightly around the waist and possessing short sleeves with powerful elastic gripping my biceps. I could hear the zips squeaking into place, the final one being at the back of my neck to close a high stiff collar which held my head in an attitude of supplication, my chin pointing at the sky. For the final touch, Grier produced a black rubber skullcap. I shrank away from the thing, but he insisted. "Stand still a wee minute longer. We might as well do the job right."

When he had finished he stood back admiringly. I must have been a grotesque sight, sheathed from head to foot in gleaming black, my arms sticking out almost at right angles. "Well, come on, it's time we got on wi' the job." He hurried toward the byre; I plodded ponderously after him. Our arrival caused a sensation. There were present the farmer, two cowmen and a little girl. The men's cheerful greeting froze on their lips as my menacing figure paced slowly in. The little girl burst into tears and ran.

"Cleansing" is a dirty, smelly job for the operator and a bore for the onlooker, who may have to stand around for twenty minutes with nothing to see. But this was one time the spectators were not bored. The men never took their eyes away from me as I stood like a suit of armor against the wall. I knew what they were thinking. Just what was going to happen when this formidable unknown went into action? Anybody dressed like that must have some tremendous task ahead of him. The intense pressure of the collar against my larynx kept me out of any conversation and this must have added to the mystery. The little girl had plucked up courage and brought her brothers and sisters to look at me. Screwing my head around painfully, I tried to give them a reassuring smile.

I couldn't say how long I stood there, but Grier at last finished his job and called out, "All right, I'm ready for you now." The atmosphere became suddenly electric. The men straightened up. This was the moment they had been waiting for.

With some difficulty I headed for the tin of pessaries. It was only a few yards away, but it seemed longer as I approached like a robot, head in the air, arms extended stiffly on either side. After a few contortions I bent, I got my hand into the tin, then had to take the paper off the pessary with one hand. The men watched, fascinated. I did a careful about-face and paced back with measured tread. Grier took the pessary and inserted it in the uterus.

I glanced down my nose at the men; their expressions had changed to open disbelief. Surely no man could be wearing that outfit just to hand over a pessary. But when Grier started the complicated business of snapping open the studs and sliding me out of it, they realized the show was over; and fast on the feeling of letdown came amusement.

As I tried to rub some life back into my swollen arms, which had been strangulated by the elastic sleeves, I was surrounded by grinning faces. Pulling together the shreds of my dignity, I put on my jacket and got into the car. Grier stayed to say a few words to the men, but he wasn't holding their attention; it was all on me, huddling in the seat. They couldn't believe I was true.

Back at the surgery the Border terrier raised his head and tried bravely to wag his tail when he saw me. I gathered him up in a blanket and was preparing to leave when I saw Grier through the partly open door of a storeroom. He had the wooden box on a table and he was lifting out the rubber suit, but there was something peculiar about the way he was doing it; his body shook and jerked, the mottled face was strangely contorted and a half-stifled wailing issued from his lips.

I stared in amazement. I would have said it was impossible, yet it was happening right in front of me. There was not a shadow of a doubt—Angus Grier was laughing.

Milk fever is one of the straightforward conditions we treat. It is a disease caused by excessive drain on the body mineral reserves of recently calved cows during the establishment of the milk flow. But, looking down into the stream in the dim early light, I realized that this case was one of its more bizarre manifestations. The illness had struck immediately after calving, and the cow had slithered down the muddy bank into the water. She was unconscious when I arrived, her hindquarters completely submerged, the head resting on a shelf of rock. Her calf, sodden and pathetic in the freezing rain, trembled by her side.

Dan Cooper's eyes were anxious. "We're too late," he said. "I can't see her breathing."

"Pretty far gone, I'm afraid," I replied. "But if I can get some calcium into her vein she might still come around."

"Damn, I 'ope so," Dan grunted. "She's one of my best milkers."

I pulled out the syringe box and selected a wide-bored needle. My fingers, numb with cold, could hardly hold it. The water was deeper than I thought and it was over my boot tops at the first stride. Gasping, I bent down and dug my thumb into the jugular furrow at the base of the neck. The vein came up, and as I pushed the needle in the blood ran warm and dark over my hand. I fumbled the flutter valve from my pocket, pushed a bottle into the cup end and inserted the other end into the needle. The calcium began to flow into the vein.

Standing there in the icy stream, I tried to keep out the black thoughts—about all those people I knew who were still in bed and would only leave it when their alarm clocks rang. I should have been a doctor—they treated their patients in nice warm bedrooms.

I pulled the needle from the vein. There was no response to the injection, so I began to run more calcium under the skin, futile though it seemed. It was when I was rubbing away this subcutaneous injection that I noticed the eyelids quiver.

A quick ripple of relief and excitement went through me. "She's still with us, Dan." I flicked her ear, and her eyes opened wide. "We'll wait a few minutes and then try to roll her onto her chest."

Within a quarter of an hour she was beginning to toss her head about and I knew it was time. I caught hold of her horns and pulled while Dan and his tall son pushed at her shoulder. After several concerted heaves the cow took over herself and settled on her chest. Immediately everything looked rosier; when a cow is lying on her side she always has the look of death on her.

I was pretty sure then that she would recover, but I couldn't leave her lying in the stream. She didn't seem to relish her situation, either, but it was another half hour and my teeth were chattering uncontrollably before she finally staggered to her feet.

"Well, that's a licker!" Dan said. "Ah never thought she'd stand again. Must be good stuff you gave her."

I laughed with delight. The spectacular effects of intravenous calcium were still enough of a novelty to intrigue me. For generations, cows with milk fever had just died. Then inflation of the udder had saved many; but the calcium was the thing—when they got up within an hour, I always felt like a successful conjurer.

We guided the cow, still rocky on her legs, up the bank toward the house. Dan and his son held the calf in a sack slung between them. The tiny animal swung to and fro, screwing up its eyes against the hard world it had entered.

We left the cow knee-deep in straw in a warm shed, licking her calf vigorously. In the porch of the house we pulled off our boots. I poured about a pint of water from each one. Mrs. Cooper had the reputation of being a firebrand who exercised an iron rule over Dan and her family, but from my previous contacts with her I had the feeling that Dan didn't do so badly. I thought so again as I saw her now, square-built but comely, plaiting a little girl's pigtails in readiness for school. A crackling fire was mirrored in the gleaming brass of the hearth, and above the clean farmhouse smell there was a hint of frying home-cured bacon. She sent Dan and the boy upstairs to change their socks; then she turned a calm gaze on me as I dripped on her linoleum.

"All right, off with the socks," she rapped out. "And your coat, and roll up your trousers, and sit down here, and dry your hair with this." A clean towel landed on my lap and Mrs. Cooper bent over me. "Don't you ever think of wearing a hat?"

"Not keen on them, I'm afraid," I mumbled as she poured hot water into a bowl and added mustard.

"Here, stick your feet in this." I gave an involuntary yelp as I made contact with the bubbling mixture, but she shot a fierce glance at me and I took care to keep my feet in it. I was sitting, teeth clenched, enveloped in steam, when she pushed a pot of tea into my hand. It was old-fashioned treatment but effective. By the time I was halfway through the tea I felt as though I were being consumed by fire. The riverbed chill was a vanishing dream. She topped up my bowl with another scalding quart, then grabbed chair and bowl and swiveled me around to the table, still with my feet in the water. Dan and the children were already at their breakfast, and in front of me was a plate with two eggs, a rough-cut piece of bacon and several sausages. I had learned enough of Dales ways by this time to keep quiet at meals. At first I had thought it incumbent on me to provide light conversation in return for their hospitality, until the questioning glances they exchanged with each other silenced me effectively. But the first mouthful of that homemade Yorkshire sausage almost made me break my newfound rule. It was an effort to restrain my cries of congratulation. Mrs. Cooper, though, must have noticed my rapt expression. Casually she rolled a few more links onto my plate.

"Killed a pig last week," she said, pulling open the pantry door. I could see the dishes heaped with chopped meat, spareribs, liver, the rows of pies with the jelly gleaming on their pale gold crusts.

I finished my meal, pulled on a thick pair of socks borrowed from Dan and my dry shoes. I was about to leave when Mrs. Cooper tucked a parcel under my arm. I knew it contained further samples from the pantry. Her eyes dared me to say much about it, but I had to mutter a few words of thanks.

THE church clock was chiming a quarter past nine when I pulled up outside Skeldale House. I felt good—warm, full of superb food and the satisfying memory of the cow's recovery. And there on the back seat was a parcel of sausages I would never forget.

I took the surgery steps at a jump and trotted along the passage, but as I rounded the corner my progress was halted. Siegfried was standing there, rigid, his back pressed against the wall. Between us, through the half-open door of the office, Miss Harbottle was clearly visible. Siegfried held up a warning hand. Then he began to creep past the door. But Miss Harbottle called to him. He gave me a despairing glance, then went slowly into the room.

I thought wonderingly of how things had built up until it was naked war now between these two. Siegfried was the employer, he held the reins and it had appeared that Miss Harbottle would be helpless in the face of his obstructive strategy. But Miss Harbottle was a resourceful fighter, and for a week now she had been playing Siegfried like an expert fisherman with a salmon. She had a new weapon; she had taken to writing his clerical idiocies on slips of paper—misspellings, errors in addition, wrong entries, all faithfully copied down. She would wait until her employer was under pressure, then she would push one under his nose and say, "How about this?"

The end was unvarying—mumbled apologies from Siegfried, and Miss Harbottle, radiating self-righteousness, correcting the entry.

As Siegfried went into the room I watched, impelled by morbid curiosity. Miss Harbottle, looking brisk, was tapping an entry in the book with her pen while Siegfried muttered replies. His teeth were clenched and his eyes had started to bulge.

The phone rang and the secretary answered it. Her employer was making for the door when she called happily, "Colonel Brent for you." Like a man in a dream he turned back. The colonel, a racehorse owner, was a thorn in our flesh; a call from him was always liable to send up the blood pressure. I could see it was that way this morning. At the end Siegfried crashed the receiver down and leaned on the desk, breathing heavily.

Then, as I watched, unbelieving, Miss Harbottle fished out one of her slips and held it in Siegfried's face. "How about this?" she asked.

I resisted the impulse to close my eyes. There was a tense interval while Siegfried stood quite motionless. Then with a scything sweep of his arm he snatched the slip from Miss Harbottle's hand

and began to tear at it with fierce intensity. As he tore he leaned forward over the desk and his glaring eyes approached ever nearer to Miss Harbottle, who slowly edged back till her chair was jammed against the wall.

It was a weird picture. Miss Harbottle straining back, her mouth slightly open, her tinted curls bobbing in alarm, and Siegfried, his ravaged features close to hers, tearing paper with insane vigor. The scene ended when Siegfried hurled the torn-up slip at the wastepaper basket. It fell in a gentle shower, like confetti, as Siegfried, still without speaking, strode from the room.

In the kitchen, Mrs. Hall opened Mrs. Cooper's parcel—a pie, some liver and the exquisite sausages. She turned a quizzical eye on me. "You look kind of pleased with yourself, Mr. Herriot."

I leaned back against the dresser. "I've just been thinking, Mrs. Hall. It must be very nice to be the principal of a practice, but you know, it's not such a bad life being an assistant."

SIEGFRIED had gone to Brawton so I took the six-o'clock surgery alone. "First, please," I called as I looked into the waiting room. There was an old lady with a cat in a cardboard box, two small boys trying to keep hold of a very active dog, and somebody I didn't recognize at first. Then I remembered—it was Lord Hulton's farm manager, Soames, of my first case. But he was a vastly different Soames. He came into the surgery wearing an ingratiating smile. He radiated anxiety to please. And the most interesting thing was that his right eye was puffed and closed and surrounded by an extensive area of bluish black flesh. His head bobbed up and down as he spoke.

"I hope you don't mind my coming to see you, Mr. Herriot. The fact is I have resigned my post with his lordship and am looking for another. I was wondering if you and Mr. Farnon would put in a word for me if you heard of anything."

I was too astonished to say much. I replied that we would do what we could, and he thanked me effusively and bowed out.

When I asked Siegfried what he made of it, he smiled. He knew the whole story. "Remember I told you he was working one or two

shady sidelines? Well, it all mounted up. And then he got careless. He was out on his ear before he knew what had happened."

"And how about the lovely black eye?"

"Oh, he got that from Tommy. You must have seen Tommy when you were there. He's the horseman."

My mind went back to that uncomfortable night and to the quiet man holding the horse's head. "Yes—big chap."

"Right. I'd hate to have him punch me in the eye. Soames gave him a hell of a life, and as soon as Tommy heard about the sacking he paid a visit just to settle the score."

Tommy, I thought, had settled something for me, too.

5

I REALIZED, quite suddenly, that spring had come. It was late March and I had been examining some sheep in a hillside fold. On my way down, in the lee of a small pinewood, I leaned my back against a tree and was aware all at once of the sunshine, warm on my closed eyelids, the clamor of the larks, the muted sea sound of the wind in the high branches. And though the snow still lay in long runnels behind the walls, there was the feeling of change, almost of liberation.

In April the roadside banks were bright with the fresh yellow of the primroses. And in April, too, came the lambing. It came in a great tidal wave, the most vivid and interesting part of the veterinary surgeon's year, the zenith of the annual cycle, and it came as it always does, when we were busiest with our other work. For in the spring all the livestock were feeling the effects of the long winter, and just as we were wondering how we could cope with the coughs and colds and pneumonias, the wave struck us. The odd thing is that for most of the year sheep hardly entered into our lives. They were just woolly things on the hills. But for these two months they almost blotted out everything else.

First came the early troubles, the pregnancy toxemias, the prolapses. Then the lambings in a concentrated rush, followed by the calcium deficiencies, the horrible gangrenous mastitis when the udder turns black and sloughs away, and the diseases which beset the lambs themselves—swayback, pulpy kidney, dysentery. Then, by the end of May, the flood receded. Sheep became woolly things on the hills again.

But in this first year I found a fascination in the work which has remained with me. Lambing, it seemed to me, had all the thrill and interest of calving without the hard labor. It was usually uncomfortable in that it was performed in the open; it didn't seem to occur to the farmers that the ewe might prefer to produce her family in a warm place or that the vet might not enjoy kneeling in his shirt sleeves in the rain. The actual job was a song. Lambs are usually born in twos or threes and some wonderful mix-ups occur—tangles of heads and legs all trying to be first out, and it is the vet's job to sort them around and decide which leg belongs to which head. I reveled in this. It was a pleasant change to be for once stronger than my patient, but I didn't overstress this advantage; gentleness is important in lambing.

And the lambs. All young animals are appealing, but the lamb has been given an unfair share of charm. The moments come back—of a bitterly cold evening when I had delivered twins on a wind-scoured hillside, the lambs shaking their heads convulsively and within minutes one of them struggling upright and making its way, unsteady, knock-kneed, toward the udder while the other followed resolutely on its knees. And the shepherd, his purpled, weather-roughened face almost hidden by his heavy coat, giving a slow chuckle. "How the 'ell do they know?"

He had seen it happen thousands of times and he still wondered. So do I.

And another memory of two hundred lambs in a barn on a warm afternoon. We were inoculating them against pulpy kidney, and there was no conversation because of the high-pitched protests of the lambs and the unremitting deep baaing from nearly a hundred ewes milling anxiously around outside. I couldn't conceive how these ewes could ever get their own families sorted out from that mass of almost identical little creatures. It would take hours.

It took about twenty-five seconds. When we had finished injecting we opened the barn doors, and the outpouring lambs were met by a rush of distraught mothers. At first the noise was deafening, but it died away rapidly to an occasional bleat as the last stray was rounded up and the flock headed calmly for the field.

Through May and early June my world became softer and warmer. The cold wind dropped and the air, fresh as the sea, carried a faint breath of the thousands of wild flowers which speckled the pastures. At times it seemed unfair that I should be paid for my work; for driving out in the early morning, with the fields glittering under the first pale sunshine and the wisps of mist still hanging—life was idyllic.

There was only one jarring note—May and June was the time of the horse. The foaling, hard but interesting work, was then mostly finished, and as the weather grew warmer the farmers wanted the year-old colts castrated. And I didn't like castrations.

I was not, am not and never will be a horseman. It is difficult to define the term, but I am convinced that horsemen are either born or made in earliest childhood. I have the knowledge of equine diseases and I know how to treat sick horses efficiently, but that power of the real horseman to soothe and mentally dominate an animal is beyond my reach. I don't try to kid myself about that. It is unfortunate, because there is no doubt horses know. It is quite different with cows; they don't care. If a cow feels like kicking you she will kick you; she doesn't give a damn whether you are an expert or not. But horses know.

One morning when the season was at its height and I had had about enough of the equine race, Siegfried called to me as he was going out. "James, there's a horse with a tumor on its belly at Wilkinson's. Get along and take it off, will you?"

Feeling a little disgruntled at fate having handed me something on top of the seasonal tasks, I boiled up my instruments and drove off, wondering as usual about the horse, whether it would be wild or quiet, and how big it would be. Maybe it was just a yearling; they did get those little dangling growths sometimes. Over the six miles I managed to build up a comfortable picture of a soft-eyed little colt, shaky on its legs.

At Wilkinson's the yard was empty except for a lad of about ten who didn't know where the boss was. "Well, where is the horse?" I asked.

The lad pointed to the stable. "He's in there."

I went inside. At one end stood a high box stall, and from within I heard a deep-throated whinnying and snorting followed by a series of tremendous thuds against the sides of the box. A chill crept through me.

I opened the top half door and there, looking down at me, was an enormous animal—a chestnut stallion with a proud arch to his neck and feet like manhole covers. Surging swathes of muscle shone on his shoulders and quarters, and when he saw me he laid back his ears and lashed out viciously against the wall. A foot-long splinter flew in the air as the great hoof crashed on the boards. I turned to the lad. "How old is that horse?"

"Over six years, sir."

I tried a little calm thinking. How did you go about tackling a man-eater like this? He must weigh over a ton. I shook myself; I hadn't even had a look at the tumor I was supposed to remove. I peeped into the stall. I could see it plainly dangling from the belly; probably a papilloma, about the size of a little cauliflower. Nice narrow neck to it; a few cc's of local in there and I could twist it off easily with the spoons.

But the snag was obvious. I would have to go under that shining barrel of an abdomen within easy reach of the great feet and stick a needle into those few inches of skin. Not a happy thought.

I pulled my mind back to practical things—hot water, soap, a towel. I went to the house to wash up, and by the time I was back at the box stall I'd somehow managed to twist my face into a smile.

"My chaps are getting a halter on him," the farmer said, but his words were cut short by an enraged squealing from the box. My mouth went dry. The stable doors flew open and the great stallion catapulted out into the yard, dragging two big men along on the end of the halter shank. They were unable to stop the plunging. I imagined I felt the ground shudder under my feet as the hoofs crashed down.

After much maneuvering the men got the horse standing with his off side against the wall of the barn. One of them looped a twitch onto the upper lip and tightened it expertly; the other took a firm grip on the halter. "Ready for you now, sir."

I pierced the rubber cap on the bottle of cocaine. Ten cc's. If I could get that into him the rest would be easy. Walking up to the horse was like watching an action from a film—it wasn't really me doing this. The near-side eye flickered dangerously as I passed my left hand over the muscles of the neck, down the smooth quivering flank and along the abdomen till I was able to grasp the tumor. I had the thing in my hand now. I pulled gently downward, stretching the brown skin joining the growth to the body. I would put the local in there—it wasn't going to be so bad. The stallion laid back his ears and gave a warning whicker. I took a long careful breath, brought up the syringe with my right hand, placed the needle against the skin, then thrust it in.

The kick was so explosively quick that at first I felt only surprise that such a huge animal could move so swiftly. It was a lightning outward slash that I never even saw and the hoof struck the inside of my right thigh, spinning me around helplessly. When I hit the ground I lay still, feeling only a curious numbness.

"Are you all right, Mr. Herriot?" Mr. Wilkinson was bending over me. The voice was anxious.

"I don't think so." I was astonished at how matter-of-fact I sounded. Calm and in charge. "I'm afraid not, Mr. Wilkinson. You'd better put the horse back—we'll have a go another day—and I wonder if you'd ring Mr. Farnon to come get me. I don't think I can drive."

My leg wasn't broken, but it developed a massive hematoma and the whole limb blossomed into an unbelievable range of colors. I was still hobbling when, a fortnight later, Siegfried and I with a small army of helpers went back and roped the stallion, chloroformed him and removed that little growth.

I have a cavity in my thigh to remind me of that day, but good came out of it. I found that the fear is worse than the reality and horse work has never worried me as much since then.

6

THE FIRST TIME I saw Phin Calvert was in the street outside the surgery. He was a thickset figure in a ragged jacket pulled wide to display a curving expanse of collarless shirt, hands tucked behind his suspenders, wisps of grizzled hair hanging in a fringe beneath a greasy cap. He was humming busily to himself.

Looking at Phin, you'd never have thought he was a prosperous farmer. So when I was called to his place I was surprised to find a substantial house and buildings and a fine dairy herd.

I could hear him even before I got out of the car.

"Hello, 'ello, 'ello! Who's this we've got, then? New chap, eh? Now we're going to learn summat!" He was grinning widely.

"My name is Herriot," I said.

"Is it now?" Phin turned to three young men standing by. "Hasn't he a nice smile, lads? A real Happy Harry!"

He led the way across the yard. "Come on, then, and we'll see what you're made of. I 'ope you know a bit about calves."

As we went into the calf house I was hoping I would be able to use some of the new drugs I had in my car; it was going to take something special to make an impact here.

There were six well-grown young animals in the house. Three of them were blundering about the pen, grinding their teeth and frothing at the mouth. One of them walked straight into the wall and stood with its nose pressed against the stone. Their apparent blindness made diagnosis easy. I began to look closely around the walls of the calf house.

Phin burst into noisy commentary. "Hey, you're as bad as t'calves, nosing about there. What d'you think you're lookin' for?"

"Paint, Mr. Calvert. I think your calves have lead poisoning."

Phin said what all farmers say at this juncture. "They can't have. I've had calves in here for thirty years and they've never taken any harm before. There's no paint in here, anyway."

"How about this?" I pulled at a piece of loose board.

"Oh, that's nobbut a bit of wood I nailed down there last week to block up a hole. Came off an old hen house."

I looked at the twenty-year-old paint hanging off in the loose flakes which calves find so irresistible. "This is what's done it," I said. "Look, you can see the tooth marks."

Phin studied the board. "All right. What do we do now?"

"First thing is to get this painted board out of here and then give all the calves Epsom salts. Have you got any?"

Phin gave a bark of laughter. "Aye, I've got a sackful, but can't you do better than that? Aren't you going to inject them?"

It was embarrassing. The specific antidotes to metal poisoning had not been discovered, and the only thing which sometimes helped was magnesium sulfate—which is, of course, Epsom salts.

"There's nothing to inject," I said. "I can't guarantee the salts. But try two heaped tablespoonfuls three times a day."

"Oh 'ell, you'll skitter the poor buggers to death!"

"Maybe so, but there's nothing else for it," I said.

Phin took a step toward me so that his face, deeply wrinkled, was close to mine. The suddenly shrewd brown eyes regarded me steadily. "Right," he said. "Come in and have a drink."

He stumped into the farm kitchen ahead of me and let loose a bellow that shook the windows. "Mother! Feller 'ere wants a glass o' beer. Come and meet Happy Harry!"

Mrs. Calvert appeared with magical speed and put down glasses and bottles. SMITH'S NUTTY BROWN ALE. It was a historic moment, though I didn't know it then; it was the first of an incredible series of Nutty Browns I was to drink at that table.

At the end of a fortnight all the calves were eating normally. One still showed a trace of blindness, but this too soon cleared up.

It wasn't long before I saw Phin again. I was in the office with Siegfried when the outer door banged and I heard a voice raised in song—hi-ti-tiddly-rum-te-tum.

"Well, well, well!" Phineas bawled heartily at Miss Harbottle. "It's Flossie! And what's my little darlin' doing this fine day?"

There was not a flicker from Miss Harbottle's granite features. She directed an icy stare at the intruder, but Phin swung around and stabbed a finger at me. "There's my man. I want him out to my place right sharpish."

"What's the trouble?" I asked. "Is it the calves again?"

"Damn, no! It's me good bull. He's puffin' like a bellows—like pneumonia but worse than I've known. He's in a 'ell of a state. Looks like he's peggin' out." For an instant Phin lost his jocularity.

I had heard of this bull—pedigree Shorthorn, show winner, the foundation of his herd. "I'll follow you home, Mr. Calvert."

"Good lad. I'm off, then." Phin paused at the door, a wild figure, tieless, tattered. He turned again to Miss Harbottle and contorted his features into a preposterous leer. "Ta-ra, Floss!"

For a moment the room seemed very empty and quiet except for Miss Harbottle's acid, "Oh, that man! Dreadful! Dreadful!"

Phin's bull stood as though rooted to the middle of the pen. His great rib cage rose and fell with the most labored respirations I had ever seen. His mouth gaped wide, a bubbling foam hung around his lips and his flaring nostrils; his eyes, almost starting from his head in terror, stared at the wall in front of him. This battle for breath looked like a losing one. He didn't even move when I inserted my thermometer.

"Poor aud beggar," Phin muttered. "He's bred me the finest calves I've ever had. He's as quiet as a sheep, too. I've seen me grandchildren walk under 'is belly. I hate to see him sufferin'. If you can't do no good, just tell me and I'll get the gun."

I read the thermometer. One hundred and ten degrees Fahrenheit. Ridiculous! I shook it and pushed it back in. I gave it nearly a minute so that I could get in some thinking. It still said a hundred and ten. What was this? Could be anthrax . . . and yet . . . Phin was waiting for me to say something, and I looked above his head to the square of deep blue and a tufted cloud moving across the sun. As it passed, a single dazzling ray made me close my eyes and a faint bell rang in my mind. "Has he been out today?" I asked.

"Aye, all morning. It was that grand and warm."

The bell became a triumphant gong. "Get a hose, quick."

"A hose? What the 'ell . . ."

"Yes, quick as you can—he's got sunstroke."

He had the hose fixed in less than a minute. I began to play the jet of cold water all over the huge form. I kept this up for about five minutes, but it seemed a lot longer as I waited for some sign of improvement. I was beginning to think I was on the wrong track when the bull gulped. It was something—he had been unable to swallow his saliva before, in his desperate efforts to get air into his lungs; and surely the breathing was slowing down a bit?

Then the bull shook himself, turned his head and looked at us. There was an awed whisper from Phin: "By gaw, it's working!"

I enjoyed myself after that. I can't think of anything in my working life that has given me more pleasure than standing in that pen directing the lifesaving jet and watching the bull savoring it. He liked it on his face best, and as I worked my way up from the tail and along the steaming back he would turn his nose full into the water, rocking his head blissfully from side to side.

Within half an hour he looked almost normal, though his chest was still heaving. I tried the temperature. A hundred and five.

"He'll be all right now," I said. "But one of your lads should keep the water on him for twenty minutes or so. I must be going."

"You've time for a drink," Phin grunted.

In the farm kitchen he stared into his glass of Nutty Brown. "Harry," he said. "I'll tell you, you've flummoxed me." He rubbed his chin in disbelief. "I don't know what to say to you."

It wasn't often that Phin lost his voice. At the next meeting of the farmers' discussion group a learned gentleman expounded on the advances in veterinary medicine and how the farmers could now expect the newest drugs and procedures.

It was too much for Phin. He jumped to his feet and cried, "Ah think you're talking a lot of rubbish. There's a young feller in Darrowby not long out of college and it doesn't matter what you call 'im out for, he uses nowt but Epsom salts and cold water."

I HAD been away for two weeks, down in Brawton helping out Angus Grier, who'd been kicked by a colt. It wasn't long, but it was enough to bring home to me afresh that working in the high country had something for me that was missing elsewhere. My first day at home I had a visit which took me up over the Brenkstone Pass to Sildale, and when I had ground my way to the top I pulled the car to the side and got out. That quotation about not having time to stand and stare has never applied to me.

In my year at Darrowby I must have stood here scores of times. In the winter the low country was a dark trough between the snow-covered distant mountains. But today it was an endless patchwork of fields slumbering in the afternoon sun. The air was heavy with the scents of summer, and the peace I always found in the silence of the moors filled me utterly.

At these times I often seemed to stand outside myself, calmly assessing my progress. It was easy to flick back over the years—right back to the moment I had decided to become a veterinary surgeon. I was thirteen when I felt a conviction that this was for me. And yet what was it based upon? Only that I liked dogs and cats and didn't care for the idea of an office life. I knew nothing about agriculture or farm animals, and though in college I learned about these things, my future was to be small-animal surgery. This lasted right up to the time I qualified—a kind of vision of treating people's pets in my own animal hospital with fully equipped operating theater, laboratory and x-ray room; not just modern but revolutionary.

How on earth, then, did I come to be sitting on a high Yorkshire moor, smelling vaguely of cows? The job at Darrowby had been a godsend, but I had thought it only a stepping-stone to my real ambition. Now, in a year everything had switched around.

Maybe it was spending one's days in this high clean-blown land, or something to do with the incredible sweetness of the air in the old wild garden at Skeldale House. Or perhaps the daily piquancy of life with Siegfried and Tristan. Or that treating cows and pigs and sheep and horses had a fascination I had never even suspected; and this brought with it a new concept of myself as a tiny wheel in the great machine of British agriculture. There was a kind of solid satisfaction in that.

Anyway, it had all changed for me, and my work consisted now of driving from farm to farm across the roof of England with a growing conviction that I was a privileged person.

I got back into the car and headed for my last visit of the day.

It was to Terry Watson, a young farm worker who kept two cows of his own. One of them, he said, had summer mastitis. The condition was just about incurable and usually resulted in the cow losing a quarter (the area of the udder which supplies each teat with milk) and sometimes even her life.

Terry's cow looked very sick. She had limped in from the field at milking time, swinging her right hind leg wide to keep it away from the painful udder, and now she stood trembling in her stall, her eyes staring anxiously in front of her. I drew at the affected teat, and a stream of dark foul-smelling serum spurted out.

"No mistaking it, Terry," I said. I felt my way over the hot swollen quarter. "It looks bad, I'm afraid."

Terry's face was grim. He was in his early twenties, had a wife and a small baby and was one of the breed who was prepared to labor all day for somebody else and then come home and start work on his own stock. His two cows, his few pigs and hens made a big difference to somebody who had to live on thirty shillings a week. "What's going to happen, then?" he muttered. "Can you do owt for her?"

"I'll give her an injection, Terry, and you must strip the teat out as often as you can, but it's a poor outlook."

"Aye, ah know that." He watched me gloomily. "She'll lose her quarter, won't she, and maybe she'll even peg out. Look, is there nowt I can do myself?" Terry Watson's thin cheeks were pale and as I looked at the slender figure I thought, not for the first time, that he didn't look robust enough for his hard trade.

"Well, the cases that do best are the ones that get the most stripping," I said. "That rubbish in her quarter can't do any harm if you draw it right out, but that would be about every half hour. And bathe the udder with warm water and massage it well."

"What'll I rub it with? Ah've got goose grease."

"Okay, use that." Goose grease was the all-purpose lubricant and liniment for man and beast.

Terry dropped down onto the milking stool and looked up at me defiantly. "Right," he said. "I'm startin' now."

Early the next morning I looked in at the Watsons'. Terry was exactly where I had left him, eyes closed, cheek resting against the cow's flank.

"Hello, you're having another go, I see."

When I spoke the cow looked around, too, and I saw with a thrill of pleasure that she was looking at me with the casual interest of the healthy bovine and, best of all, her jaws were moving with that slow, regular, lateral grind that every vet loves to see. "Terry, she just doesn't look like the same cow!"

The young man seemed hardly able to keep his eyes open, but he smiled. "Have a look at her udder."

The tissue was smooth and yielding. As the animal showed no sign of discomfort, I drew on the teat with thumb and forefinger; the quarter was nearly empty, but I did manage to squeeze out a single jet of pure white milk. "What's going on here, Terry? Have you switched cows on me?"

"Nay, guvnor, it's same cow all right—she's better, that's all."

"She's normal. I've never seen anything like it."

"Aye, I know you haven't." Young Mrs. Watson had appeared at the door holding her baby. "You've never seen a man that would rub and strip a cow right round the clock, have you?"

"Round the clock?" I said.

"Since you left last night. Never been to bed, nor in for a meal. Great fool—it's enough to kill anybody."

"Good Lord, man," I said. "You've done the impossible. Go in now and rest."

"Nay, I can't do that." He shook his head and straightened his shoulders. "I've got me work to go to and I'm late as it is."

A LOT of the Dales farms were anonymous and it was a help to find this one so plainly identified. HESTON GRANGE it said on the gate. I got out of the car and undid the latch. It was a good gate that swung easily on its hinges. The farmhouse lay below me, massive, gray stone, with a pair of bow windows which some prosperous Victorian had added to the original structure.

I walked around the buildings shouting, but there was no reply, so I knocked at the door.

A voice answered, "Come in," and I opened the door into a huge stone-flagged kitchen hung with hams and bacon. A dark girl in a checked blouse and green linen slacks was kneading dough. "Sorry I couldn't let you in. I've got my hands full." She smiled and held up her arms, floury white to the elbow.

"That's all right. My name is Herriot. I've come to see a calf."

"Yes, we think he's broken his leg. Just a minute, I'll come with you. My father's in the fields. I'm Helen Alderson, by the way. Meg," she called, and an old woman appeared. "Take over this bread, will you, while I show Mr. Herriot the calf?"

Outside, she laughed. "We've got a bit of a walk, I'm afraid. He's in one of the top buildings." She pointed to a stone barn high on the fellside.

I looked at the girl. "Oh, I don't mind in the least."

Following her across a narrow bridge, I was struck by a thought: This new fashion of women wearing slacks might be a bit revolutionary, but there was a lot to be said for it. The girl kept up a brisk pace through a pinewood, out again into the hot sun on open moor and over rocky outcrops. She was swinging along with easy strides, but I was beginning to puff and was glad to reach the barn.

My patient was very small and very sorry for himself with his dangling foreleg, and the Aldersons' diagnosis had been correct.

"Clean fracture of the radius and ulna," I said. "It should do well with a plaster on it." I soaked my plaster bandages in water and then, while the girl held the calf's head, applied them to the leg till it was encased from elbow to foot.

When I was satisfied that the plaster was set she released him and the little animal trotted away. "Look," she cried. "He's putting his weight on it already! And doesn't he look happier!" I smiled. The calf felt no pain now, and the fear which always demoralizes a hurt animal had magically vanished.

"He certainly has perked up quickly," I said. My words were almost drowned by a bellow outside the door which the calf answered with a high-pitched bawl. It was a deafening duet.

"That's his mother," the girl shouted. "She's been hanging about all morning wondering what we'd done with her calf."

I opened the door and we both laughed as the big cow rushed in, almost knocking me down, and began pushing her calf around with her muzzle and making muffled lowing noises.

"I'll come back in a month and take the plaster off," I said.

As we left the barn the sunshine and the sweet warm air met us like a high wave. "You're lucky to live here," I said. "You don't need me to tell you."

We sat down on the warm grass and she pointed out the mountains to me—Heskit Fell and Eddleton, Wedder Fell and Colver and Sennor. She spoke the wild Nordic names of them as though they were old friends. "A lot of people find it too bare and wild," she said. "It seems to frighten them."

I laughed. "As far as I'm concerned I can't help feeling sorry for all the thousands of vets who don't work in the Yorkshire Dales." Then almost without knowing, I was telling her about my student days, my hopes and aspirations. I surprised myself with my flow of talk and I felt I must be boring her. But she nodded as though she understood. It came to me that it had been a long time since I had talked to a girl my own age. I didn't want to leave, and when I said "I'll see you in a month" it sounded like an awful long time.

"Helen Alderson?" Siegfried said over lunch. "Lovely girl."

Tristan, across the table, gave a long low whistle.

Siegfried went on. "Her mother died a few years ago and she runs the whole place. Cooks and looks after her father and a younger brother and sister." He spooned some mashed potatoes onto his plate. "Any men friends? Oh, half the young bloods in the district are chasing her, but she seems a choosy sort."

7

THE card dangled above the old lady's bed. It read GOD IS NEAR, but it wasn't like the usual religious text. It didn't have a frame or ornate printing. It was just a strip of cardboard with plain lettering which might have said NO SMOKING or EXIT, and it was looped carelessly over an old gas bracket so that Miss Stubbs could look up and read GOD IS NEAR from where she lay.

There wasn't much more Miss Stubbs could see; perhaps a few feet of privet hedge through the frayed curtains, but mainly it was just the cluttered little room which was her world.

The room was on the ground floor and in the front of the cottage, and as I came up through the wilderness which had once been a garden I could see the dogs watching me from where they stood behind the old lady's bed. And when I knocked, the place erupted with their barking. It was always like this. I had been visiting regularly for over a year and the pattern never changed: the furious barking; then Mrs. Broadwith, who looked after Miss Stubbs, would push all the animals but my patient of the day into the kitchen and I would go in and see Miss Stubbs in her bed with the card hanging over it.

She had been there for a long time and would never get up again. But she never mentioned her illness and pain to me; all her concern was for her three dogs and two cats.

Today it was old Prince and I was worried about him. It was his heart—just about the most spectacular valvular incompetence I had ever heard. He was pleased as ever to see me, his long fringed tail waving gently—that Irish setter tail attached to the bulging black and white body, with shaggy head and upstanding Alsatian ears. Miss Stubbs often used to call him "Mr. Heinz," and though he may not have had fifty-seven varieties in him, Prince's hybrid vigor had stood him in good stead. With a heart like his he should have been dead long ago.

"I thought I'd best give you a ring, Mr. Herriot," Mrs. Broadwith said. "He's been coughing right bad this week and this morning he was a bit staggery. Still eats well, though."

"I bet he does." I ran my hands over the fat on the ribs. "It would take something drastic to put old Prince off his grub."

Miss Stubbs laughed from the bed and the old dog, his mouth wide, eyes dancing, seemed to be joining in the joke. I put my stethoscope over his heart. The beat was a good bit faster than last time; he was on oral digitalis, but it wasn't doing its job. Gloomily I moved the stethoscope over the chest and listened without enthusiasm to the symphony of whistles and squeaks which signaled the workings of Prince's lungs. The old dog stood very erect and proud. He always took it as a tremendous compliment when I examined him and there was no doubt he was enjoying himself now. His was not a painful ailment.

Straightening up, I patted his head and he responded immediately by trying to put his paws on my chest. He didn't quite make it, and even that slight exertion started his ribs heaving and his tongue lolling. I gave him an intramuscular injection of digitalin and another of morphine hydrochloride, which he accepted with apparent pleasure as part of the game.

"I hope that will steady his heart and breathing, Miss Stubbs. You'll find he'll be a bit dopey and that will help, too. I'm going to leave you some more medicine for his bronchitis."

The next stage of the visit began now as Mrs. Broadwith brought in a cup of tea and the rest of the animals were let out of the kitchen. Ben, a Sealyham, and Sally, a cocker spaniel, were closely followed by the cats, Arthur and Susie, who stalked in gracefully and began to rub against my legs.

It was the usual scenario for the many cups of tea I had drunk with Miss Stubbs. "How are you today?" I asked.

"Oh, much better," she said and, as always, changed the subject. She liked to talk about her pets and about the days when her family were alive. She loved to describe the escapades of her brothers, and today she showed me an old photograph of them—three young men in the knee breeches of the 1890s smiled up at me, and the impish humor in their faces came down undimmed over the years.

"My word, they look really bright lads, Miss Stubbs," I said.

"Oh, they were young rips!" She laughed, and for a moment her face was radiant, transfigured by her memories.

Sitting there drinking tea, with the dogs lying beside us and the cats making themselves comfortable on the bed, I felt afraid of the responsibility I had. Except for her memories, the one thing which brought some light into the life of the brave old woman was the transparent devotion of this shaggy bunch, whose eyes were never far from her face. And they were all elderly. A fourth dog, a truly ancient golden Labrador, had died a few months ago. And now I

GOD

had Prince with his heart; Sally beginning to drink a lot of water, which made me wonder if she was starting with a pyometra; and Ben growing steadily thinner with his nephritis. The cats were better, though Susie was a bit scraggy and I kept up a morbid kneading of her furry abdomen for signs of lymphosarcoma. Arthur, a huge neutered tom, ailed not at all except that his teeth tended to tartar up.

This must have been in Miss Stubbs's mind, because when I had finished my tea she asked me to look at his mouth.

"Yes, there's a bit there. Might as well fix it."

Arthur was a living denial of all those theories that cats are cold-natured, selfish and the rest. His fine eyes, framed in the widest cat's face I have ever seen, looked out on the world with an all-embracing benevolence. His every move was marked by dignity. As I started to scrape his teeth, his chest echoed with a booming purr like a distant outboard motor. I accidentally nicked his gum. He casually raised a massive paw as if to say, Have a care, chum, but his claws were sheathed.

My next visit was less than a month later and was in response to an urgent summons from Mrs. Broadwith—Ben had collapsed. In ten minutes I was threading my way through the front garden with the animals watching from their window. As I went into the little room I saw Ben lying on his side, very still, by the bed. It wasn't often these nephritis cases went off so suddenly.

"Well, it was quick, Miss Stubbs. I'm sure the old chap didn't suffer at all." My words sounded lame and ineffectual.

The old lady was in full command of herself. No tears as she looked down at her companion of so many years. My idea was to get him out as quickly as possible and I pulled a blanket under him and lifted him up. "Wait a moment," Miss Stubbs said, and, still with no change of expression, she reached out and touched Ben's head. Then she lay back as I hurried from the room.

In the kitchen I had a whispered conference with Mrs. Broadwith. "I'll run down t'village and get Fred Manners to come and bury him," she said. "Could you stay with the old lady while I'm gone? Talk to her, like, it'll do her good."

I went back and sat down by the bed. "You know, Mr. Herriot," Miss Stubbs said casually, "I'll be the next to go."

"Oh, nonsense! You're feeling a bit low, that's all. We all do when something like this happens." But I was disturbed. I had never heard her even hint at such a thing before.

"I'm not afraid," she said. "There's something better waiting for me. I've never had any doubts." There was silence between us as she lay looking up at the card on the gas bracket.

Then the head on the pillow turned to me again. "I have only one fear." The brave face changed with startling suddenness, as if a mask had dropped, and she grasped my hand. "It's my dogs and cats, Mr. Herriot. I'm afraid I might never see them when I'm gone and it worries me so. You see, I know I'll be reunited with my parents and my brothers, but . . . but . . ."

"Well, why not with your animals?"

"That's just it." For the first time I saw tears on her cheeks. "They say animals have no souls."

"Who says?"

"Oh, I've read it. A lot of religious people believe it."

"Well, I don't." I held her hand firmly. "If having a soul means being able to feel love and loyalty and gratitude, animals are better off than a lot of humans. You've nothing to worry about."

"Oh, I hope you're right. I lie at night thinking about it."

"I know I'm right, Miss Stubbs, and don't you argue with me. They teach us vets all about animals' souls."

She laughed with a return of her old spirit. "I'm sorry. I won't talk about this again. But before you go—I want you to be absolutely honest with me. I know you are very young, but . . . what, truly, are your beliefs? Will my animals go with me?"

"Miss Stubbs," I said, swallowing once or twice. "I'm afraid I'm a bit foggy about all this, but I'm absolutely certain of one thing. Wherever you are going, they are going, too."

She stared at me, but her face was calm again. "Thank you, Mr. Herriot. I know you are being honest with me. That is what you really believe, isn't it?"

"I do," I said. "With all my heart I believe it."

It was not much more than a month later that I learned I had seen Miss Stubbs for the last time. I was on my rounds and a farmer happened to mention that her cottage was up for sale.

"But what about Miss Stubbs?" I asked.

"Oh, went off sudden about three weeks ago."

"Mrs. Broadwith isn't staying on in the house, then?"

"Nay, I hear she's staying at t'other end of the village."

"Do you know what's happened to the dogs and cats?"

About dogs and cats he knew nothing. I lost no time in tracking Mrs. Broadwith down. She was settled in a tiny but attractive house, and she answered my knock herself.

"Oh, come in, Mr. Herriot. It's good of you to call." We sat facing each other across a scrubbed table. "It was sad about the old lady. But she just slept away at the finish."

"I'm glad of that. I've only just heard."

Mrs. Broadwith looked around the room. "I was real lucky to get this place—it's just what I've always wanted."

"What's happened to the animals?" I blurted out.

"Oh, they're in t'garden." She got up and opened the door and with a surge of relief I watched my old friends pour in. Arthur was on my knee in a flash, arching himself ecstatically against my arm while his outboard motor roared softly above the barking of the dogs. Prince, wheezy as ever, tail fanning the air, laughed up at me delightedly between barks.

"I couldn't be parted from them," Mrs. Broadwith said. "They'll have a good home with me as long as they live."

I looked at her Yorkshire country face, its grim lines belied by the kindly eyes. "This is wonderful," I said. "But won't you find it just a bit . . . er . . . expensive to feed them?"

"Nay. I 'ave a bit put away."

"Well fine, fine. I'll look in now and then." I rose to go.

"There *is* one thing—before they sell off the things at the cottage, could you get us what's left of your medicines?"

I took the key and drove to the other end of the village. The door creaked open and inside the silence was like a heavy pall. Nothing had been moved. The bed with its rumpled blankets was still there.

I picked up half-empty bottles, a jar of ointment, old Ben's tablets—a lot of good they had done him.

I wouldn't be coming here anymore. At the door I paused and read for the last time the card which hung over the empty bed.

I WAS about to spend that evening as I spent all Tuesday evenings—staring at the back of Helen Alderson's head at the Darrowby Music Society. It was a slow way of getting to know her, but I had been unable to think of a better idea.

Since the morning I'd set the calf's leg, I had scanned the daybook regularly in the hope of getting a visit to the farm. But the Aldersons seemed to have lamentably healthy stock. And the really crushing blow came when Helen's father rang up to say he had taken off the calf's plaster himself and didn't need me to do it. For the first time I cursed the self-reliance of the Dalesmen. With the courage of desperation I joined the music society.

That was weeks ago and, I reflected miserably, I couldn't remember how many soprano soloists and male choirs had come and gone. Tonight a string quartet was scraping away, and my eyes, as usual, were focused on Helen, sitting between two old ladies. Those two old girls were always there, cutting out any chance of private conversation. And it was not the sort of place where you could just up and say, "What are you doing on Saturday night?"

The scraping stopped, everybody clapped and the vicar got up and beamed on the company. "And now, ladies and gentlemen, I think we might stop for fifteen minutes as I see our willing helpers have prepared tea. The price, as usual, is threepence." There was laughter and a pushing back of chairs.

I went to the rear of the hall with the others. People regarded a vet who liked music as an interesting curiosity so they tended to buttonhole me, but tonight I managed to edge myself as if by accident near Helen.

"Good evening, Mr. Herriot, are you enjoying it?" Why did she *always* say that? And "Mr. Herriot"! But what could I do? "Call me Jim" would sound great. I replied, "Good evening, Miss Alderson. Yes, it's nice, isn't it?" Things were going with a bang again.

I munched my biscuit while the old ladies talked about Mozart. It was about time I gave up the whole thing.

The vicar approached, his gaze twinkling from Helen to me. "Perhaps our young friends would take the washing up tonight?"

Washing up teacups suddenly seemed like the promised land.

The scullery had a sink and a few shelves and just about room for the two of us. I began to run the hot water. Now, I thought, I can work the conversation to where I want it. But we didn't talk about anything but music. We were nearly through the pile of crockery, and I was near panic when I lifted the last cup from the soapy water. Helen tried to take it from me to dry, but I clung to the handle while I waited for inspiration. It was developing into a tug-of-war. Then I heard a hoarse croak which I only just recognized as my own voice. "Can I see you sometime?"

For a moment she didn't answer. Was she surprised, annoyed? Anyway, she flushed. "If you like."

"Saturday evening?" She nodded, dried the cup and was gone.

I went back to my seat with my heart thudding. The strains of mangled Haydn from the quartet went unheeded. Did she really want to come out? Had I hustled her into it against her will? My toes curled with embarrassment at the thought, but for better or for worse it was a step forward. I had done it at last.

I LOOKED out at the autumn mist dissolving in the early sunshine. There was a chill in the old house this morning, as though a cold hand had reached out to remind us of hard months ahead.

"It says here," Siegfried said, adjusting his paper against the coffeepot, "that farmers have no feeling for animals."

I buttered a piece of toast. "Cruel, you mean?"

"Not exactly. This chap maintains that to a farmer livestock are purely commercial—there's no affection in it."

"Well, they'd all go mad if they were like Kit Bilton." Kit was a truck driver who, like most of the workingmen of Darrowby, kept a pig for family consumption. The snag was that when killing time came Kit couldn't bear it.

I happened to go into his house once and found his wife and

daughter hard at it cutting up the meat while Kit huddled miserably by the fire. He was a huge man who could throw a twelve-stone sack of meal onto his wagon with a jerk of his arms, but he seized my hand and sobbed. "He was like a Christian was that pig, Mr. Herriot."

"But Kit isn't a real farmer." Siegfried sawed off a slice of Mrs. Hall's home-baked bread. "The question is, can the dairy farmer milking maybe fifty cows become really fond of any of them, or are they just milk-producing units?"

"You put your finger on it. It's numbers," I said. "The farmers with only a few stock always have names for them—Daisy, Mabel, I know one called Kipperlugs. These people are fond of their animals. But I agree, I don't see how the big men can be."

Siegfried stretched luxuriously. "Well, I'm sending you to see a really big man this morning—John Skipton of Dennaby Close. He's got some tooth rasping to do on a couple of old horses."

I always felt at my most medieval when I was caught up in large-animal dentistry, and before the draft horse was replaced by tractors it was a regular task. I looked with distaste at the tooth instruments: the vicious long-armed forceps, sharp-jawed shears, mouth gags, hammers and chisels, files and rasps. It was rather like a quiet corner in the Spanish Inquisition.

Dennaby Close was not just a substantial farm; it was a monument to a man's endurance and skill. The fine old house and extensive buildings, the great sweep of lush grassland along the lower slopes of the fell were all proof that old John Skipton had achieved the impossible; he had started as an uneducated farm laborer and was now a wealthy landowner.

The miracle hadn't happened easily; old John had a lifetime of toil behind him that would have killed most men. He had conquered, but to some people it seemed that he had himself been conquered in the process. He had had no time for a family or creature comforts—his poorest workers lived in better style than he did—and he'd driven himself so fiercely that he couldn't stop.

I paused as I got out of the car and stood marveling again at the house, whose elegance had withstood three hundred years of the

Dales climate—the graceful manor with its tall leaded windows, the massive chimneys towering over moss-grown roof tiles. There should have been a cavalier in ruffles and hose pacing beneath the wide stone arch. But there was just tattered old John stumping impatiently toward me.

"Hello, young man," he cried. "We'll have to walk down to t'river; 'osses are down there."

I eased my box of instruments from the car. It seemed to be filled with lead. The old man seized a pitchfork, stabbed it into a bale of hay, hoisted it effortlessly over his shoulder and set off at a trot. I stumbled after him, puffing and trying to put away the thought that he was at least fifty years older.

About halfway down we came across a group of men repairing a gap in one of the dry stone walls. One of the men looked up. "Nice mornin', Mr. Skipton," he sang out cheerfully.

"Never mind t'mornin'. Get on wi' some work," grunted old John, and the man smiled as though he had received a compliment.

At last we reached the river. The two horses were standing in the pebbly shallows, nose to tail; they had been rubbing their chins gently along each other's backs. A high cliff overhanging the far bank made a perfect windbreak for them, while on our side clumps of oak and beech blazed in the sunshine.

"They're in a nice spot, Mr. Skipton," I said.

"Aye, they can keep cool in the hot weather and they've got the barn when winter comes." John pointed to a low thick-walled building. "They can come and go as they please."

The sound of his voice brought the horses out of the river at a stiff trot. The mare was a chestnut and the gelding a bay, but both coats were flecked with gray. The deep cavities above their eyes showed their years. For all that, they capered around John, stamping their feet, throwing their heads about, pushing his cap over his eyes with their muzzles.

"Get by!" he shouted. "Daft awd beggars." But he tugged at the mare's forelock and ran his hand along the gelding's neck.

"When did they last do any work?" I asked.

"Oh, about twelve years ago. They're retired like. They've

earned it." For a moment he stood silent, then he spoke as if to himself. "They were two slaves when I was a slave." He looked at me and for a revealing moment I read in the pale blue eyes something of the struggle he had shared with the animals.

"But twelve years! How old are they, anyway?"

John's mouth twisted up. "You're t'vet. You tell me."

I stepped forward confidently and looked at the mare's teeth. "I've never seen anything like this," I gasped. The incisors were immensely long and all of the usual marks had long since gone. I laughed. "It's no good, I'd only be guessing."

"She's about thirty. Gelding's a year or two younger. She's had fifteen grand foals and never ailed except a bit of teeth trouble. It's time they were both rasped again. Gelding's the worst—has a right job champin' his grub."

A quick exploration of the mare's mouth revealed what I suspected—the outside edges of the upper teeth were overgrown and jagged and were irritating the cheeks, while the inside edges of the lower molars were doing the same to the tongue.

"With those sharp edges rubbed off she'll be as good as new, Mr. Skipton." A few minutes' work with the rasp reduced the points. "I don't want to make them too smooth," I said, "or she won't be able to grind her food."

John grunted. "Good enough. Now have a look at t'other."

I had a feel at the gelding's teeth. "Soon put him right, too," I said. I pushed at the rasp, but the thing wouldn't go fully to the back of the mouth. I reached in again with my fingers, and I came upon something like a great chunk of bone projecting down from the roof of the mouth. I shone my pocket flashlight over the back of the tongue and saw that the last upper molar was overlapping the lower one so far that it was like a barb about three inches long stabbing down into the tender tissue of the gum.

That would have to come off; it meant using those great long-handled shears. They gave me the willies. You fastened the sharp blades onto the tooth and began to turn the crossbar slowly, slowly. Soon the tooth began to groan and creak under the tremendous leverage and you knew that any second it would crack off like a rifle in your ear. That was when all hell usually broke loose—not because of pain, because the overgrown part had no nerve supply; it was the noise that caused the trouble.

I produced the dreadful instrument from my crate and with it a Haussmann's gag to hold the mouth wide. It was easy to see then—another great prong at the other side of the mouth exactly like the first. Great, great, I had two to chop off.

The old horse stood patiently, eyes almost closed, while I went through the motions with my toes curling. When the sharp cracks came the eyes opened wide, but he never even moved.

"Good job I got you along, young man," old John said. "Reckon he'll feel a lot better now." And he turned and stumped up the hill at a furious pace. I panted along in the rear, changing my box from hand to hand every few minutes. About halfway up, the heavy thing slipped out of my grasp. This gave me a chance for a breather. I looked back at the horses; they had returned to the shallows and were playing, chasing each other.

Back in the farmyard, John paused awkwardly. "Thank ye, young man," he said, and turned abruptly away while I dumped my box in the car. It was then that I saw the man who had spoken to us on the way down. He was sitting in a sunny corner with his dinner packet.

"You've been down to see t'pensioners, then? By gaw, awd John should know the way."

"Regular visitor, is he?"

"Regular? Every day God sends. Rain, snow or blow. And allus has summat with him—bag o' corn, straw for their bedding."

"And he's done that for twelve years?"

The man unscrewed his thermos flask. "Aye, them 'osses haven't done a stroke o' work all that time and he could've got good money for them from the meat merchants. Odd, isn't it?"

"You're right," I said. "It's odd."

Just how odd it was occupied my thoughts all the way back to the surgery. We had just about decided at breakfast that the man with a lot of animals couldn't be expected to feel affection for individuals among them. John Skipton must have hundreds.

Yet what made him trail down that hill every day in all weathers? Why had he filled the last years of those old horses with peace and beauty? Given them a final ease he denied himself?

It could only be love.

8

"The Reniston, eh?" I said uneasily. "Bit grand, isn't it?"

Tristan peered up through the usual cloud of smoke. "Of course it's grand. It's the most luxurious hotel this side of London, but you want to impress this girl, don't you? Well, ring her up and tell her you're taking her to the Reniston. The food is wonderful, there's a dinner dance every Saturday night." He sat up suddenly and his eyes widened. "Can't you see it, Jim? The music oozing out of Benny Thornton's trombone and you, full of lobster thermidor, floating round the floor with Helen snuggling up to you. If you are prepared to spend about a fortnight's wages you can have a really good night."

I hardly heard the last part, I was concentrating on the blinding vision of Helen snuggling up to me.

Tristan broke in. "Have you got a dinner jacket?"

"I hired one at Brawton for Mrs. Pumphrey's party, but there's no time to get one for tonight. I do have a dinner suit, but I got it when I was about seventeen. I doubt if I could get into it."

Tristan waved this aside. "That doesn't matter, Jim. As long as you're wearing the proper gear they'll let you in, and with a big good-looking chap like you the fit of the suit is unimportant."

We extracted the suit from the bottom of my trunk. I had cut quite a dash in it at college dances, but the fashion now was all for comfortable jackets and unstarched shirts. This outfit was rigidly of the old school, including an absurd little waistcoat with lapels, and a stiff shiny-fronted shirt with a wing collar. But the real problem appeared when I put it on. Hard work, Pennine air and Mrs. Hall's good food had filled me out and the jacket failed to meet across my stomach by six inches. I seemed to have got taller, too, because there was a generous space between the bottom of the waistcoat and the top of the trousers. The trousers themselves were skintight up top and oddly baggy below the knees.

Tristan's confidence evaporated. We decided to call on Mrs. Hall. She was an unemotional woman and endured the irregular life at Skeldale House without noticeable reaction, but when she saw me her facial muscles went into a long twitching spasm. She finally overcame the weakness and became very businesslike.

"A little gusset at the back of your trousers will work wonders, Mr. Herriot, and I think if I put a bit of silk cord across the front of your jacket it'll hold it nicely. Mind you, there'll be a bit of space like, but I shouldn't think that'll worry you. And I'll give the whole suit a good press—makes all the difference."

I REALLY went to work on myself that night, scrubbing and anointing and trying a whole series of different partings in my hair before I was satisfied. Tristan, as master of the wardrobe, brought the suit tenderly upstairs, still warm from Mrs. Hall's ironing.

When I was finally arrayed Tristan circled around me, pulling and patting and making delicate adjustments here and there. Eventually he stopped and surveyed me from the front. "Fine, Jim, fine," he said. "You look distinguished, you know. It's not everybody who can wear a dinner jacket—so many people look like conjurers, but not you."

I had arranged to pick up Helen at seven o'clock and as I stood outside her house a strange unease crept over me. When I had come here before it had been as a veterinary surgeon—the man who knew, who came to render assistance in time of need. It had never occurred to me how much this affected my outlook every time I walked onto a farm. Now I had come to take this man's daughter out. He might not like it, might positively resent it. I took a deep breath and knocked.

Helen's young brother let me in. The boy had a hand over his mouth in an attempt to hide a grin. His little sister was pretending to concentrate on her homework, but she, too, wore a fixed smirk. They seemed to find the situation funny.

Mr. Alderson was reading the *Farmer and Stock-Breeder*, his stockinged feet stretched out toward a blazing pile of logs. "Come in, young man, and sit by the fire," he said absently. I had the uncomfortable impression that it was a frequent and boring experience for him to have young men calling for his older daughter. I sat down and he returned to his magazine. I stared into the fire till my eyes ached. Then I studied the oil painting above the mantelpiece. Mr. Alderson turned a page. The large wall clock ticked on. Spluttering noises came from the children.

After about a year I heard footsteps on the stairs, then Helen came into the room. She was wearing a blue dress—the kind without shoulder straps that seems to stay up by magic. Her dark hair shone under the kitchen light, and over one white arm she held a camel's hair coat. I felt stunned. She was like a rare jewel in a rough setting. She gave me her friendly smile. "Hello, I hope I haven't kept you waiting too long."

I muttered something in reply. She kissed her father, who didn't look up but waved vaguely. There was another outburst of giggling from the table.

In the car I felt unusually tense. For a mile or two inane remarks about the weather were all that kept the conversation going. I was beginning to relax when I drove over a little humpbacked bridge into a dip in the road. Then the car suddenly stopped. The engine coughed once, then left us silent in the darkness. And there was something else; my feet and ankles were freezing cold.

"My God!" I shouted. "We've run into a bit of flooded road. I'm terribly sorry about this—your feet must be soaked."

But Helen was laughing. She had her feet tucked up on the seat, her knees under her chin. "Yes, I am a bit wet, but it's no good sitting about like this. Hadn't we better start pushing?"

We waded out into the black icy water. We managed to push the little car out of the flooded patch. I dried the plugs and got the engine going and we squelched back into the car.

Helen shivered. "I'm afraid I'll have to go home and change my shoes and stockings. And so will you. We can go back by the Fensley road."

Mr. Alderson was still reading. He gave me a baleful glance

when he learned that I needed to borrow a pair of his shoes and socks, and rose, groaning, from his chair.

Helen followed him upstairs and I was left alone with the children. They studied my sodden trousers with undisguised delight. I had wrung most of the surplus water out of them, but the final result was remarkable. Mrs. Hall's knife-edge crease reached to just below the knee. Then there was chaos. And as I stood by the fire to dry, a gentle steam rose about me.

Mr. Alderson reappeared at length and dropped some shoes and rough socks at my feet. I pulled on the socks quickly, but the shoes! They were dancing slippers from the early days of the century and their cracked patent leather was topped by wide black silk bows. Mr. Alderson had dug himself deep into his chair and had found his place again among the pig prices. I had the feeling that if I asked for a plainer pair he would attack me with the poker. I put the slippers on.

We took a roundabout road to avoid the flood, but I kept my foot down and we made good time.

By day the Reniston dominated Brawton like a vast medieval fortress, bright flags fluttering arrogantly from its four turrets, but tonight it was like a dark cliff with a glowing cavern at street level where the Bentleys discharged their expensive cargoes. I tucked the Austin away quietly at the back of the parking lot. A magnificent commissionaire opened the door for us and we trod noiselessly over the rich carpeting of the entrance hall.

We parted there to get rid of our coats, and in the men's room, as I scrubbed some of the Austin's oil from my hands, I looked up in the mirror at the white-jacketed attendant hovering behind me with a towel. The man, clearly fascinated, was staring at my pierrot shoes and rumpled trouser bottoms. As he handed over the towel he smiled broadly.

I met Helen in the reception hall and we went over to the desk. "What time does the dinner dance start?" I asked.

The girl at the desk looked surprised. "I'm sorry, sir, there's no dance tonight. We only have them once a fortnight."

Helen met my dismay with a smile. "It doesn't matter," she said.

"Well, we can have dinner, anyway." I tried to speak cheerfully, but a little black cloud seemed to be forming just above my head. Would anything go right tonight? The dining room didn't help my morale. As big as a football field, with great marble pillars, a carved painted ceiling. All the ornate splendor of Victorian days lived on in this tremendous room. Most of the tables were occupied by the usual clientele, a mixture of county aristocracy and industrialists from the West Riding. I had never seen so many beautiful women and masterful-looking men under one roof, and I noticed with a twinge of alarm that though the men were wearing everything from dark lounge suits to hairy tweeds, there wasn't a dinner jacket in sight.

A majestic figure in white tie bore down on us. He looked like a Roman emperor. His eyes flickered expertly over me and he spoke tonelessly. "You want a table, sir?"

"Yes please," I mumbled, only just stopping myself from saying "sir" to the man in return. "A table for two."

"Are you staying, sir?"

This question baffled me. How could I possibly have dinner here if I wasn't staying? "Yes, I am staying."

The emperor made a note on a pad. "This way, sir."

He moved with great dignity among the tables while I followed abjectly in his wake with Helen, trying to ignore the heads which turned to have a second look as I passed.

The table was nicely situated and a swarm of waiters descended on us, pulling out our chairs and shaking out our napkins. When they had dispersed the emperor took charge again.

"May I have your room number, sir?"

I stared up at him over my dangerously billowing shirtfront. "Room number? Oh, I'm not living in the hotel."

"Ah, *not* staying." He fixed me with an icy look, and, muttering something to one of the waiters, he strode away.

It was about then that the black cloud descended, enveloping me in misery. The evening was a disaster and would get worse. I must have been mad to come to this sumptuous place dressed up like a knockabout comedian. I took a menu card from a waiter.

Everything was in French, but somehow I ordered the meal. As we ate I tried desperately to keep a conversation going—in vain. Long deserts of silence began to stretch between us. Worst of all was the little voice which kept telling me that Helen had never really wanted to come out with me anyway.

We rode most of the way home in strained silence. By the time we drew up outside the farm my head had begun to ache. We shook hands and Helen thanked me for a lovely evening. There was a tremor in her voice and in the moonlight her face was anxious and withdrawn. I said good night and drove away.

THE longer I worked in Darrowby the more the charms of the Dales beguiled me. And there was one solid advantage of which I became more aware every day—the Dales farmers really knew how to handle animals. To a vet whose patients are constantly trying to thwart him or injure him it was a blessing.

In my weakened condition the morning after the Reniston horror, I looked with particular satisfaction at the two men holding my patient the cow. It wasn't a difficult job—just an intravenous injection—but still it was reassuring to have two such sturdy fellows to help me. Maurice Bennison, as tough as one of his own hill beasts, had a horn in his right hand while the fingers of his left gripped the nose. His brother George, whose job it was to raise the vein for me to push the needle in, held the choke rope limply in enormous hands and grinned down at me amiably from his six feet four inches.

"Right, George," I said. "Tighten up that rope and lean against the cow to stop her coming round on me." I pushed my way between the cow and her neighbor, past George's unyielding bulk, and bent over the jugular vein. It was standing out very nicely. I poised the needle and thrust quickly into the vein.

"Lovely!" I cried as the dark blood fountained out and spattered thickly on the straw bedding beneath. "Slacken your rope, George . . . George! For God's sake, get your weight off me!"

Because George had apparently decided to rest his full two hundred pounds on me instead of the cow, and as I tried desperately to connect the tube to the needle I felt my knees giving way. I shouted again, louder, but he was inert, his chin resting on my shoulder. I fell flat on my face and lay there writhing under the motionless body. George was unconscious.

"Maurice," I gasped, crawling out from beneath his brother. "Get him out, quick, before the cows trample him." Maurice dropped the cow's head, grabbed George by the ankles and hauled. George shot out from under the cows, his head beating a brisk tattoo on the cobbles, to continue his sleep on the byre floor. Without a word Maurice moved back to his post by the cow and waited for me to continue with my injection. But I found that sprawled body distracting. "Look, couldn't we sit him up against the wall and put his head between his legs?" I suggested apologetically. To humor me, Maurice grabbed George's shoulders and trundled him over the floor with the expertise of a man used to throwing around bags of potatoes. Even propped against the stones, the poor fellow didn't look so good.

"Don't you think we might give him a drink?" I said.

But Maurice had had enough of pampering George. "Nay, nay, he'll be right," he muttered testily. "Let's get on with t'job."

The incident started me thinking about people's reactions to the sight of blood. Even though it was only my second year of practice I had already learned that it was always the biggest men who went down, especially superconfident types. I suppose it was a bit early to start compiling statistics, but I had never seen a woman or small man pass out, however squeamish they might feel.

This sort of thing, I had found, was always just around the corner. I suppose we must have more trouble in this way than our medical colleagues, because they do most of their cutting and carving in hospitals, whereas vets have to operate on the spot. This means that the owners and attendants of the animals are pulled in as helpers and subjected to some unusual sights. Anyway, in a very short time I became a fair authority on the various manifestations of "coming over queer."

One of my most vivid recollections is of a summer evening when I had to carry out a rumenotomy on a cow. As a rule I was inclined to play for time when I suspected a foreign body—there were so many other conditions with similar symptoms that I was never in a hurry to make a hole in the animal's side. But this time diagnosis was clear. To clinch it, the farmer told me he had been repairing a hen house in the cow pasture—nailing up loose boards. I knew where one of the nails had gone.

The farm was right on the main street of the village, and as I laid out my instruments a row of grinning faces watched from above the half door of the box, encouraging me with ribald shouts. It occurred to me I could use an extra pair of hands. "How would one of you lads like to be my assistant?" I asked. After much shouting, a huge youth with a shock of red hair ambled into the box. Magnificent sight he was, and the bright blue eyes and ruddy high-cheekboned face reminded me that Norsemen had been around the Dales a thousand years ago. This was a Viking.

I had him roll up his sleeves and scrub while I infiltrated the cow's flank with anesthetic. When I gave him artery forceps and scissors to hold he pranced around, making stabbing motions at the cow and roaring with laughter.

"Maybe you'd like to do the job yourself?" I asked.

The Viking squared his great shoulders. "Aye, I'll 'ave a go," and the heads above the door cheered lustily. As I poised my scalpel with its new razor-sharp blade over the cow, the air was thick with earthy witticisms. I had decided that this time I really would make the bold incision recommended in the surgery books; it was about time I advanced beyond the stage of pecking nervously at the skin. "A veritable blow" was how one learned author had described it. Well, that was how it was going to be.

With a quick motion of the wrist I laid open a ten-inch wound. I stood back for a few seconds admiring its clean-cut edges. Only a few capillaries were spurting onto the glistening, twitching abdominal muscles. At the same time I noticed that the noises from the heads above the door had been replaced by an eerie silence.

"Forceps, please," I said, extending my hand back. Nothing happened. I looked around; the top of the half door was bare—not a face in sight. There was only the Viking spread-eagled on the floor, chin pointing to the roof. The attitude was so theatrical that I thought he was playacting. But no, the Viking was out cold.

The farmer, who was holding the cow's head, glanced at me with a flicker of amusement. "Looks like you and me for it, then, guvnor." He tied the halter to a ring on the wall, washed his hands methodically and took up his place at my side. Throughout the operation he passed instruments, swabbed blood and clipped sutures, whistling tunelessly through his teeth. When I produced the offending nail from the cow's depths, he raised his eyebrows and said "'Ello, 'ello," then whistled again.

We were too busy to do anything for the Viking. Halfway through he sat up, shook himself, then got to his feet and strolled with elaborate nonchalance out of the box. The poor fellow seemed to be hoping that perhaps we had noticed nothing unusual.

9

If only my car had had any brakes I would certainly have enjoyed looking down on Worton village from the high moor—the old stone houses straggling along the riverbank, with their bright little gardens and green clipped lawns. But the whole scene was clouded by the thought that I had to get down that road with its one-in-four gradient and those two villainous bends. It was like a malevolent snake coiling almost headlong from where I sat. And, as I said, I had no brakes.

Of course the vehicle had originally been fitted with the means of bringing it to a halt, and, during most of the year I had driven it, a violent pressure on the pedal would have the desired effect, though with a certain amount of veering about on the road. But now the response was nil.

I had brought the matter up with Siegfried and he had expressed concern. "That won't do at all, James. I'll have a word with Hammond about it. Leave it with me." And a few days later, "Oh Lord, yes. I've been meaning to fix it up with Hammond. Don't worry, James. I'll see to it."

Finally I had to tell him that the only way I had of stopping the car was to crash it into bottom gear. "Oh bad luck, James. Must be a nuisance for you." So I asked Mr. Hammond down at the garage if he had heard anything from Siegfried. He hadn't.

There wasn't much I could do. It was Siegfried's car.

I looked again down the steep track. The sensible thing, of course, would be to go back into Darrowby and take the low road into Worton. But that meant a round trip of ten miles and I could actually see the farm I wanted to visit just a thousand feet below. In fact, there was old Mr. Robinson now, pottering across the yard with a bucket. I could almost reach out and touch him. I had to make up my mind: to Darrowby or over the top? At last I did what I always did—took the quick way down.

But this hill really was a beauty, and as I nosed gingerly onto it, the whole world seemed to drop away from me. With the gear lever in low I headed, dry-mouthed, down the strip of tarmac, which now looked to be almost vertical. As the first bend rushed up at me the little engine started a rising scream of protest. When I hit the curve I hauled the wheel around desperately to the right, the tires spun for a second in the stones and loose soil of the bank, then we were off again.

This was a longer stretch and even steeper. As I hurtled into the bend the thought of turning at this speed was preposterous, but it was that or over the edge. Terror-stricken, I dragged the wheel to the left. One side of the car lifted and I was sure we were over. It rocked from side to side for a horrible second or two before it finally decided to stay upright, and I was once more on my way. I was aware of a curious numbness. I seemed to have reached the ultimate limits of fear when at last the road began leveling out. I had made it.

It wasn't till I veered onto the final straight that I saw the sheep. Hundreds of them, only yards away. A river of woolly backs lapping from wall to wall. My speed had dropped, but I was still going downhill. Without hesitation I turned and drove straight into a wall.

There didn't seem to be much damage. A few stones slithered down as the engine stalled and fell silent. I sank back in my seat, relaxing my clenched jaws, releasing, finger by finger, my fierce grip on the wheel while the sheep flowed past. I took a sideways glance at the man who was shepherding them. He was a stranger to me and I prayed he didn't recognize me either, because at that moment the role of unknown madman seemed to be the ideal one. Best not to say anything; appearing around a corner and driving deliberately into a wall is no basis for a rewarding conversation.

The sheep were still passing by and I could hear the man calling to his dogs. But I kept up a steady stare at the stones in front of me until he had passed me by.

I suppose some people would have asked me what the hell I was playing at, but not a Dales shepherd. He went quietly by without invading my privacy, but when I looked in the mirror after a few moments I could see him in the middle of the road staring back at me, his sheep temporarily forgotten.

THERE is a piercing clarity about the memory of my brakeless period which has kept it fresh over the years. I suppose it lasted only a few weeks, but it could have gone on indefinitely if Siegfried himself hadn't become involved. It was when we were going to a case together. For some reason he decided to take the Austin and settled in the driver's seat. I cowered next to him as he set off at his usual brisk pace.

Hinchcliffe's farm lies about a mile on the main road outside Darrowby. It is a massive place with a wide straight drive leading down to the house. We weren't going there, but as Siegfried spurted to full speed I could see Mr. Hinchcliffe in his big Buick ahead of us proceeding in a leisurely way along the middle of the road. As Siegfried pulled out to overtake, the farmer suddenly stuck out his hand and began to turn into his farm—directly across our path. Siegfried's foot went down hard on the brake pedal and his eyebrows shot right up as nothing happened. We were going straight for the side of the Buick and there was no room to go around back of it.

Siegfried didn't panic. He turned with the Buick and the two cars roared side by side down the drive, Mr. Hinchcliffe staring at us with bulging eyes. He stopped at the front door, but we continued around the house because we had to.

Fortunately it was one of those places with a circular drive, and we rattled through the stackyard and back to the front of the house behind Mr. Hinchcliffe, who had got out and was looking around the corner to see where we had gone. He turned in astonishment and, openmouthed, watched us as we passed; but Siegfried, retaining his aplomb to the end, inclined his head and gave a little wave before we shot up the drive. Just as we returned to the main road I had a look back at Mr. Hinchcliffe. He was still watching us and there was a certain rigidity in his pose which reminded me of the shepherd.

Siegfried steered carefully into a lay-by and stopped. For a few moments he stared straight ahead and I realized he was having a little difficulty getting his patient look properly adjusted; but when he finally turned to me his face was transfigured, almost saintly. I dug my nails into my palms.

"Really, James," he said. "I can't understand why you keep things to yourself. Heaven knows how long your car has been in this condition, yet never a word from you." He raised a forefinger and his patient look was replaced by one of sorrowing gravity. "Don't you realize we might have been killed back there? You really ought to have told me."

I WAS used to this aspect of Siegfried's character and could usually laugh it off. But a day or two after the Hinchcliffe episode it was suddenly too much.

Siegfried was bending over the daybook. "Now let's see what we've got this morning. Barnett, Gill, Dent . . . Oh, and I'd better see Scruton's calf—you've been attending it, I know, but I'm going right past the door. Can you tell me about it?"

"It's been breathing a bit fast and running a temperature around a hundred and three—not pneumonia, I think. I suspect it may be developing diphtheria—there's a swelling on the jaw and the throat glands are up."

All the time I was speaking, Siegfried continued to write, stopping once to whisper to Miss Harbottle. Then he looked up brightly. "Pneumonia, eh? How have you been treating it?"

"I said I didn't think it was pneumonia. I've been injecting prontosil and I left liniment to rub on the throat region."

But Siegfried was writing hard again. He tore a page from the pad and gave it to me. "Right, you've been applying liniment to the chest. Which liniment exactly?"

"Lin. methyl. sal. Not on the chest. On the throat." But Siegfried had turned away to tell Miss Harbottle the order of his visits and I was talking to the back of his head.

Finally he stood up. "Well, let's get on. But why the devil are you rubbing liniment on the calf's throat?"

"Well, I thought it might relieve the inflammation a bit."

"But James"—he was wearing his patient look again—"don't you think it would do more good on the chest wall?"

"No, I don't. Not in a case of calf diphtheria."

Siegfried laid his hand on my shoulder. "My dear old James, start at the beginning. Speak slowly and calmly so you won't become confused. You were treating a calf with pneumonia . . ."

I thrust my hands deep into my coat pockets and began to churn among the thermometers and scissors and little bottles which always dwelt there. "Look, I told you right at the start that I suspected early diphtheria and that there was a fever of a hundred and three."

Siegfried was looking past me at the window. "Just look at that snow. Don't you think, James, that with that temperature you should be injecting prontosil? Just a suggestion, James—I wouldn't interfere."

"But hell, I *am* using prontosil!" I shouted. "I've been doing my damnedest to get this across to you, but what chance—"

"Come come, dear boy. No need to upset yourself." Siegfried's face was transfigured by an internal radiance. Tolerance and affection flowed from my boss in an enveloping wave. I battled with an impulse to kick him swiftly on the shin. "James, James. We haven't all got the gift of communication. You're the most excellent fellow, but must apply yourself to this. It is simply a matter of marshaling your facts—only a question of practice, I'm sure." He gave an encouraging wave of the hand and was gone.

I strode quickly through to the stock room and, seeing a big empty cardboard box on the floor, dealt it a vicious kick. I put so much venom into it that my foot went clear through the cardboard, and I was plunging about the room swearing and trying to shake the box loose when Tristan came in. "What's up, Jim? Has my big brother been getting under your skin?"

I sank down on a crate. "I don't know. Why should he get under my skin now? It's never bothered me before. What the hell's wrong with me?"

Tristan looked at me thoughtfully. "There's nothing much wrong with you, Jim, but I can tell you one thing—you've been just a bit edgy since you went out with the Alderson girl."

"Oh God," I groaned. "Don't remind me. Anyway, I've not seen her since, so that's the end of that and I can't blame her."

"Yes, but look at you. If she's given you the old heave-ho, so what? Do you know how many times I've been spurned?"

"Spurned? I never even got started."

"All right, but you're going around like a bullock with bellyache. I've been watching you working all hours, and I tell you this dedicated vet thing is all right up to a point. But you've got to live a little. Think of all the lovely lasses just waiting for a big handsome chap like you to gallop up on his white horse." He leaned over and slapped my knee. "Tell you what. Why don't you let me fix up a nice little foursome?"

"Ach, I don't know. I'm not keen, really."

"Nonsense!" Tristan said. "Don't be so monkish."

I was awakened late that night by a heavy weight crashing down on the bed. "Jim," said a voice breathing beer-scented smoke. "I bring you glad tidings. Remember that little nurse Brenda you've seen me around with? Well she's got a pal—Connie, another nurse. The four of us are going dancing at the Poulton Institute on Tuesday."

"You mean me, too?"

"I do. You're going to have the best time you've ever had."

It was a new experience for me to be standing outside the hospital waiting for the nurses to come off duty, but Tristan's experience showed, mainly in the shrewd position he took up in a dark corner of the gas company's doorway. From there he could look across into the hospital and the long white corridor leading to the nurses' quarters. There was another advantage to this stance: if Siegfried should happen to pass that way, Triss would be invisible.

At half past seven he nudged me. Two girls had come out of the hospital. "That's Connie, Jim, that lovely coppery blonde."

We went over and Tristan introduced me with characteristic charm. I was beginning to feel better. There *was* something therapeutic in having two pretty girls look up with parted lips and shining eyes as though I were the answer to their every prayer.

They were remarkably alike except for the hair. Brenda's was very dark. Both of them projected a powerful image of bursting health—fresh cheeks, white teeth, lively eyes and something else which I found particularly easy to take—a simple desire to please.

Tristan opened the back door of the car with a flourish. "Be careful in there, Connie—he looks quiet, but he's a devil."

Both girls giggled as we set off at breakneck speed. Tristan was in full cry and the girls laughed in delight at everything he said. I could feel Connie shaking. The little car, swaying around a sharp corner, had thrown her against me and she stayed there quite naturally with her head on my shoulder, her hair against my cheek. She smelled cleanly of soap and antiseptic. My mind went back to Helen—I didn't think much about her these days. It was a question of practice, to scotch every thought of her as soon as it came up. I was getting pretty good at it now. Anyway, that was all over.

I put my arm around Connie and she lifted her face to me. Ah well, I thought as I kissed her. Tristan's voice rose in song from the front seat, Brenda giggled, the old car sped on.

We came at last to Poulton, whose single street straggled untidily uphill to a green with an old stone cross. Back of it on a steep mound was perched the institute hall. But Tristan was not planning to go straight to the dance. "There's a lovely little pub here. We'll just have a toothful to get us in the mood."

We had the small stone pub to ourselves. The landlord's cheerful round face lit up at the sight of Tristan. "Now then, Mr. Farnon, are you very well?"

"Never better, Mr. Peacock, and how are you?"

"Nicely, sir, nicely."

"Mr. Peacock keeps some of the finest draft Magnet in Yorkshire," Tristan said to us. "Perhaps you'd be kind enough to bring us two pints and two halves, Mr. Peacock."

I noticed there was no question of asking the girls what they would like, but they seemed quite happy. The landlord reappeared from the cellar, puffing slightly, with a tall enameled jug from which he poured a thin brown stream, varying the height expertly till he had produced a white frothy head on each glass.

Tristan raised his pint and looked at it with quiet reverence. He took a sip, which he retained in his mouth for a few seconds. He closed his eyes for a long time and when he opened them they were rapturous, as though he had seen a beautiful vision.

"It's an experience," he whispered. "Keeping beer in the wood is a skillful business, but you, Mr. Peacock, are an artist." Raising his glass in salute, he drained it with an easy upward motion of the elbow. Little oohs of admiration came from the girls.

I was always at a disadvantage in the company of a virtuoso like Tristan, but as the landlord kept revisiting with his jug it seemed to become easier. I was soothed and comforted. Tristan was right—I had been needing this. I hadn't realized at first that Connie was one of the most beautiful creatures I had ever seen. I had failed to notice the perfection of her skin, the mysterious greenish depths of her eyes. And the laughing mouth, shining even teeth and little pink tongue. Everything I said was brilliantly witty, and she looked at me in open admiration. It was profoundly reassuring. Time slowed down and finally there was no past or future, only Connie and the warm untroubled present.

I was surprised when Tristan pulled at my arm. I had forgotten he was there. It was suddenly important that I should tell my friend how deeply touched I was by his concern for me. "My dear old chap," I said thickly. "May I take this opportunity of telling you that I consider that in all Yorkshire there is no finer gentleman breathing than T. Farnon."

The face across from me swam into focus. "You honor me, old friend. Let us now have one for the road and get on to this dance."

We did so, taking, at last, affectionate leave of Mr. Peacock. After the brightness of the inn the darkness pressed on us like a blanket, and we groped our way up the hill to the institute. A cheerful young farmer took our money and we were soon swallowed up in a tight mass of young men in stiff dark suits and girls in bright dresses, all sweating happily as they swayed and wheeled. On a low platform at one end four musicians were playing their hearts out—piano, accordion, violin and drums. At the table at the other end several comfortable middle-aged women presided over thick sandwiches, jugs of milk and homemade pies, and trifles generously laid with whipped cream.

I launched out confidently with Connie. There was a lot of twirling and stamping and the noise was deafening. I loved it and whirled Connie lightly among the throng. I was dimly aware of bumping people, but, try as I might, I couldn't feel my feet touching the floor. I decided I'd never been so happy. After half a dozen dances we floated toward the food table. We each ate an enormous wedge of ham-and-egg pie which was so exquisite that we had another, then some of the trifle. It was about halfway through the next waltz that I began to feel my feet on the boards again—quite heavy and dragging somewhat. Connie felt heavy, too, slumped in my arms.

She looked up. Her face was very white. "Feeling queer—'scuse me." She began to tack erratically toward the ladies' room. A few minutes later she staggered out, her face no longer white. It was green. "Fresh air, Jim. Take me outside."

I took her out into the darkness and it was as if I had stepped aboard a ship; the ground pitched under my feet. Holding Connie's arm, I retreated hastily to the wall of the institute and leaned against it. But the wall, too, was heaving about. "Oh," I moaned at the stars. "Why did I drink all that beer?"

But I had to look after Connie. I put my arm around her. "Come on, we'd better start walking." We began to reel blindly around the building, and I forgot that the institute was perched on that steep little hill. There was an instant when we were treading on nothing. We finished in a tangled muddy heap on the road.

I lay there peacefully till I heard a pitiful whimpering nearby. Connie! A compound fracture at least! But when I helped her up I found she was unhurt, and so, surprisingly, was I. We must have been as relaxed as rag dolls when we fell. We climbed back up to the institute and stood just inside the door. Connie was unrecognizable; her beautiful hair hung in straggling wisps, and tears coursed slowly through the muddy smears on her cheeks. My suit was plastered with clay and so, I could feel, was my face. We stood close, leaning miserably on each other. My stomach heaved and tossed.

Then I heard somebody say, "Good evening." It was a woman's voice and very close. There were two figures looking at us with interest. They seemed to have just come in. I concentrated fiercely on them and they swam into focus for a few seconds. It was Helen and a man. A man with a pink scrubbed face, shining fair hair and a spotless overcoat. He was staring at me distastefully. They went out of focus and there was only Helen's voice. "We thought we'd look in on the dance. Are you enjoying it?"

Then, unexpectedly, I could see her clearly. She was smiling her kind smile, but her eyes were strained as she looked from me to Connie. I stood there gazing at her calm beauty. It seemed, for a moment, that it would be the most natural thing in the world to throw my arms around her. Instead I nodded dumbly.

"We'll be off, then," she said, again smiling. "Good night."

The fair-haired man gave me a cold nod and they went out.

FORTUNATELY I have the kind of job where things can suddenly happen that brighten my day. When I was feeling my worst, there was that letter from the Bramleys. You don't find people like the Bramleys now; radio, television and the motorcar have carried the outside world into the most isolated places, so that the people you used to meet on the lonely farms are rapidly becoming like people anywhere else. There are still a few left, of course, and when I come across any of them I like to make some excuse to sit down and talk and listen to the old Yorkshire words and expressions which have almost disappeared.

But even in the 1930s, when there were many places still untouched, the Bramleys were unique. There were four of them—three brothers, all middle-aged bachelors, and an older sister, also unmarried. Scar House, their ancient farm, lay deep in the hills. There was no road to it, only a rutted track, but that didn't bother the Bramleys because the outside world held no great attraction for them. Miss Bramley made occasional trips to Darrowby on market days. Herbert, the middle brother, had come into town once in 1929 to have a tooth out. Apart from that they stayed contentedly at home.

A call to Scar House always came as rather a jolt because it meant a trek of at least two hours. One night at about eight o'clock I headed out to see one of their horses with colic. My eyes were half closed against the steady drizzle when I left the car, but about half a mile ahead I could see the lights of the house winking among the trees. After twenty minutes or so of slithering in and out of puddles and opening a series of broken, string-tied gates, I reached the farmyard. I was about to knock on the back door when I stopped with my hand poised. I found I was looking through the kitchen window, and in the interior, dimly lit by an oil lamp, the Bramleys were sitting in a row.

They weren't grouped around the fire but were jammed tightly on a long, high-backed wooden settle which stood against the far wall. The strange thing was the almost exact similarity of their attitudes—all four had their arms folded, feet stretched out in front of them. The men had removed their heavy boots and were stocking-footed, but Miss Bramley wore an old pair of carpet slippers. I stared, fascinated by the curious immobility of the group. They were not asleep, not talking or reading or listening to the radio—in fact, they didn't have one—they were just sitting. I had never seen people just sitting before and I stood there for some minutes to see if they would move, but nothing happened. It occurred to me that this was probably a typical evening; they worked hard all day, had their meal, then they just sat till bedtime.

A month or two later I discovered another unexpected side of the Bramleys when they started having trouble with their cats. I knew they were fond of cats, by the number and variety which swarmed over the place, but what I was unprepared for was their utter desolation when the cats started to die. Miss Bramley was on the doorstep at Skeldale House nearly every day, carrying an egg basket with another pitiful patient huddling miserably inside. Even today, with the full range of modern antibiotics, the treatment of feline enteritis is unrewarding. I did my best with what I had. I even took some of the cats in at the surgery, but the mortality rate was high. Most farmers look on cats simply as pest killers. Not the Bramleys.

One morning Miss Bramley came in with a fresh consignment of invalids. "Is it going to go through 'em all?" she quavered.

"Well, it's very infectious—to young cats particularly."

Miss Bramley's face twitched uncontrollably. A couple of tears wandered among the network of wrinkles on her cheeks. "It's Topsy's kittens I'm worried about," she gasped out at length. "There's five of 'em and they're the best we've got."

I rubbed my chin. I had heard a lot about Topsy, one of a strain of incomparable ratters and mousers. Her last family were only about ten weeks old and it would be a crushing blow to the Bramleys if anything happened to them. But what the devil could I do? There was, as yet, no protective vaccine—or, wait a minute—I remembered I'd heard a rumor.

I pulled out a chair. "Just sit down a few minutes, Miss Bramley. I'm going to make a phone call." I was soon through to the laboratory I'd thought of, and half expected a sarcastic reply. But they were kind and cooperative. They had had encouraging results and would be glad to let me have five doses of the new vaccine if I would inform them of the result.

I hurried back to Miss Bramley. "I've ordered something for your kittens. I can't guarantee anything, but have them down here on Tuesday morning."

Stivers

The vaccine arrived promptly and as I injected the tiny creatures Miss Bramley extolled the virtues of the Topsy line. "Look at the size of them ears! Did you ever see bigger uns?"

I hadn't. The ears were enormous, saillike, and they made the ravishingly pretty little faces look even smaller.

Miss Bramley nodded and smiled with satisfaction. "Aye, you can allus tell. It's the sure sign of a good mouser."

"Now," I said, "we can only wait. Please do let me know the outcome of this."

I didn't hear from the Bramleys for several months. Then came the day that the grubby envelope was pushed under the surgery door. The letter inside—the one that made me feel so good—was a model of conciseness. It was written in a careful, spidery scrawl: "Dere Sir, Them kittens is now big cats. Yrs trly, R. Bramley."

AND then there were the gypsies.

As I stopped my car by the shabby, ornate caravan, some unreal quality in the tableau kept me motionless in my seat, staring, forgetful of my reason for being here. The grass bank was wide on this loop of the road and there were five of them squatting around the fire—a man and woman and three little girls. They sat very still, regarding me blankly through the drifting smoke while a few big snowflakes settled lazily on the children's tangled hair. Finally I wound down the window and called, "Are you Mr. Myatt? I believe you have a sick pony."

"Aye, that's right." The man, a thin, dark-skinned, unshaved little figure, got up and came over to the car holding out something in his hand. It was a ten-shilling note and I recognized it as a gesture of good faith.

The gypsies who occasionally wandered into Darrowby were always regarded with a certain amount of suspicion. We had been caught out once or twice, enough so that Siegfried had shouted to me as I left the house this morning, "Get the brass if you can." But he needn't have worried—Mr. Myatt was on the up-and-up.

My patient was a piebald of about thirteen hands with good clean legs and a look of class about him. The other animals moved around on their tethers, watching us with interest, but the piebald stood as though carved from stone.

Even from a distance I could tell what was wrong with him. That crouching posture could be produced only by acute laminitis—inflammation, accompanied by heat, pain and lameness—a result of overeating. All four feet must be affected, because he had his hind feet right under his body in a desperate attempt to take his full weight on his heels.

"Has he been getting any extra food, Mr. Myatt?"

"Aye, he getten into a bag of oats last night." In his strange accent he managed to convey that the pony had broken loose and gorged himself, and that he had given him castor oil.

The temperature was a hundred and four and the pulse was rapid and bounding. I passed my hand over the trembling hoofs, feeling the abnormal heat; then I looked at the taut face, the dilated nostrils and terrified eyes. Anybody who has had an infection under a fingernail can have an inkling of the agony a horse goes through when the sensitive laminae of the foot are inflamed and throbbing against the unyielding wall of the hoof. "Can you get him to move?"

The man pulled the halter, but the pony refused to budge. I helped; as we pulled together Mrs. Myatt slapped the pony's rump. He took a couple of stumbling steps, groaned as though the ground were red-hot and crouched again on his heels.

I'd have to give him what relief I could. The first thing was to get rid of that bellyful of oats. I gave an injection of arecoline and I showed Mr. Myatt how to tie cloths around the hoofs so that he could keep soaking them with cold water. The pony evacuated his bowel, but his pain was undiminished. I knew it would stay like that until the inflammation subsided—if it did. I couldn't stop it.

As I turned over these gloomy thoughts the three little girls went up to the pony. The biggest put her arms around his neck and laid her cheek against his shoulder while the others stroked the shivering flanks. There were no tears, but it was easy to see how much he meant to them.

I gave Mr. Myatt a bottle of tincture of aconite. "Get this down him every four hours, and keep putting cold water on the feet. I'll come and see him in the morning."

I closed the car door, and through the smoke and the drifting snowflakes I could see the children still stroking their pony.

"Well, you got the brass, James," Siegfried said at lunch. "What was the trouble?"

"Worst case of laminitis I've ever seen. I've done the usual things, but I'm pretty sure they aren't going to be enough."

"Not a very bright prognosis, then?"

"Really black. And he's a grand little animal, lovely piebald. I wish there were something else I could do!"

Siegfried dropped two thick slices of mutton on my plate. "These are rotten jobs, lad, I know, but it's no good worrying."

"Ach, I'm not worrying, exactly, but—maybe it's those people—they're something new to me. Right out of the world. And three raggedy little girls absolutely crazy about that pony."

I could see the glint in Siegfried's eyes that came whenever the talk turned to horses, but I knew he wouldn't push in.

"I wish you'd come and have a look," I said. "Maybe there's something you could suggest. Do you think there could be?"

Siegfried stared in front of him for a few seconds. "Obviously, James, this is a right pig of a case. We have to pull something special out of the bag and I've got an idea." He gave me a crooked smile. "You may not like it."

"If you can help this pony, I don't care what you do."

"Right, come on, then." And he led me through to the instrument room. I was surprised when he opened the cupboard where old Mr. Grant's instruments were kept. When Siegfried had bought the practice, the old vet's instruments had come with it. It would have been logical to throw them out, but maybe Siegfried felt as I did about them. The polished wooden boxes of shining odd-shaped scalpels, the enema pumps, the ancient firing irons—they were a silent testament to sixty years of struggle. I often used to picture the old man wrestling with the same problems I had. But Mr. Grant was dead and gone and had taken with him all the skills I was doggedly trying to accumulate.

Siegfried pulled out a flat leather box and unfastened the clasp. Inside lay a fleam and a round polished blood stick.

I stared in astonishment. "You're going to *bleed* him, then?"

"Yes, my boy. I'm going to take you back to the Middle Ages."

"But have you ever done it?"

"I've done it. And I've seen some funny things after it, too." He cleaned the fleam and dropped it into the sterilizer.

The gypsies were again hunched over the fire when we got there and Mr. Myatt, sensing that reinforcements had arrived, scrambled to his feet and held out another ten-shilling note.

Siegfried waved it away. "Let's see how we get on, Mr. Myatt." He strode over to where the pony trembled in his agonized crouch.

"Poor little beggar," he said softly. "You weren't exaggerating, James. Bring that box from the car, will you?"

When I came back he was tying a choke rope around the base of the pony's neck. "Pull it up tight," he said. As the jugular rose up tense and turgid in its furrow he quickly clipped and disinfected a small area and inserted a plaque of local anesthetic. Finally he opened the leather box and extracted the fleam.

Everything seemed to start happening then. Siegfried placed the little blade of the fleam against the bulging vein and without hesitation gave it a confident smack with the stick. Immediately an alarming cascade of blood spouted from the hole. Mr. Myatt gasped and the children set up a sudden chatter. I understood how they felt. I was wondering how long the pony could stand this outflow without dropping down.

When at least a gallon had come away Siegfried seemed satisfied. "Slacken the rope, James," he cried, then rapidly closed the wound on the neck with a pin suture. "Come on, now, lend a hand, everybody! We've got to get him into that brook!"

He was clearly enjoying himself, and his presence was having its usual effect. The Myatts were spurred into action and even the pony seemed to be taking an interest. All five gypsies pulled at his halter, Siegfried and I looped our arms behind his thighs, everybody gave encouraging shouts and at last he began to move. It was a painful process, but he kept going—through the gate and across the field to the shallow stream. There were no banks to speak of and it was easy to push him out into the middle. As he stood there with the icy water rippling around his inflamed hoofs I fancied I could read in his eyes a faint dawning of an idea that things were looking up at last.

"Now he must stand in there for an hour," Siegfried said. "And then you'll have to make him walk round the field. Then another hour in the water. As he gets better you can give him more and more exercise, but he must come back to the brook. There's a lot of work for somebody here, so who's going to do it?"

The three little girls came shyly around him and looked up, wide-eyed, into his face. Siegfried laughed. "You three want the job, do you? Right. I'll tell you just what to do."

He pulled out the bag of peppermint drops which was always somewhere in his bulging pockets, and I settled in for a long wait. I had seen him in action with children, and when that bag came out everything stopped. It was the one time Siegfried was never in a hurry.

The little girls each solemnly took a sweet, then Siegfried squatted on his heels and addressed them like a professor with his class. They soon began to thaw and put a word in for themselves. The smallest launched into a long account of the remarkable things the pony had done when he was a foal, and Siegfried listened, nodding gravely. There was all the time in the world.

His words obviously went home, because over the next few days whenever I passed the gypsy camp I could see the three wild little figures with the pony in the brook or dragging him around the field. I didn't need to butt in—he was improving all the time.

I wondered what to make of it. Was it my imagination, or had that pony seemed to feel relief almost immediately after the blood-letting? Was it really right to bash a hole in the jugular and release about a bucketful of the precious fluid? I still don't know. I never dared try it myself.

But Siegfried had done the trick all right. About a week later I saw the Myatts on their way out of Darrowby, the red caravan rocking across the marketplace, with Mr. Myatt up front wearing a black velvet cap. Tethered to various parts of the caravan the family of horses clopped along, and right at the rear was the piebald, going well.

The little girls were looking out of the back door. I waved and they looked at me unsmiling. Then one of them shyly lifted her hand. The others followed suit and my last sight was of them waving eagerly back.

10

"COULD Mr. Herriot see my dog, please?"

Familiar enough words coming from the waiting room, but it was the voice that brought me to a slithering halt. It couldn't be, of course it couldn't, but it sounded like Helen. I applied my eye without hesitation to the crack in the door. Tristan was standing there looking down at somebody beyond my range of vision. All I could see was a hand resting on the head of a sheep dog and two silk-stockinged legs—nice legs, not skinny. My cogitations were cut short as a head bent over to speak to the dog and I had a close-up profile of the small straight nose, and the dark hair falling across the milky smoothness of the cheek.

I was still peering, bemused, when Tristan shot out of the room and collided with me. Stifling an oath, he grabbed my arm and hauled me along the passage.

"It's her! The Alderson woman!" he said in a hoarse whisper. "And she wants to see you! Not Siegfried. Mr. Herriot himself."

As I stood hesitating he opened the door and tried to propel me back up the passage. "What *are* you waiting for?" he hissed.

"Well, it's a bit embarrassing, isn't it? Last time she saw me I was so pie-eyed I couldn't even speak."

Tristan struck his forehead with his hand. "She's asked to see you—what more do you want? No. Wait. Stay right there." He returned in a second with a white lab coat. "Just back from the laundry. Jim—the immaculate young surgeon."

I stood unresisting as he worked my arms into the starched sleeves, but struck away his hand when he started to straighten my tie. With a final encouraging wave he headed for the back stairs, and I, giving myself no more time to think, marched into the waiting room. Helen looked up and smiled. And it was just the same smile. Nothing behind it. Just the same friendly steady-eyed smile as when I first met her.

We faced each other in silence for some moments; then when I didn't say anything she looked down at the sheep dog.

"It's Dan. We're so fond of him—he's one of the family."

I patted his head. "I see he's holding up a hind leg."

"Yes, he jumped over a wall this morning and he's been like that ever since. He can't put any weight on the leg."

"Right. Bring him down to the operating room and I'll have a look. Take him on in front of me, will you, so I can watch how he walks." Watching how Helen walked distracted me over the first few yards, but it was a long passage and by the time we had reached the door I had managed to drag my attention back to my patient. And glory be, it was a dislocated hip.

My feelings were mixed. This was a major injury, but the chances were I could put it right and look good in the process. Because I had found, in my brief experience, that one of the most spectacular procedures in practice was the reduction of a dislocated hip. Maybe I had just been lucky, of course.

I hoisted Dan onto the table and examined him. There was no doubt about it. The dog stared resolutely ahead, panting nervously but apparently resigned to his fate. "Nice good-natured dog," I said. "And a bonny one, too. He's dislocated his hip. It's a nasty thing, but with a bit of luck I ought to be able to put it back."

Helen patted the handsome head and the tail waved slowly. "What happens if it won't go back?"

"He'd have to form a false joint up there. He'd be very lame for several weeks and probably always have a slightly short leg."

"Oh dear," Helen said. "Do you think he'll be all right?"

"I think he's got a good chance, mainly because you haven't hung about for days before bringing him in."

"Oh, good. When will you be able to start on him?"

"Now. I'll give Tristan a shout. This is a two-man job."

"Couldn't I help? I'd like to, if you wouldn't mind."

I looked at her doubtfully. "Well, I don't know. You mightn't like playing tug-of-war with Dan in the middle. He'll be anesthetized, of course, but there's usually a lot of pulling."

Helen laughed. "Oh, I'm quite strong. And not a bit squeamish. I'm used to animals, you know."

"Right," I said. "Slip on this spare coat and we'll begin."

The dog didn't flinch as I pushed the needle into his vein, and as the Nembutal flowed in his head began to slump against Helen's arm. Soon he was as limp as any rag doll. I took hold of the affected leg and spoke across the table. "I want you to link your hands underneath his thigh and try to hold him there when I pull."

I suppose there must be a foolproof way of doing this job—a method which works the very first time—but success has always come to me only after a fairly long period of trial and error, and it was the same today. I tried all sorts of angles, rotations and twists on the flaccid limb, trying not to think of how it would look if this just happened to be the one I couldn't put back. I was wondering what Helen, hanging on determinedly to her end, must be thinking of this wrestling match when I heard the muffled click. It was a sweet and welcome sound. I flexed the joint once or twice. The femoral head was once more riding smoothly in its socket.

"Well, that's it," I said. "Hope it stays put. The odd one does pop out, but I've got a feeling this is going to be all right."

Helen ran her hand over the silky ears of the sleeping dog. "Poor old Dan. How long will it be before he comes round?"

"Oh, he'll be out for the rest of the day. When he starts to wake up I want you to be around to steady him so he won't fall and put the thing out again. Perhaps you'd give me a ring and tell me how he's doing."

I gathered Dan up in my arms and was staggering along the passage with him when we met Mrs. Hall carrying a tea tray.

"I thought you and the young lady might fancy a cup," she said. I looked at her narrowly. This was unusual. Was it possible she had joined Tristan in playing Cupid?

"Well, thanks very much, Mrs. Hall. I'll just put this dog outside first." I settled Dan under his blanket in Helen's car and went back to find Helen already sitting with a cup in her lap, and I thought of the other time I had drunk tea in this room with a girl. Diana Brompton! Surely the toughest of all Siegfried's followers.

This was a lot different. During the struggle in the operating room I had been able to observe Helen at close range, and I had discovered that her mouth turned up at the corners as though she were about to smile; also that the deep warm blue of the eyes made a dizzying partnership with the rich black-brown of her hair.

And this time the conversation didn't lag. Maybe it was because I was on my own ground—perhaps I never felt fully at ease unless there was a sick animal involved somewhere—but Mrs. Hall's teapot was empty and the last of the biscuits gone before I finally saw Helen off and started on my rounds.

The same feeling of easy confidence was on me that night when I heard her voice on the phone. "Dan is up and walking about," she said. "He's a bit wobbly, but he's sound on that leg."

"Great, the first stage is over. He's going to be fine."

"Thank you so much. We were terribly worried, especially my young brother and sister. We're very grateful."

"Not at all, I'm delighted, too. He's a grand dog." I hesitated for a moment—it had to be now. "I see the Plaza's showing a film about the Hebrides and I thought maybe . . . I wondered if perhaps, er . . . you might come and see it with me."

A pause. My heart did a quick thud-thud.

"All right," Helen said. "Yes, I'd like that. When? Friday night? Well, thank you—good-by till then."

I replaced the receiver with a trembling hand. Why did I make such heavy weather of these things? But it didn't matter—I was back in business.

Tristan was unpacking the U.C.M.s—Universal Cattle Medicine. We half believed the assurance we had read so often on its label: "Never Fails to Give Relief." Our specific remedies were so few and the possibilities of error so plentiful that it was comforting to be able to hand over the old standby. Whenever an entry of Siegfried's or mine appeared in the daybook stating, "Visit attend cow, 1 U.C.M.," it was a pretty fair bet we didn't know what was wrong with the animal.

Tristan was lifting the tall shapely bottles of ruby fluid out of the elegant tea chest they came in and stacking them on the shelves in deep rows. When he saw me he ceased his labors. He sat down and pulled out the inevitable Woodbine.

"You're taking her to the pictures, then?"

"Yes," I said, feeling vaguely uneasy under his eye. "In about an hour. Anything wrong with going to the pictures?"

"No no. No no no, Jim. A very wholesome pursuit."

"But you don't think I should be taking Helen there."

"I never said that. It's just that . . . I thought you might have gone in for something a bit more . . . well . . . enterprising."

I gave a bitter laugh. "Look, I tried enterprise once."

"So tonight you play safe at the Darrowby Plaza."

Shivering in the tub in the vast drafty bathroom, I couldn't keep out the thought that Tristan was right. I rarely went to the local cinema myself, and taking Helen there was indeed a form of cowardice. But as I closed the door of Skeldale House and looked along the street to where the first lights of the shops beckoned in the dusk, I felt a lifting of the heart. It was as though a fleeting fragrance of spring had touched me. The promise was there—of sunshine and warm grass and softer days. And tonight was another beginning, no matter how small.

You had to look closely or you could easily miss the Plaza, tucked in as it was between Pickersgill's, the ironmonger's, and Howarth's, the chemist's. Its entrance was no wider than the average shopfront. But what puzzled me was that the place was dark, though the show was due to start in ten minutes. I hadn't dared tell Tristan that I had played it safe to the point of arranging to meet Helen here. With a car like mine—well, I had thought it prudent to eliminate all transport hazards. "Meet you outside the cinema." It wasn't very bright, was it?

But then I saw her picking her way across the marketplace cobbles. She smiled and waved, as if being taken to the Darrowby Plaza was the biggest treat a girl could wish for, and everything was suddenly absolutely right. I felt a surging conviction that nothing was going to spoil this night. When she told me that Dan was running about again like a puppy with no trace of a limp, my euphoria was at high tide.

My only worry was the uninhabited look of the cinema entrance. "Strange," I said. "You don't suppose the place isn't open tonight?"

"I'm sure these people are waiting, too," Helen said.

I had been too distracted to notice them; there were a few couples, middle-aged, and some small boys. They didn't seem worried. And there was no cause. Exactly two minutes before the picture was due to start a bicycle came to a screeching halt outside the entrance, a man in a very old raincoat jumped off, inserted a key in the lock and threw wide the doors. Reaching inside, he flicked a switch and a single neon strip flickered fitfully above our heads. Then he whipped off the raincoat, revealing faultless evening dress. The manager had arrived.

While this was going on a very fat lady appeared from nowhere and wedged herself into the paybox. The show was ready to roll.

We all began to shuffle inside. Maggie Robinson, the blacksmith's daughter, who was taking the tickets, was intrigued by the sight of us. She giggled, darted glances at Helen and all but dug me in the ribs. Clearly the management were determined that their patrons shouldn't feel cold. We might have been plunging into a tropical jungle. Maggie steered us through the stifling heat to our places. I noticed that there was no arm between the seats. "Them's the courting seats," Maggie blurted out and fled.

But it was all right sitting there with Helen. I felt fine except for a tendency to gasp like a goldfish in the airless atmosphere. I was settling down cozily when a little man in front of us turned slowly around. His mouth was pursed grimly and he fixed his eyes on mine in a long challenging stare. We faced each other for several silent moments.

"She's dead," he said.

A thrill of horror shot through me. "Dead?"

"Aye, she is. She's dead." He dragged the word out slowly.

I swallowed. "Well, I'm sorry to hear that. Truly sorry."

He regarded me with a peculiar intensity as though he expected me to say more. Then with apparent reluctance he turned away.

I looked helplessly at the rigid back in a heavy overcoat. Who was this man? I knew the face from somewhere. And *what* was dead? Cow? Ewe? Sow? My mind began to race over recent cases, but that face didn't seem to fit in anywhere. I often had trouble identifying people outside their usual environment.

Helen was looking at me questioningly and I managed a wan smile. But the spell was shattered. The little man's head was swiveling again. "Ah don't think there was ever owt wrong with her stomach," he declared.

"You don't, eh?"

"No, young man, ah don't." He dragged his eyes unwillingly from my face and turned toward the screen again.

The effect of this second attack was heightened because the lights went off suddenly and an incredible explosion of noise blasted my eardrums. It was the newsreel. The sound machine, like the heating system, had apparently been designed for something like the Albert Hall and I cowered back under the assault. As a voice bellowed details of month-old events I closed my eyes and tried again to place the man in front of me.

I searched my memory and had got back about three weeks without result when the news finished. There was a blessed respite of a few seconds before the uproar broke out again. This was the feature, described outside as a tender love story. I can't remember the title, but there was a lot of embracing, which would have been all right except that every kiss was accompanied by a chorus of long-drawn sucking noises from the little boys downstairs.

And all the time it got hotter. I unbuttoned my shirt collar, but I was beginning to feel decidedly light-headed. The little man in front, still huddled in his heavy coat, seemed unperturbed. Twice the projector broke down and we stared for several minutes at a blank screen. Maggie Robinson, standing in the aisle, never looked at the screen. She kept her eyes fixed on Helen and me throughout, with a knowing leer. About halfway through the film, however, she was suddenly brushed aside as a large form reeled up the aisle and into our row.

It was Gobber Newhouse, the town drunk. Barging past us, Gobber rested briefly on Helen's lap, trod on my toe and finally spread his enormous carcass over the seat on my left. He heaved and squirmed about until he found a comfortable position and with a final cavernous belch composed himself for slumber. With his snores reverberating in my ear and a dense pall of stale beer drifting over me, the tender love story never had a chance.

It was a relief when it came to an end and the lights went up, but I was worried that Helen was upset. I had noticed as the evening wore on that her lips had a tendency to twitch and that she kept drawing her brows down in a frown. Maggie appeared providentially with a tray around her neck and I purchased two chocolate ices.

I had taken only one bite when I noticed a stirring under the overcoat in front of me. "Ah knew," the little man said, fixing me with that hostile stare. "Right from start, ah did, that you were on the wrong track. Aye, I've been among beasts for fifty years and they never go on like that when it's the stomach."

"Don't they? You're probably right."

The little man shook a forefinger at me. "For one thing, a beast wi' a bad stomach is allus hard in its muck."

"Yes, yes, quite," I said hastily, glancing at Helen. This was just what I needed to complete the romantic atmosphere.

He sniffed, and once again we were plunged into blackness and noise. I was lying back quivering when it came through to me that something was wrong. What was this strident Western music? Then the title flashed on the screen. *Arizona Guns.*

I turned to Helen in alarm. "What's going on? This is supposed to be the Scottish film, isn't it?"

"It's supposed to be." Helen paused and looked at me with a half smile. "But I'm afraid it isn't going to be."

I slumped wearily in my seat. No dance at the Reniston, wrong picture tonight. Well, I was a genius in my own way.

"I'm sorry," I said. "I hope you don't mind too much."

She shook her head. "Not a bit. Anyway, let's give this one a chance. It may be all right."

But as the ancient horse opera crackled out its cliché-ridden message I gave up hope. This was another of those evenings. I watched apathetically as the posse galloped for the fourth time past the same piece of rock and I was totally unprepared for the deafening fusillade of shots which rang out. It made me jump and it even roused Gobber from his sleep.

" 'Ellow! 'Ellow! 'Ellow!" he bawled, thrashing around him with his arms. A backhander on the side of the head drove me violently against Helen's shoulder and I was beginning to apologize when I saw that her twitching and frowning had come on again. Her whole face seemed to break up. She began to laugh, silently and helplessly.

I had never seen a girl laugh like this. It was as though it was something she had wanted to do for a long time. She abandoned herself utterly to it, lying with her head on the back of the seat, legs stretched out in front of her, arms dangling by her side. When she had got it all out of her system, she put her hand on my arm. "Look," she said faintly. "Next time, why don't we just go for a walk?"

Never mind Gobber and that little man in front and Maggie's leers and the steady trickle of sweat down my back. Never mind anything. "Next time," she had said.

ALMOST before I knew what was happening, "next time" had become a pattern; around eight o'clock my feet began to make of their own accord for Heston Grange. Of course I didn't go every night; there was my work, there were the proprieties, and there was Mr. Alderson.

Helen's father was an expert stockman and his farm could compare with the best, but a good part of his mind often seemed to be elsewhere since his wife's death a few years ago, so Helen told me. When things weren't going well he carried on long muttered conversations with himself, but when he was pleased he was inclined to break into a loud tuneless humming. On my professional visits I could often locate him by tracking down this characteristic droning among the farm buildings.

And at first when I came to see Helen I think he never even noticed me—I was just one of the crowd of young men who hung around his daughter; but as my visits became more frequent he regarded me with what I first felt to be dislike, but was in fact alarm. I couldn't blame him. He was devoted to Helen, he naturally desired a grand match for her, and there was one such in the offing—young Richard Edmundson, whose father was an old friend of the Aldersons and farmed nearly a thousand acres. Richard was the young man who had been with Helen at the dance at the Poulton Institute that night of dreadful memory; and Richard was very keen indeed. An impecunious young vet was a poor bargain, I could see that. So when Mr. Alderson was around, my visits to Heston were most uncomfortable affairs. We always seemed to be looking at each other out of the corners of our eyes, which was a pity, because I instinctively liked him.

It was always a relief when I got out of the house with Helen. Everything was right then; we went to village dances, we walked for miles along the old grassy mine tracks among the hills, or sometimes she came on my evening calls. And everything we did was somehow meaningful.

11

I MIGHT have gone on indefinitely walking and talking with Helen, and avoiding her father, but for a conversation I had with Siegfried. We were sitting in the big room at Skeldale House before bedtime, talking over the day, when he laughed. "I had old Harry Forster in tonight paying his bill. He was really funny. 'It's a nice little nest you have here, Mr. Farnon,' he kept saying, and then, very sly, 'It's time there was a bird in this nest, you know.' "

I laughed, too. "Well, you should be used to it by now. People won't be happy until they've got you married off."

"Wait a minute, not so fast. It was you Harry had in mind."

"What do you mean?"

"Well, just think. Didn't you say you had run into the old boy one night when you were walking over his land with Helen? He thinks it's time you were hitched up, that's all."

I lay back and gave myself over to laughter. "Me! Married! That'll be the day. Can you imagine it? Poor old Harry."

Siegfried leaned forward. "What are you laughing at, James? He's quite right—it's time you were married."

"What are *you* on about?" I looked at him incredulously.

"He's right. You ought to get married, and soon."

"Oh come on, Siegfried. I'm only starting. I've no money, no nothing. I've never even thought about it."

"Never . . . Well, tell me this, are you courting Helen Alderson or aren't you?"

"Well, I'm . . . I've been . . . oh, I suppose you could call it that."

Siegfried settled comfortably back and assumed his judicial expression. "Good. You admit you're courting the girl. Now let us take it a step further. She is, from my own observation, extremely attractive—in fact, she nearly causes a traffic pileup when she walks across the cobbles on market day. It's common knowledge that she is intelligent, equable and an excellent cook. Perhaps you would agree with this?"

"Of course I would," I said, nettled at his superior air. "But why are you going on like a high court judge?"

"Because, James, you seem to have an ideal wife lined up and you are doing nothing about it. So stop playing around and let us see a little action."

"But it's not that simple," I said, my voice rising. "I'd have to be a lot better off, and anyway, I've only been going to the house for a few weeks—surely you don't start thinking of getting married as soon as that. And her old man doesn't like me."

Siegfried put his head on one side and I gritted my teeth. "Now, old lad, there's something I have to tell you for your own good. Caution is often a virtue, but in your case you carry it too far. You've got to learn to take a chance, to lash out a bit. As it is, you are confined to a narrow range of activity by your own doubts."

"The original stick-in-the-mud, in fact, eh?"

"Oh, come now, James. I didn't say that. But there's another small point. Until you get married I'm afraid I'll not get the full benefit of your assistance. Frankly, you are so besotted that you don't know what you're doing half the time."

"What the devil are you talking about? I've never—"

"Kindly hear me out, James. You've developed a disturbing habit of staring into space when I'm talking to you. There's only one cure, my boy."

"And it's a simple little cure, isn't it!" I shouted. "No money, no home, but leap into matrimony with a happy cry."

"Ah-ah, you see, there you go again, looking for difficulties." He gazed at me with pitying affection. "No money, you say. Well, one of these days you'll be a partner here. Your plate will be out on those railings in front of the house, so you'll never be short of your daily bread. As to a home—look at all the room in this house. You could set up a private suite upstairs."

My head was beginning to swim. "You make it all sound so easy."

"But it *is* easy!" Siegfried shot upright in his chair. "Get that girl into church before the month is out!" He wagged a finger at me. "Learn to grasp the nettle of life, James. And remember"—he clenched his fist and struck an attitude—"*There is a tide in the affairs of men, which, taken at the flood . . .*"

"Okay, okay," I said. "That's enough. I get the message."

I don't suppose I am the first person to have had his life fundamentally influenced by one of Siegfried's outbursts. But there is no doubt he is responsible for the fact that I was the father of a grown-up family while I was still a young man, because when I brought the subject up with Helen she said yes, she'd like to marry me. She seemed surprised at first—maybe she expected it would take me a few years to get off the ground. Anyway, before I had time to think much more about it we had set our eyes on an early date and were making plans for furnishing our prospective flat at Skeldale House.

But one cloud bulked large on the horizon. As I walked hand in hand with Helen, my thoughts in the air, she kept bringing me back to earth with an appealing look.

"Jim, you'll really have to speak to Dad. It's time he knew."

I HAD been warned long before I qualified that country practice was a dirty stinking job. I had accepted the fact, but there were times when this side of my life became almost insupportable. Like now, when even after a long hot bath I still smelled. As I hoisted myself from the steaming water I sniffed at my arm and there it was—a malodorous memory striking triumphantly through all the soap and antiseptic. Nothing but time would remove it.

Something in me rebelled at the idea of crawling into bed in this state. I looked with desperation along the row of bottles on the bathroom shelf. I stopped at Mrs. Hall's bath salts. This was something I'd never tried, and I tipped a handful into the water. For a moment my head swam as the rising steam was suddenly charged with sweetness; then on impulse I shook most of the jar's contents into the bath. For a long time I lay there smiling as the oily liquid lapped around me.

The whole process had a stupefying effect on me, and even as I sank back on my pillow a delicious slumber claimed me. When the bedside phone (we now each had one) boomed in my ear the sense of personal affront was even stronger than usual. Blinking sleepily at the clock, which said one fifteen a.m., I lifted the receiver and mumbled into it, but I was jerked suddenly wide-awake when I recognized Mr. Alderson's voice. Candy was calving and something was wrong. Would I come right away?

There has always been a "this is where I came in" feeling about a night call. And as my lights swept the cobbled marketplace it was there again, a sense of returning to fundamentals, of really being me. My mind was ticking over anxiously.

Because Candy was something special. She was the house cow, a pretty little Jersey, all of whose rich yellow offering found its way onto the family table (her golden creamy butter was to dream about), sole member of her breed in the herd and Mr. Alderson's particular pet. I couldn't blame him, because I sometimes wish all cows were Jerseys, gentle doe-eyed creatures you can push around without any trouble, and even if they kick you it's a love tap compared with the clump from a craggy Friesian. But apart from all that, Mr. Alderson just liked the animal. He would pat her head and hum to himself every time he passed her. I must not make a ham-fisted job of calving Candy.

Helen's father was an efficient farmer. In the lighted box stall two buckets of water were steaming in readiness, and Stan and Bert, the cowmen, were waiting with their boss. Candy was lying in comfortably deep straw and she was not straining, but she had a preoccupied, inward look as though all was not well with her.

"There's nowt in there," Mr. Alderson said. "She'd been on for a few hours and not showing so I popped me hand in and there's no head, no legs, nowt. And not much room, either. That's when I rang you."

This sounded very strange. I hung my jacket on a nail and began thoughtfully to unbutton my shirt. It was when I was pulling it over my head that I noticed Mr. Alderson's nose wrinkling. The farm men, too, sniffed and looked at each other wonderingly. Mrs. Hall's bath salts, imprisoned under my clothing, had burst from their bondage in a sickly wave. Hurriedly I began to wash my arms, but it seemed only to get worse. Nobody said anything. These men weren't the type to make the ribald remark which would have enabled me to laugh the thing off. There was no ambiguity about this scent; it was voluptuously feminine.

Cringing inwardly, I knelt to make my examination and in a moment my embarrassment was forgotten and my spirits plummeted. Torsion of the uterus. I sat back on my heels.

"She's got a twisted calf bed. There's a live calf in there but no way out for it. I can barely get my hand through."

Mr. Alderson rubbed his chin. "What can we do, then?"

"We'll have to try to correct the twist by rolling the cow over while I keep hold of the calf. It's a good job there's four of us."

"And that'll put everything right, will it?"

I swallowed. Sometimes rolling worked and sometimes it didn't, and in those days we hadn't quite got around to performing cesareans on cows. But if I was unsuccessful, I faced the prospect of telling Mr. Alderson to send Candy to the butcher. I banished the thought quickly.

"It'll put everything right," I said. It had to. I stationed Bert at the front legs, Stan at the hind and had the farmer holding the cow's head on the floor. Then I reached in through the tiny opening, thanking God for my small hands, and grasped the calf's foot. "Now roll her," I gasped, and the men pulled the legs around in a clockwise direction. I held fiercely to the little foot as the cow flopped onto her other side.

Nothing seemed to be happening. "Push her onto her chest," I panted, but as they rolled her onto her brisket I gave a yell of pain.

"Get her back, quick! We're going the wrong way!" The smooth band of tissue had tightened on my wrist in a grip of frightening power. I thought I'd never get out. I gritted my teeth and took a fresh grip on the calf's foot. "Okay, try her the other way."

This time we went through a hundred and eighty degrees. Nothing happened. Taking a quick breather, I lay face down while the sweat sprang out on my back, sending out fresh exotic vapors from the bath salts.

"Right. One more go!" I cried. And oh it was beautiful to feel everything magically unraveling and my arm lying free in a wide uterus with all the room in the world and the calf already beginning to slide toward me. Candy summed up the situation immediately. She gave a determined heaving strain and popped the calf wet and wriggling into my arms.

"By gum, it was quick at t'finish," Mr. Alderson murmured.

Thankfully I soaped my arms in one of the buckets. After every delivery there is relief, but in this case it was overwhelming. It no longer mattered that I smelled like a ladies' hairdressing salon. I just felt good. I said good night to Bert and Stan as they returned to their beds, giving a final incredulous sniff when they passed me. Mr. Alderson was having a word with Candy while he dried her calf. He seemed fascinated by the unbelievably tiny heifer with its large dark limpid eyes and expression of trusting innocence. In a moment the tuneless humming broke out like a joyful paean.

There would never be a better time. I spoke up firmly. "Mr. Alderson," I said. "I would like to marry your daughter."

The humming switched off abruptly and he turned slowly until he was facing me. His eyes searched mine unhappily. "You'd better come in the house," he said.

The farmhouse kitchen looked lost and forsaken with the family abed. Mr. Alderson put away his buckets, hung up the towel and washed his hands methodically; then he pottered through to the parlor and I heard him clinking about in the sideboard. When he reappeared he bore a tray on which a bottle of whisky and two glasses rattled gently. The tray lent the simple procedure an air of formality which was accentuated by the heavy cut crystal of the glasses and the virgin, unopened state of the bottle.

Mr. Alderson set the tray down on a small table beside the chair he always sat in. Nobody said anything. He peered at the cap of the bottle like a man who had never seen one before, then unscrewed it with slow apprehension. Finally he poured out two measures with the utmost gravity and precision, and with a last touch of ceremony he proffered the laden tray.

I took my drink and waited expectantly.

Mr. Alderson looked into the lifeless fireplace for a minute or two. He pursed his lips as though about to whistle, but instead took a gulp of whisky which sent him into a paroxysm of coughing. When his breathing had returned to normal he sat up straight, fixed me with two streaming eyes and cleared his throat. "Aye well," he said. "It's grand hay weather."

I agreed with him. "Mind you," he said. "A night's rain would do a lot o' good."

I gave my opinion that it undoubtedly would and the silence fell again. My host kept drinking his whisky as though he were getting used to it. And I could see that it was having a relaxing effect; the strained lines on his face were beginning to smooth out and his eyes were losing their hunted look. But nothing more was said until he had replenished our glasses. Then he looked down at the rug and spoke in a small voice.

"James," he said. "I had a wife in a thousand."

I was so surprised I hardly knew what to say. "Yes, I know," I murmured. "I've heard a lot about her."

"Aye," he went on, his voice full of gentle yearning. "She was the grandest lass for miles around and the bonniest." He looked up at me suddenly with the ghost of a smile. "Nobody thought she'd ever have a feller like me, you know. But she did."

He began to tell me about her, without self-pity, but with a wistful gratitude for the happiness he had known. And I discovered that Mr. Alderson was different from a lot of the farmers of his generation, because he said nothing about her being a "good worker." I had been shocked more than once by newly widowed men who, when I commiserated with them, said only, "Aye, she was a grand worker." But Mr. Alderson said that his wife had been beautiful, and kind, and that he had loved her very much. He talked about Helen, too, and how like her mother she was in every way. Though he never said so, I had the feeling all the time that he meant all this to concern me; the fact that he was talking so freely seemed a sign that the barriers were coming down.

Actually he was talking a little too freely. In my experience, even the burliest Yorkshiremen couldn't take whisky, and Mr. Alderson normally hardly drank at all. I was getting worried. But there was nothing I could do. He was lying back in his chair now, completely at ease, his eyes alight with his memories, gazing above my head. After one long passage he dropped his eyes and stared at me for a moment before he managed to place me. It seemed to remind him of his duties as host and he reached for the bottle, but as he did so he caught sight of the clock.

"Well, dang it, it's four o'clock. It's hardly worth goin' to bed, but I suppose we'd better have an hour or two's sleep." He jumped briskly to his feet, looked around him for a moment in a businesslike sort of way, then pitched head first with a sickening clatter among the fire irons. Frozen with horror, I started forward, but I needn't have worried because he bounced back to his feet at once and looked me in the eye as if nothing had happened.

"Well, I'd better be off," I said. "Thanks for the drink." I realized that the chances of Mr. Alderson saying "Bless you, my son," or anything like that were remote. But I had a comforting impression that all was going to be well. He made a creditable attempt to usher me out, but his direction was faulty and he tacked helplessly away from me across the kitchen floor. I hesitated only a second. "I'll just walk up the stairs with you, Mr. Alderson," I said in a matter-of-fact voice, and he made no resistance as I took his arm.

As we creaked our way upstairs he stumbled and would have gone down had I not grabbed him around the waist. He looked up at me and grunted, "Thanks, lad," and we grinned at each other for a moment.

At his bedroom door he stood hesitating as though about to say something. But finally he just nodded and ducked inside.

I waited outside the door, listening in some anxiety to the bumps and thumps from within; but I relaxed as a loud tuneless humming came through the panels. Everything most certainly was going to be all right.

12

CONSIDERING we spent our honeymoon tuberculin testing, it was a big success. It compared favorably, at any rate, with the experiences of a lot of people I know who celebrated this milestone in their lives by cruising for a month on sunny seas and still wrote it off as a dead loss. For Helen and me it had all the ingredients—laughter, fulfillment and camaraderie—and yet it only lasted a week. And, as I say, we spent it tuberculin testing.

The situation had its origins one morning at the breakfast table when Siegfried, red-eyed after a bad night with a colicky mare, was opening the mail. He drew his breath in sharply as a thick roll of forms fell from a Ministry of Agriculture envelope.

"God Almighty! Look at all that testing!" He read feverishly down the long list. "And they want the Ellerthorpe lot next week without fail—it's very urgent." He glared at me for a moment. "That's when you're getting married, isn't it?"

I shifted uncomfortably. "Yes, I'm afraid it is."

Siegfried snatched a piece of toast from the rack and began to slap butter on it like an exasperated bricklayer. "Well, this is just great, isn't it? The practice going mad, a week's testing right at the top of the Dale, away in the back of beyond, and you drifting gaily off on your honeymoon smack in the middle of it." He crunched savagely on his toast.

"I'm sorry, Siegfried," I said. "I didn't mean to land you in this mess, but I couldn't know the practice would get so busy now or that they'd throw all this testing at us."

Siegfried pointed a finger at me. "That's just it, James—you don't look ahead. You just go belting straight on, and to hell with the consequences." He paused to cough up a few crumbs which he had inhaled in his agitation. "I can't see what all the hurry is—you've got all the time in the world to get married, you're just a boy. And you hardly know this girl, you've only—"

"But wait a minute, you said—"

"No, let me finish, James. Marriage is a very serious step. Why in God's name does it have to be next week? Next year would have been soon enough, but no, you've got to rush in and tie the knot. It isn't so easily untied, you know."

"Oh hell, Siegfried, you know perfectly well it was you who—"

"One moment! Your precipitate marital arrangements are going to cause me a considerable headache, but believe me I wish you well. I hope all turns out for the best, but I must remind you of the old saying: 'Marry in haste, repent at leisure.'"

I could stand no more. I leaped to my feet and yelled at him. "Damn it, it was your idea! I was all for waiting. . . ."

But Siegfried wasn't listening. His face broke into a seraphic smile. "Now, now, now, James, sit down and calm yourself. You mustn't mind my speaking to you like this—you are very young and it's my duty." He was all of six years older, but he donned the mantle of omniscient graybeard without effort. I dug my fingers into my knees and decided to let it pass. Besides, I was beginning to worry about leaving him snowed under. I stared out the window while he went on about the improvidence of youth. Then suddenly I had one of my infrequent ideas.

"Look, I wouldn't mind spending my honeymoon round Ellerthorpe. It's wonderful at this time of year and we could stay at the Wheat Sheaf. I could do the testing from there."

He stared in astonishment. "But what would Helen say?"

"She wouldn't mind. We were only going off touring. And it's funny, but Helen and I have often said we'd like to stay at the Wheat Sheaf sometime—there's something about that pub."

Siegfried shook his head decisively. "No, James. I won't hear of it. I'll manage. Forget it and go away and have a good time."

"No. I really like the idea." I scanned the list quickly. "I can start testing at the Allens' and do all those smaller ones round there on Tuesday, get married here on Wednesday and go back for the second injection and readings on Thursday and Friday. I can knock hell out of that list by the end of the week."

Siegfried looked at me as though he were seeing me for the first time. He argued and protested, but for once I got my way.

On Tuesday at noon I had finished testing the Allens' huge herd, scattered for miles over the stark fells at the top of the Dale, and was settling down with the hospitable folk for the inevitable "bit o' dinner." Mr. Allen was at the head of the scrubbed table and facing me were his two sons, Jack and Robbie, superbly fit and tough young men whose handling of the wild scattered beasts I had watched with awe all morning.

I always had to stand a bit of leg-pulling from Mrs. Allen, a jolly talkative woman; on previous visits she had ribbed me mercilessly about being a slowcoach with the girls. I knew she would start on me again today so I bided my time. It came as she dumped a huge slab of roast ham on the table.

"Now then, Mr. Herriot, it's time you found a nice girl. I'm always at you, but you take not a bit o' notice." She was passing the mashed potatoes when I dropped my bombshell.

"Well, as a matter of fact, Mrs. Allen," I said airily, "I've decided to accept your advice. I'm getting married tomorrow."

She stopped with her spoon in midair. "Married tomorrow?"

"That's right. I thought you'd be pleased."

"But . . . you're coming here Thursday and Friday."

"Of course. I have to finish the test, haven't I? I'll be bringing my wife. I'm looking forward to introducing her to you."

Mr. Allen stopped sawing at the ham. His wife gave an uncertain laugh. "You're kidding. You'd be off on your honeymoon—"

"Mrs. Allen." I held up my hand. "I wouldn't joke about a serious matter like that. Let me repeat—tomorrow is my wedding day and I'll be bringing my wife along on Thursday to see you."

Deflated, she heaped our plates and we all fell to. I knew she was in agony, dying to know more. As I was leaving she put a hand on my arm. "You really don't *mean* it, do you?"

I smiled and got into the car and waved. "Good-by and thank you. Mrs. Herriot and I will be along first thing on Thursday."

OF THE wedding I have only one vivid memory. It is of Siegfried, just behind me in the church, booming Amen at regular intervals—the only time I have ever heard a best man do this. It was an incredible relief when Helen and I could drive away. We were passing Skeldale House when Helen grasped my hand. "Look!" she cried excitedly. "Look over there!"

Underneath the Farnon brass plate, which was slightly askew as usual, was a brand-new one. On a black background, bold white letters read J. HERRIOT M.R.C.V.S. VETERINARY SURGEON.

I looked back down the street to try to see Siegfried, but we had said our good-bys and I would have to thank him later. So I drove out of Darrowby with a feeling of swelling pride because I knew what the plate meant—I was a partner, a man with a real place in the world. The thought made me slightly breathless. In fact, we were both a little dizzy and we cruised for hours around the countryside, getting out when we felt like it, walking among the hills, taking no account of time. It must have been nine o'clock before we realized we had gone far out of our way.

It was very dark when we rattled down the steep narrow road into Ellerthorpe. The Wheat Sheaf was an unostentatious gray stone building with no light over the door, and as we went into the slightly musty-smelling hallway the gentle clink of glasses came from the public bar on our left. Mrs. Burn, the elderly widow who owned the place, appeared and scrutinized us unemotionally.

"We've met before, Mrs. Burn," I said, and she nodded. I apologized for our lateness and was wondering whether I dare ask for a few sandwiches when the old lady spoke up, unperturbed.

"Nay," she said. "It's all right. We've been expecting you and your supper's waiting." She led us to the dining room, where her niece, Beryl, served a hot meal in no time. Thick lentil soup, stew with mushrooms, vegetables obviously concocted by a culinary genius. We had to say no to the gooseberry pie and ice cream.

It was like that all the time at the Wheat Sheaf. It was aggressively unfashionable, needing paint, crammed with hideous furniture. But at mealtimes it was easy to see how it had won its reputation. They were the big moments of the day. What captivated Helen and me, though, was the peace, the sleepy insinuating charm of the place. I still often pass the Wheat Sheaf, and as I look at its ancient stone frontage, quite unaltered by the passage of a mere thirty years, the memories are fresh and happy and warm: our footsteps echoing in the empty street when we took our last walk at night, the old brass bedstead almost filling the little room, the dark rim of the fells bulking against the night sky beyond our window, faint bursts of laughter from the bar downstairs.

I PARTICULARLY enjoyed, too, our very first morning when I took Helen to do the test at the Allens'. As I got out of the car that Thursday I could see Mrs. Allen peeping around the kitchen curtains. She was out in the yard at once, her eyes popping at the sight of my bride. Helen was one of the pioneers of slacks in the Dales, and she was wearing a bright purple pair which would in modern parlance knock your eye out. The farmer's wife was partly shocked, partly fascinated, but she soon found that Helen was of the same stock as herself and within seconds the two were chat-

tering busily. I judged from Mrs. Allen's ever widening smile that Helen was putting her out of her pain by explaining all the circumstances. Finally Mr. Allen had to break into the conversation. "If we're goin' we'll have to go," he said gruffly.

We began the second day of the tests on a sunny hillside where a group of young animals had been penned. Jack and Robbie plunged in among the beasts while Mr. Allen took off his cap and courteously dusted the top of the wall. "Your missus can sit 'ere," he said.

I paused. My missus! I looked over at Helen as she sat cross-legged on the stones, her notebook on her knee, pencil at the ready, and as she pushed back the shining dark hair from her forehead she caught my eye and smiled; and as I smiled back I became aware suddenly of the vast swelling glory of the Dales around us, and of the scent of clover and warm grass, more intoxicating than wine. And it seemed that my first two years at Darrowby had been leading up to this moment; that the first big step of my life was being completed right here, with Helen smiling at me and the memory, fresh in my mind, of my new plate hanging in front of Skeldale House.

I might have stood there indefinitely, in a sort of trance, but Mr. Allen cleared his throat in a marked manner and I turned back to the job in hand.

"Right," I said, placing my calipers against a beast's neck. "Number thirty-eight, seven millimeters and circumscribed," I called out to Helen. "Number thirty-eight, seven, C."

"Thirty-eight, seven, C," my wife repeated as she bent over her book and started to write.

Notes on Dr. Herriot—as remembered from lunch:

Sprightly and twinkle-eyed in appearance; as warm and outgoing in conversation—and as funny—as in print. He quite simply and without fanfare loves his life as a vet, loves animals and people with a wry but calm acceptance of nonperfection in critters generally.

His daughter is a medical intern in a Yorkshire hospital; his son is a veterinarian, now also a partner in the practice that still includes its founders, Siegfried and Triss. Siegfried—as might have been expected—married a beautiful girl. Triss is a big administrator in the Ministry of Agriculture.

I asked Herriot how he wrote his books, how he ever had time to. His wife made him do the first one (*All Creatures Great and Small* combines two books first published in Great Britain) because she was afraid all the stories of old-style Yorkshire people would be forgotten. So he got a typewriter, closed the bedroom door on himself, and started in at the end of the day. But he couldn't stand missing the family, and so he just sat in the back of the living room with the "telly" on and the kids watching it, and there he wrote. His third book is just out in London, and a fourth is in the works (taking him through World War II, during which he served in the RAF).

It was April when he was in the United States, and I asked him when he was going home. He said, in his wonderful Scot-talk, "Why, tomorrow. You may not know, but this is the busiest time of the year coming up—the lambing season—and I must be back for that." He loves to walk over the moors and up the old tracks left by the mine carts; he has several dogs who go along.

What he does, in toto, is exude a feeling about life that is completely whole and healthy and good. It's this quality that has made his book go—not the slightest streak of the preacher, just the vigorous enjoyer.

—J.S.

The Salamander

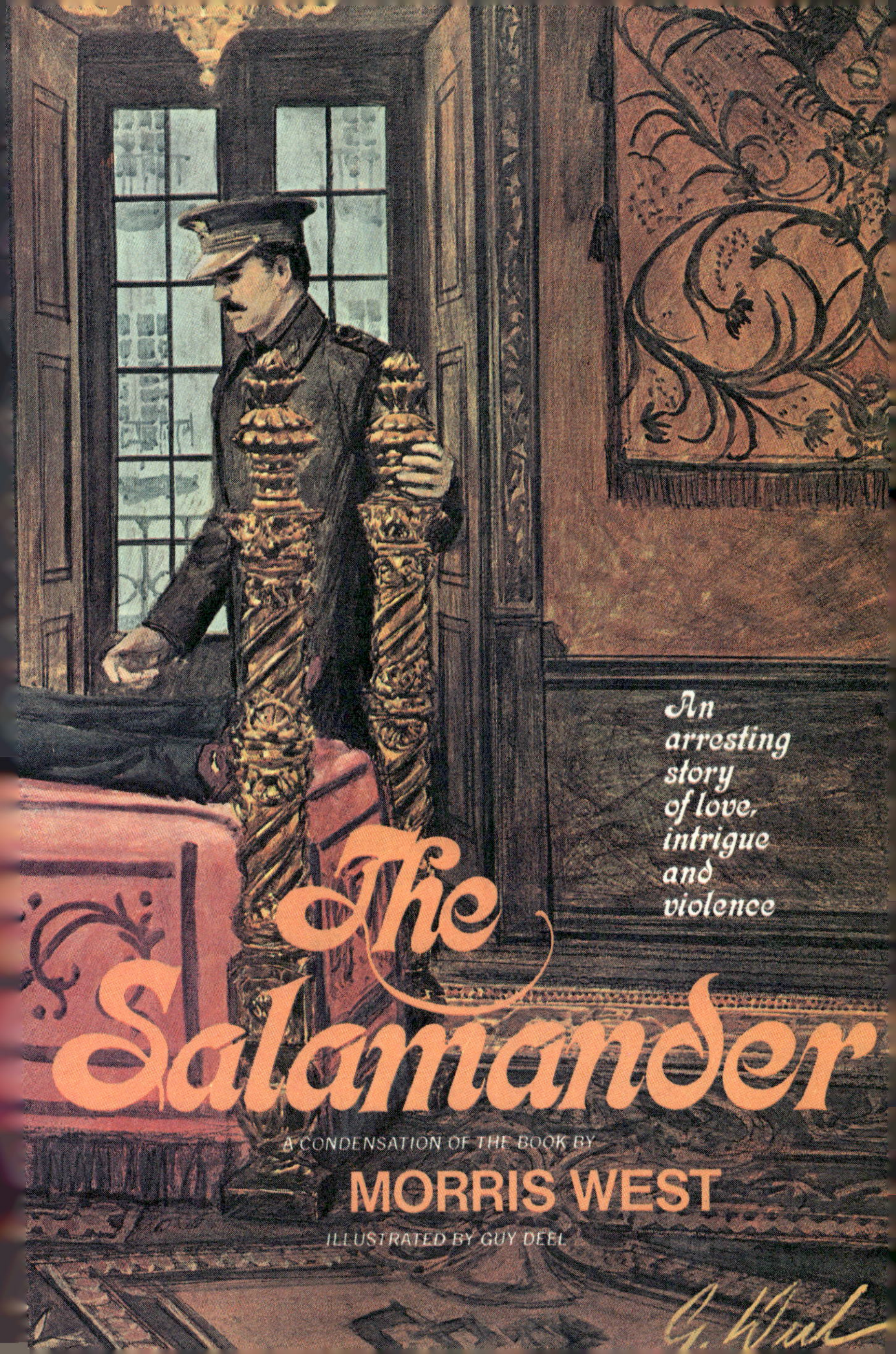
An arresting story of love, intrigue and violence
The Salamander
A CONDENSATION OF THE BOOK BY
MORRIS WEST
ILLUSTRATED BY GUY DEEL

A high-ranking Italian general is found dead. Suicide? Or murder?

An artfully wrought card depicting a salamander—the legendary beast that lives in fire and symbolizes man's survival—is discovered near the corpse.

Colonel Dante Matucci of the Service of Defense Information sets in motion a thrilling chase through the dark underworld of Italy, through its fashionable society, through politics and high finance. As he exposes a dangerous plot to convert a democracy into a dictatorship, Matucci must determine the price of his own survival as a self-respecting man *and* as a servant of a modern state. Like the salamander, he will survive the flames.

one

Between midnight and dawn, while his fellow Romans were celebrating the end of Carnival, Count Pantaleone, general of the military staff, died in his bed. A bachelor in his early sixties, a soldier of spartan habit, he died alone.

At seven in the morning his servant, a retired sergeant of cavalry, found him lying on his back, fully clothed, gape-mouthed and staring at the coffered ceiling. The servant crossed himself, closed the dead eyes with two fifty-lire pieces and telephoned the general's aide, Captain Girolamo Carpi.

Carpi telephoned the Director. The Director telephoned me, Dante Matucci, colonel of carabinieri—the national police—attached for special duty to the Service of Defense Information.

The service is usually called by its Italian initials, SID (Servizio Informazione Difesa). Like every other intelligence service it spends a huge amount of taxpayers' money perpetuating itself, and somewhat less in scavenging information to protect the republic from traitors, spies and saboteurs. You will gather I am skeptical about its value, as men who work in it tend to become. However, that's a digression. . . .

Count Pantaleone was dead. I was appointed to stage a clean

exit for the corpse. The army supplied me with a senior medical officer and a military advocate. We drove together to the general's apartment. Captain Carpi received us. So far, so good. No neighbors on the landing. No relatives yet informed. I had no great respect for Carpi, but I had to commend his discretion.

The medical officer made a cursory examination and decided that the general had died from an overdose of barbiturates, self-administered. He wrote a certificate, countersigned by the military advocate, which stated the cause of death as cardiac arrest. It was not a false document. The general's heart had stopped.

When an army ambulance had removed the body, I remained in the apartment with Carpi and the servant, who made us coffee. While we drank it, I questioned him. His answers established a series of simple facts.

The general had dined out. He had returned twenty minutes before midnight and retired immediately. The servant had secured doors and windows, set the burglar alarm and gone to bed. Visitors or intruders? None. The alarms had not been triggered. Telephone calls? No way to know. The general had a private line in his bedroom. The general's demeanor? Normal. He was a taciturn man. Hard to know what he was thinking at any time. That was all.

I dismissed the servant to the kitchen. Carpi then poured us two glasses of the general's whiskey.

"What do we tell his friends—and the press?" he asked.

"You saw the death certificate: cardiac arrest."

"And the autopsy report?"

"My dear Captain, for an ambitious man you are very naïve. There will be no autopsy. The general's body has been taken to a mortuary where it will be prepared for a brief lying-in-state. We want him seen and mourned as a noble servant of the republic. Then we want him forgotten. You can help us."

"How?"

"Your patron is dead. You did well for us. You deserve a better appointment. I'd suggest something far away from Rome—perhaps Sardinia. You will find promotion a lot quicker there."

"I'd like to think about it."

"No time, Captain Carpi! You pick up your transfer papers this morning. You deliver them, signed, by five this afternoon. You will have a new posting immediately after the funeral. You are in a delicate position, you will remember. You agreed to spy on a superior officer. SID is grateful, but your fellow officers would despise you. Any indiscretion would therefore damage your career and expose you to great personal danger."

"I understand."

"Good. You may go now. Leave me your key, please. *Ciao!*"

Carpi was one of those weak, handsome fellows who always need a patron, and who will always betray him to a more potent one. I had used him to report on Pantaleone's political activities. Now he was a nuisance. He left me sitting with my whiskey, trying to set my thoughts in order.

The Pantaleone affair had all the makings of a political time bomb—although not one in a thousand citizens would recognize his name; and of those who did, not one in ten would understand the magnitude of the conspiracy which had been built around it. The Director understood; so did I. I had dossiers on all the principal participants, and had been chafing at my impotence to do anything about them. They were not criminals—at least not yet. They were all high men—ministers, deputies, industrialists, service officers, bureaucrats—who looked to a day when the confusions of Italy—unstable government, industrial unrest, a faltering economy and a very frustrated people—would bring the country to the brink of revolution. On that day, which was closer than many people imagined, the conspirators hoped to seize power and present themselves as saviors of the republic. If a handful of Greek colonels had done it, they reasoned, why couldn't a larger and more powerful group of Italians do it better.

Their figurehead had been that passionate patriot, General Massimo Pantaleone. Now the general had removed himself from the scene. Why? Was there someone new in the wings? If so, when would he reveal himself? I would have to answer these questions, and the margin for error was very slim. Even a hint that an investigation was in progress, let alone that the army had notarized a dubious document, would be headline news and split the country apart. Conspiracy has been endemic to Italy since Romulus and Remus; but if the dimensions of this plot were made known—there would be blood in the streets, maybe also mutiny in the armed services, whose political loyalties were deeply divided between Left and Right! I had made no idle threat to Captain Carpi. If he tried to sell his information, an accident would be speedily arranged for him.

Meantime, I had my own work to do. I began to comb the apartment for papers. I went through drawers and cupboards and pockets. I shook out every book in the library. I removed the blotter from the desk pad. I tested everywhere for secret places. I lifted ornaments and peered into vases. Even so, I nearly missed the card.

It was lying on its edge against the baseboard, behind the bedside table. On one side was a drawing, done by hand in India ink—a salamander with a coronet on its head, couched in a bed of flames; on the other, an inscription written in perfect copperplate—*Un bel domani, fratello.*

"One fine tomorrow, brother." A very Italian phrase. Was it a vain hope, a promise of reward, a threat of vengeance, or a rallying cry? The word brother was ambiguous, too, and the salamander made no sense at all. I decided to refer it to the specialists. I took a clean envelope from the desk, sealed the card inside it and put it in my pocket.

It was time then for a private chat with the servant. I found him in the kitchen, a dejected old man ruminating over an uncertain future. I consoled him with the thought that the general had probably remembered him in his will and that, at least, he was entitled to severance pay. He brightened and offered me wine and cheese. As we drank together he became garrulous, and I was happy to let him ramble. "He didn't have to be a soldier, you know. The Pantaleones always had money. Lands in the Romagna, apartment buildings in the city, the Frascati estate, the villa on Ponza. Of course, she's got the villa now."

"Who has?"

"You know—the Polish woman. The one he had dinner with last night. Anders. She's been his girl friend for years. Although he never brought her here. He didn't want people to think he was enjoying himself. I knew about her, of course. Good-looking woman . . . Someone ought to tell her what's happened."

"I'll do that. Where does she live?" The question was a blind. I knew the answer and a great deal more about Lili Anders.

"Parioli. The address is in the general's notebook."

"I'll find it."

"Hey! You're not taking any of the general's stuff away, are you? I'm responsible. I don't want any trouble."

"I'm taking his papers. We can't leave confidential documents lying around. Anything that doesn't belong to the army we'll return to his lawyer. I'll give you an official receipt. All right?"

"If you say so. Wait a moment! Who *are* you?"

"Matucci. Carabinieri."

"Carabinieri! There's nothing wrong, is there?"

"Nothing at all. Normal procedure with an important man."

"Who's going to make the arrangements, tell his friends?"

"The army."

"So what do I do? Just sit around here?"

"People will telephone. Take their names and numbers and we'll arrange for someone to call them back. You'll still be paid, don't worry. Tell me, where did the general dine last night?"

"At the Chess Club."

"Thanks. I'll be on my way." I scribbled a receipt, shoved the documents into a valise of the general's and walked out into the sunshine. It was ten minutes after one. The alleys were busy with Romans going home for lunch and siesta.

I have to tell you frankly, I don't like the Romans. I'm a Tuscan, and these people are first cousins to the Hottentot. They are the worst cooks in Italy, devoid of the most elementary graces. They have seen everything and learned nothing. They have known imperial grandeur, papal pomp, war, famine and plague; yet they will bow the knee to any tyrant who offers them an extra loaf of bread and a free ticket to the circus. Yesterday it was Benito Mussolini, drunk with rhetoric, haranguing them from the balcony of the Piazza Venezia. Tomorrow it might be another—and my job was to discover where that one was now.

I shook myself out of my reverie, walked half a block to my car and drove to the office. I might have saved myself the trouble. My two senior clerks were out at lunch, number three was flirting with the typist, and the data bank was out of action because the power supply had been interrupted by a two-hour strike. There was a message from the Ministry of the Interior, under whose jurisdiction the SID comes, requesting "immediate contact on a most urgent matter." When I called I was told that my man was entertaining some foreign visitors and might possibly be back at four o'clock. "Urgent"—these Romans!

I dumped the bag of documents on my desk and shouted for number three clerk to sort and collate them. Then, because the strike had put the elevator out of action, I climbed three flights to the forensic laboratory, where there had to be someone alive. As usual it was old Stefanelli, who according to local legend slept every night in a bottle of formaldehyde and emerged fresh as a marmoset at sunrise every morning. He was a tiny wizened fellow, easily ten years past retirement age, who managed by a combination of patronage and talent to hang on to his job. Because what other technicians burst their brains to learn, Stefanelli knew. Sprinkle a speck of dust in his palm and he would name you the region and even make a reasonable guess at the village from which it came. Give him a drop of blood, two nail clippings and a lock of hair, and he would build you the girl who owned them. He was a tetchy and troublesome genius who would spit in your eye if you crossed him, or slave twenty-four hours at a stretch for a man he trusted. When I came in, puffing and sour-faced, he greeted me exuberantly.

"Eh, Colonel! What have you got for Steffi today?"

"Troubles, Steffi." I handed him the salamander card. "I want a full reading on this fast: paper, penmanship, the meaning of the symbol and any prints you can lift."

Stefanelli studied the card intently for a few moments. "The card is of Japanese stock—fine-quality bonded rice. I can tell you who imports it by tomorrow. The penmanship is fantastic! So beautiful it makes you want to cry. I haven't seen anything like it since Aldo the Calligrapher died in 1935. The design obviously is a salamander, the beast that lives in the fire. But what it means here I don't know. It could be a trademark, or a member's card for a club. It could be adapted from a coat of arms. I'll show it to my old friend, Solimbene. Knows every coat of arms in Europe."

"Good. How about doing some copies of it before the others get back from lunch? I'll need one for my own inquiries."

"Where did you get this, Colonel?"

"In General Pantaleone's bedroom. He died last night."

"Pantaleone? That old *fascista!* What happened to him?"

"Natural causes. We've got a notarized certificate to prove it."

"Very convenient! Suicide or murder?"

"Suicide."

"Eh! That smells bad."

"So, Steffi, this is between you and me and the Director. Dead silence until I tell you."

Stefanelli grinned. "I don't like Fascists any more than you do, Colonel. And if we don't get a stable government soon, we'll get a *colpo di stato,* a military takeover of the government with a Fascist in the saddle. Then civil war—Left against Right, North against South. I can smell it and I'm scared. I don't want my children to suffer as we did."

"Nor I, Steffi. So we have to know who steps into the general's shoes. Call me the minute you have anything. *Ciao.*"

Now I was at loose ends. I could make no sense of the Pantaleone documents until they were collated with the general's dossier. The Director, who was the only man I could talk to freely, was not in the office. I decided to find Lili Anders.

Her apartment was on the third floor of a new condominium, all aluminum and glass, with a porter in livery and an elevator paneled in walnut. Lili Anders must be living at twice the scale on which she was taxed. I was mildly resentful by the time an elderly housekeeper dressed in black bombazine opened the door. She confronted me like a true Roman, laconic and hostile: "Yes?"

"Matucci. Carabinieri. I wish to see the Signora Anders."

"You have an appointment?"

"No."

"Then you'll have to come back later. The *signora* is asleep."

"I'm afraid I must ask you to wake her. My business is urgent."

"Do you have any identification?"

She looked at my card, swept me into the hall like a pile of dust and left.

I waited, grim and dyspeptic. Then Lili Anders made her entrance. For a woman who had just been sleeping she was beautifully turned out; every blond hair in place, no wrinkle in dress. She was polite but cool. "You wished to see me?"

"Privately, if that is possible."

She led me into the living room and closed the door. She prayed me to be seated and then stood by the mantel under an equestrian portrait of Pantaleone. "You are from the carabinieri."

"I am Colonel Matucci."

"And the reason for this visit?"

"A painful matter, I'm afraid. I regret to inform you that General Pantaleone died early this morning."

She stared at me, wide-eyed and trembling, holding on to the mantel for support. I moved toward her to steady her, but she waved me away. I crossed to the buffet, poured brandy into a goblet and handed it to her. "If you want to cry, go ahead."

"He was kind to me and gentle, but I have no tears for him."

"There is something else—he died by his own hand."

She spread her hands in a gesture of defeat. "There were too many dark places in his life; too many secrets, too many people lying in wait for him."

"Did he tell you that?"

"No. I knew."

"Then perhaps you know why he chose last night to kill himself. Why not a week ago, or next month?"

"I don't know. He had been moody for a long time, but whenever I asked him what was troubling him, he put me off."

"And last night?"

"One thing only. During dinner at the Chess Club a waiter brought him a message. He went out for about five minutes. He told me it had been a telephone call from a colleague. Nothing more was said. When he brought me home I invited him in. Sometimes he stayed, sometimes he didn't. This time he said he had work to finish at home."

I handed her the copy of the salamander card. "Have you seen this before? Or anything like it? Or heard those words?"

She studied it. "Not that I can remember. I'm sorry."

"You must in no sense reproach yourself. You have had a grievous shock. And now I have to distress you still further. I must warn you that you stand in grave personal danger."

"I don't understand."

"You have been for a long time the mistress of an important man. Even if the general told you nothing, others will believe he told you everything. Inevitably, therefore, you will come under surveillance, under pressure, possibly even under threat."

"From whom?"

"From extremists of the Right and of the Left, from foreign agents operating in the republic, even from officials of our own public security. As a foreigner residing here on a sojourn permit, you are especially vulnerable."

"But I have nothing to tell! I lived a woman's life with a man who needed comfort and affection. His other life, whatever it was, I did not share. You must believe that." She was shaken now. Her face seemed to crumple, her hands fumbled restlessly.

I leaned back in the chair and admonished her. "I wish I could believe you. But I know you, Lili Anders, chapter and verse. I know you from your first birthday in Warsaw to your recent dispatch to one Colomba, a bookbinder in Milan, identifying yourself as Falcone. You are all called by bird names, are you not? You are paid by Canarino from an account in a Zurich bank. You see, Lili, we Italians are not as inefficient as we look. We are good conspirators ourselves. I admire a good professional. But you are a problem. Another brandy? I'll have one myself, if you don't mind. *Salute!*"

She drank, clasping the glass in both hands as if it were a pillar that would support her. "What happens to me now?"

"Eh! That's a question, Lili. I could take you into custody on espionage charges. That means a long interrogation and a stiff sentence. Or I could leave you free, on certain conditions. Which would you prefer?"

"I'm tired of the game, Colonel. I'd like to be out of it."

"You can't get out, Lili. You can only change sides."

"Which means?"

"Full information on your network, and a contract with us."

"As a double agent, you mean. Can you protect me?"

"As long as you're useful, yes. Let's try some more questions. Who arranged your first meeting with the general?"

"The Marchesa Friuli. Her code name is Pappagallo."

"Parrot! The old girl looks it. What was your directive?"

"To give early warning of any attempt at a *colpo di stato* by neo-Fascist groups, and of actions designed to provoke it."

"Such as?"

"Acts of violence planned against police or carabinieri during labor demonstrations, bomb attacks that could be attributed to Maoist or Marxist groups, signs of disaffection in the armed services, any changes of political groups in the high command."

"Had there been any such changes recently?"

"No—at least not to my knowledge."

"Then why was the general depressed?"

"I was trying to find out. I had the feeling that it was personal rather than political. He had a habit of dropping cryptic remarks, then shutting up like a shellfish. The other night, for example, he said: 'There is no simple future for me, Lili, because my past is too complicated,' and then he quoted from the Bible: *A man's enemies are the men of his own house.* But he wouldn't explain."

"Anything else?"

"I'm trying to remember—Oh, yes, when we were in Venice, we

went to the opera at the Phoenix Theater. He was talking about the phoenix, the fabulous bird that rose alive from its own ashes; then he said there was another fabled creature, more remarkable and more dangerous—the salamander that lived in fire and could survive the hottest flames. Wait! That's your card."

"So it is, Lili. Did he say more about the salamander?"

"Some friends joined us. The subject was dropped."

"Well, there will be other times and other questions. You'll now be under constant surveillance. Here is my card with day and night numbers. I'd like you to be at the funeral."

"Please, no!"

"Please, yes! I want tears and grief and black mourning. You will not move back into society until I tell you. No new boy friends until you are out of mourning. Then, when you find one, I'd like to check him out."

She managed a weak smile. "Check him or me, Colonel?"

"I can't afford you, Lili. Still it's a thought to keep. One fine tomorrow . . . ? Be good now. And there's a prize for every tear at the requiem."

Half an hour later I was seated on the Via Veneto, with a sandwich and a *cappuccino,* scanning the afternoon papers. The general's death was reported only in the late bulletins, in identical terms, directly quoting the army announcement. The bloodhounds would not be in full cry until morning. By that time the general would be safely lying in state in the family chapel at Frascati.

THE obsequies of Massimo, Count Pantaleone, made a splendid piece of theater. The requiem was sung by Cardinal Dadone, the bishop of Frascati. The panegyric was delivered in ringing tones by the secretary-general of the Society of Jesus. The mass was attended by the President, ministers of the council, members of both chambers, prelates of the Roman Curia, representatives of NATO and the diplomatic corps, relatives and friends. Six field officers carried the bier to the vault, which was closed and locked by the President himself, a gesture of respect, gratitude and national solidarity not lost upon the gentlemen of the press. Lili

Anders was there, leaning on the arm of Captain Girolamo Carpi, who was visibly moved by the passing of his beloved patron.

I was among the mourners, too; but my concern was that my camera crew photograph every person there, from the cardinal to the florist. I hate funerals. I was glad when the rites were over.

At three thirty I was back in the forensic laboratory with Stefanelli. The old fellow was jumping like a grasshopper. "I told you Solimbene would recognize that card. The crowned salamander is the emblem of Francis the First. It recurs in arms derived from the house of Orléans, the duchy of Angoulême and the Farmer family in England. Solimbene is getting us a list of Italian families who use it. The pen work? Based on Aldo the Calligrapher, as I thought, probably executed by Carlo Metaponte, who forged papers for the partisans during the war and has been going straight ever since. The card is not Japanese—I was wrong there—but a passable imitation made by the Casarolis. They're giving us a list of their principal customers. The inscription makes no sense yet, but we're coming to it. How's that for forty-eight hours!"

"Great, Steffi. But we need more. How about fingerprints?"

"The only ones that we've been able to lift belong to the late lamented general. You didn't expect anything else, surely?"

"Try again, Steffi. I want miracles, and I want them yesterday."

"Everything takes time, Colonel. How was the funeral?"

"Beautiful, Steffi. I cried all through it!"

"*Requiescat in aeternum.*" Stefanelli crossed hands on his bony chest and rolled his eyes. "Have you seen the obituaries?"

"Now, when have I had time to read, Steffi?"

"I've got them here. They're worth a look."

They were. The Right wing was fulsome. The Center was respectful and only mildly censorious of the general's Fascist period. The Left achieved a kind of poetry of abuse, culminating in a doggerel that worried me a little.

Uprooted today,
The last of his line,
Pantaleone,
The rogue.

This might simply mean that the Left had helped uproot him, and that happily no successor was in sight. It might also be the opening gambit of a campaign to vilify the general. But there was nothing I could do about it. At least not one of the obituaries questioned the official version of the general's demise, which was not to say they believed it but only that it suited all parties to accept it.

While I was leafing through the papers Steffi added a spicy commentary. "Now here's a pretty thing: 'The Principessa Faubiani presents her summer collection!' You know about her, don't you? Came from Argentina, married young Prince Faubiani, set him up with a boy friend and then petitioned for separation on grounds of his impotence. That way she kept her freedom, the title and a right to maintenance. Since then she's had a new protector every couple of years—old ones now, all rich. They finance her fashion collections. The last one was a banker. I hear she has a new one—I wonder who."

"And what's your interest in fashion, Steffi?"

"My wife has a boutique on the Via Sistina. High mode for rich tourists, decorative staff, interesting gossip. All that."

"You crafty old devil!"

"Lucky, Colonel. I married for love and got money as well. Speaking of gossip, one of my wife's clients insists that Pantaleone has a brother floating around somewhere."

"Not according to Central Registry. Old Massimo had two daughters and a son. One daughter died in childbirth; the other married a Spanish diplomat and lives in Bolivia. Our general, who inherited the title, was the only male issue."

"Well, I admit the old Baroness Schwarzburg isn't the Central Registry, but she knew the old count and she claims he bred himself a bastard from the girls' governess. He paid her off, and she married someone who gave the boy a name, but the baroness couldn't remember it. She's getting doddery, of course. . . . Anyway, it's a note in the margin, if you're interested."

"I'd be interested if you could tell me why Pantaleone killed himself. . . . It's nearly five. The funeral photographs should be ready. If they're not, I'll send you three heads for pickling. Keep in touch, Steffi."

The photographs were not ready. After ten minutes of snappish dialogue with the chief of photographic records I gave up in disgust and went back to my own office. Here, at least, there was some efficiency. The general's documents were indexed, and number one clerk had made some discoveries.

"Brokers' notes, Colonel. The general has unloaded about eighty million lire' worth of prime stock in the last four weeks. Question: Where did the proceeds go? Not into his bank—there's his last statement, issued only a week ago. Then here's a letter from a real estate agency pointing out that, though the Pantaleone property has been for sale for more than two months, there has been no serious interest at the figure asked. They recommend withdrawing the property until the credit situation in Europe eases. . . . Now comes this little piece—a handwritten note from del Giudice, art dealer in Florence: 'Strongly advise against any transactions which involve you personally in a commitment to export works from the Pantaleone collection. You offer the works for sale subject to the conditions of existing law. After that, full responsibility for export rests on the purchaser.' "

"So, he was trying to sell out. Any indication why?"

"Not in these papers."

"What else have we got?"

"No other surprises. But there's a key to a safe-deposit box at the Banco di Roma. I'd like to see the inside of that."

"We will—as soon as the banks open in the morning."

"His lawyer is howling for us to release the papers."

"I'll worry about him later. I'll also have a chat with the general's brokers about the stock sale. If you want me in the next hour, I'll be at the Chess Club. After that, at home."

The Chess Club of Rome is a sacred institution. You enter it, as you hope one day to enter heaven, through a noble portico and find yourself in a courtyard of classic dimensions. You climb a flight of stairs to a series of anterooms, where servants in livery receive you with cautious deference. You tread softly, so as not to disturb the ghosts of kings and nobles who still inhabit the place. In the dining room you are awed by the whispered talk of men who deal with great affairs, and daunted by the cold eyes of dowagers sour with the virtue of age. And you will look in vain for chess players, although it is rumored that they do exist.

I was not coming to play chess. I was here to get myself put in touch—if the stars were in favorable conjunction—with those who had served Pantaleone on the eve of his death.

It was still only eight thirty and the guests were sparse. The secretary was unusually urbane and presented me to the headwaiter. He, too, was helpful, and allowed me to explain my mission to the steward. Sometime during his last meal, I said, the general had been called to the telephone, and for reasons connected with military security I wished to trace the call and contact the person who had made it. Then I had my first surprise.

"No, Colonel." The headwaiter was definite. "The general was called from the dining room, but not to the telephone. A senior member of the club had asked to speak with him in private. The steward conducted the general to him. They spoke for a few moments, the general returned to his table, the member left the club. I saw him leave."

"And who was this member?"

"The Cavaliere di Gran Croce Bruno Manzini from Bologna. He's in the club now. Came in about twenty minutes ago with the Principessa Faubiani."

"La Faubiani, eh?" I permitted myself a small grin of satisfaction—I was one up on old Steffi! "Would you give the gentleman my card and ask him to spare me a few moments?"

Manzini was an impressive figure. He must have been nearly seventy years old; his hair was snow-white, brushed back in a lion's mane over his coat collar; but his back was straight as a pine, his skin was clear, his eyes bright and humorous. He carried himself with the air of a man accustomed to deference. He announced himself with calm formality. "I am Manzini. I understand you wish to see me. May I see your official identification?"

I handed it to him and he read it carefully. "Thank you, Colonel. Now, your question."

"You were, I believe, a friend of General Pantaleone?"

"Not a friend, Colonel, an acquaintance. I had small respect for him, none at all for his politics."

"How would you define his politics?"

"Fascist and opportunist."

"And your own?"

"Private to myself, Colonel."

"I understand you had a conversation with the general here on the night he died. May I know the substance of it?"

"Certainly. Del Giudice, an art dealer in Florence, had told me that Pantaleone was about to sell the family collection. I was interested in certain items and wanted to negotiate with Pantaleone directly. It would save us both money. He said he would think about it and write to me soon."

"The Pantaleone collection is an old and important one. Why would the general want to disperse it?"

"I have no idea. May I know the reason for these inquiries?"

"At the moment I am not at liberty to disclose it, sir. And may I ask you to keep this conversation private?"

"You may not! I did not invite it. I stand upon my right to discuss it as I please, with whom I please."

"Sir, you know the organization which I represent?"

"The Service of Defense Information? I know of its existence. I am not familiar with its activities."

"You know, at least, that we deal with highly sensitive matters, both political and military."

"My dear Colonel, please! I'm an old man. I have no taste for spies, provocateurs or those who treat with them. I know that intelligence services can become instruments of tyranny. I know that they tend to corrupt the people who work in them. If you have no more questions, I trust that you will excuse me. Good evening!"

He stalked out of the room, and I let out a long exhalation of relief. This was a sturdy one. He looked you straight in the eye

and gave you clean answers crack-crack-crack, knowing that you dared not dispute him. But the important questions were still open. Why would Pantaleone, with suicide on his mind, embark on the long business of selling an estate? And why promise a letter he knew he would never write?

It was enough, more than enough, for one day. My head was stuffed with cotton and my heart full of envy for a seventy-year-old man who could afford expensive pets like La Faubiani. I drove reluctantly homeward to a hot dinner, a tepid hour of television and a cold bed.

I had a very troubled night. Shortly after ten a colleague from Milan telephoned with the news that a young Maoist being questioned in a bomb case had fallen to his death from the window of the interrogation room. There would be headlines in every morning paper. The Left would swear he had been pushed by the police. The Right would affirm that he had jumped. There would be troops on every street corner for a week, which would heighten the tension and polarize the factions even more. What a nightmare mess!

At eleven thirty Lili Anders telephoned in panic. Her network contact had summoned her to a rendezvous at the Osteria dell'Orso at midnight. What should she do? I told her to keep the rendezvous, rehearsed her in her story and then spent an anxious fifteen minutes rounding up my surveillance team to follow her.

I was just about to crawl back into bed when the telephone rang again. This was Captain Carpi's shadow. The captain was drunk and mumbling to a bar girl. What did I want done about it? Let him drink himself silly, then bundle him home.

AT NINE THIRTY next morning I sat in conference with a senior official of the Banco di Roma. He was courteous but firm. There could be no access to the late general's safe-deposit. The law demanded rigid performance of contracts between banker and client. Besides—he paused—the strongbox was empty. The general's lawyer had taken possession of its contents under an existing authority.

The brokers were more cooperative. They had indeed sold large parcels of the general's stock and had remitted the proceeds to his lawyer, Sergio Bandinelli. That ended their transaction.

Back in my office, I wrote a summons for Bandinelli to call on me within forty-eight hours. Then I settled down to examine the funeral photographs. At the end of an hour I had one small surprise. Bruno Manzini appeared in three shots, once with Cardinal Dadone, once with the Minister of Finance and the third time with an elderly peasant employed at the Villa Pantaleone. For a man who regarded Pantaleone as a Fascist and an opportunist, his presence at the funeral was a singular gesture. I wondered why he had troubled to make it. I telephoned a colleague for a copy of Manzini's dossier. Then I summoned Stefanelli.

Old Steffi was bursting with news. First, his wife had told him that La Faubiani's new protector was one Bruno Manzini, a Bolognese richer than anyone had a right to be—big in textiles, electrics, steel, even food processing.

"I know all that, Steffi."

"The hell you do! How?"

I told him. Then I showed him the photographs. "Now, Steffi. What's he doing at the funeral of a man he despised?"

"Easy. You may not like me, but you'll come to see me buried. How else can you be sure I'm dead?"

"Maybe . . . maybe. What else have you got?"

"The Casarolis sell rice paper to wholesalers only. Here's that list. But thousands of retailers sell the stuff."

"Body of Bacchus! Don't you have any good news, Steffi?"

"Solimbene called. So far he's found fifteen families in Italy who use the salamander in their coat of arms. Another paper chase, I'm afraid. . . . Did you read the headlines this morning?"

"I did."

"I'm scared, Colonel. Last night a suspect under questioning jumped or was pushed from a window. Why? Under what conditions? We have two thousand carabinieri on the streets of Milan this morning. Another thousand on extra duty in Rome. Cowing people. Stifling questions. We—the carabinieri and our colleagues in the police—are the real rulers of Milan at the moment. It's a terribly tempting blueprint, friend. We don't have to offer bread and circuses anymore, just public order, peace on the streets and buses running on time. Because we don't have a government; we have parties, factions, warring interests. And if things don't change soon, the man in the street is going to start shouting for a leader, a new *duce!*"

"What I'm trying to find out, Steffi, is who that would be."

"And when you do?"

"Say it, Steffi."

"You buried an embarrassing corpse yesterday—under orders. Suppose you stumble on another embarrassment, a live one this time—a man in our own service, for example. Suppose you're ordered then to close the file and keep your mouth shut. What will you do?"

"I'm damned if I know. Old Manzini was right. This job corrupts people. I don't know how much it's corrupted me."

"You may have to know very soon, Colonel. I'm a Jew, Colonel. You didn't know that? Well, I live in the old ghetto. In the synagogue we've got a list of names, eleven hundred people who were shipped out to Auschwitz on the Black Sabbath of 1943. Fourteen men and one woman came back. Do you know why I joined the service? So that I'd know in advance if it were ever going to happen again. . . . How old are you, Colonel?"

"Forty-two. Why?"

"You were only a boy then. But every time I see an election poster now, I get nightmares. I'm sorry if I've offended you."

"You haven't, Steffi. I'm glad you told me. Now, why don't you go play with your microscope, eh?"

But when the old man had gone, all the litter of photographs and memoranda on my desk suddenly seemed irrelevant. What was at issue was not the sordid power games of politics, but myself, Dante Matucci: who I was, and what price I would accept for my soul—if indeed I had one. To be a servant of the state was easy. The state was like God—you couldn't define it. You didn't have to ask questions about it. But I, Dante, was—or hoped

I was—a person. How much of me did the state own? How far could it legitimately direct me? To toss a living man out of a window? To shoot a rioter? To stifle a citizen with papers so he couldn't even get up in the morning without a permit?

And then there was the other side of the coin: fifty million turbulent people locked in a narrow peninsula, poor in resources, rich only in sap and energy, easy prey to agitators. How did you stop them from tearing each other to pieces if you didn't break a few heads from time to time?

I was still chewing on that sour thought when the boys from the surveillance team came to report on Lili Anders. Their tapes of the nightclub meeting were almost unintelligible. I wanted to know why.

"No time to plant anything effective, Colonel. Anyway, they only stayed half an hour. We followed them back to Anders's apartment. The contact dropped her there and drove off. Giorgio followed him. I stayed to get a report from the lady."

"Who was the contact?"

"Picchio—Woodpecker."

"What did sweet Lili have to say for herself?"

"Woodpecker asked what the general died of. A heart attack, she said. Had she known he was sick? No, but he did have occasional chest pains that he called indigestion."

"Good for Lili. Go on."

"Who brought her the news? A colonel of carabinieri, Matucci. Had he asked any significant questions? Only about Pantaleone's movements on the night of his death. She had told him the truth. Who, Woodpecker asked, were the general's heirs? She didn't know. Did she know the general's lawyer? She did. She was ordered to cultivate him, and find out all she could about the estate. Had she ever met a Major General Leporello?"

"Impossible! He's one of ours."

"It shook me, too, Colonel."

"What did Lili say?"

"She'd never met him. Had the general ever spoken of him? Not that she remembered. What was her next assignment? Sit tight, concentrate on the lawyer and await further instructions. That's it, Colonel."

"Anything from Lili's phone tap?"

"Nothing since her call to you, Colonel."

"Good. Now, let's hear about our little Captain Carpi."

"He passed out cold about three in the morning and I took him home. He's a bad drunk, Colonel."

"That's something new. Anyway, he'll sober up in Sardinia tomorrow. Thank you, gentlemen. Make sure you're fresh and sharp by eight this evening. You're still on night roster."

I grinned at their discomfiture as they slouched out. This was what the Americans called the name of the game. You walked your feet off, you knocked on doors, you waded through reams of useless information, until you came up with one item that began or completed a whole mosaic. I had one now: Why was Woodpecker, a Polish agent, interested in Marcantonio Leporello, major general of the carabinieri?

As AN investigator I have many shortcomings and two special talents. I have a photographic memory. And I know how to wait. Comes a moment in every investigation when there is nothing to do but let the chemistry of the situation work itself out. If you try to hurry it, you make mistakes. The Italians love brouhaha. Sketch them a scene and in an hour they've built you an opera. I am a colonel at forty-two because I have learned to make a virtue out of the vices of my countrymen.

But when a big thing came up, the trick was to create a zone of quiet and sit there, visible but enigmatic. It was a tactic that disconcerted my associates.

At that moment in time the Pantaleone affair was in suspension. The meaning of the salamander card was not yet deciphered. The general's lawyer had the contents of his strongbox. Manzini's presence at the funeral might mean nothing. He was simply a buyer of expensive art. There was nothing to go on, nothing—except that a Polish agent was interested in Major General Leporello. It seemed the time to have a chat with the Director.

The Director was a character in his own right. In the SID they called him Volpone—the old fox. To me he was a chameleon. One moment you saw him, the next you had lost him against the political undergrowth. He had the manners of a prince and the mind of a chess player. He had a sense of history and a conviction that it always repeated itself. He was inordinately rich, generous to those he liked and ruthless to those he did not. He insisted that I was one of those he liked. We clashed often. He had tempted me, more than once, but I had turned away with a grin and a shrug. I made no secret of my weaknesses, but I was damned if I would be blackmailed with them. And if the Director wanted to play games, I had a few of my own.

I was playing one now. Major General Leporello was a big man in the carabinieri. I wanted to know whether the Director was big enough to handle him. "Woodpecker is interested in Leporello," I said abruptly. "Why?"

The old fox sniffed the air. "Isn't it your job to tell me?"

"Leporello's dossier is marked 'Reserved to Director,' sir."

"Forgive me, I'd forgotten. Let me see now. General Leporello has spent the last five months abroad. An official tour to study riot control and counterinsurgency."

"Do you know the general personally, sir?"

"Yes. He's a sound man."

"Vulnerable?"

"He's a patriot, a devout Catholic, a Christian Democrat and financially independent. I doubt he could be bought or frightened."

"Might he be seduced?"

"By what, Colonel?"

"The ultimate infirmity—ambition. The student of counterinsurgency might decide to put it into practice."

"You're lost in fables, Matucci. What's your evidence?"

"Suggestive only. Woodpecker and his network have a commission which I quote: 'to give early warning of any attempt at a *colpo di stato* by neo-Fascist groups, or of actions designed to provoke it.' If Woodpecker is interested in Leporello, we have to be, too."

"I think not. But let me play with the idea. Anything else?"

"No, sir."

"Then permit me to offer you a compliment. I like your attitude to your work, careful and open-minded. That's rare in these times, you know."

"You are kind, sir. Thank you." I walked out a very pensive man. I had no wish to end my days in the dungeons of official disfavor. And yet . . . a military man who could control rioters and urban guerrillas might, one fine tomorrow, control the country, especially if he were a patriot, a good Christian and financially independent.

I was hardly back in my office when my secretary announced that Sergio Bandinelli was waiting to see me.

The lawyer was short, fussy and very irascible. "I am here to protest the illegal seizure of the papers from my client's domicile and to demand their immediate delivery into my hands."

"No problem. They're yours to take. As for the protest, what's the profit? You know that SID works under the President's directive and to rather special rules. Of course, if you wish to press a complaint . . ."

"Well, under the circumstances . . ."

"Good! I am encouraged to solicit your assistance."

"I am happy to assist, Colonel, provided I may reserve my position in the event of conflict of interest."

"Of course. The general's death has political consequences which I am directed to study. All his activities are of interest. Why, to begin with, was he liquidating his estate?"

"I am not at liberty to say."

"His brokers informed us that the proceeds of his shares were transmitted to you. What were you directed to do with the money?"

"I cannot tell you that, either. Legal privilege."

"Before you invoke it, let me tell you that your late client maintained relations with a member of a foreign espionage network. You yourself are under surveillance by the same network."

"Is this some kind of threat, Colonel?"

"No threat—simple fact. When you refuse to disclose what has happened to large sums of money you put yourself in jeopardy. A threat to the security of the state is involved. You are answerable for your part in your client's affairs. I ask you again—what happened to the money?"

"I reinvested it in Switzerland and Brazil."

"And if the art collection had been sold, and the land?"

"I was instructed to do the same with the proceeds."

"Have you approval from the Ministry of Finance for export of funds?"

"Well, no . . . but the nature of the transaction—"

"Would involve intermediaries who have safe channels for currency export. Who charge five percent, for which they guarantee immunity to the client. They can't guarantee that, and you know it. You can be charged with conspiracy to circumvent the law. So—why was Pantaleone exporting funds?"

"He was afraid. He had joined with the new Fascists as their military adviser and commander in chief in case of a *colpo di stato*. Their provocative tactics worried him. He felt they were not strong enough to risk a *colpo di stato* and that, if they tried, it would lead to civil war. So they began to lose faith in Pantaleone. They wanted to move him out in favor of a bolder man."

"Did Pantaleone know who that man was?"

"No. Only that it was a military man not now in the movement but who might be attracted into it when the time was right."

"Was the general frightened of a rival? Or of something else?"

"Action against himself. Some kind of revelation of his past. He had a checkered career and many enemies."

"Blackmail, in fact. Had he had any direct threats?"

"About a week ago he received a communication by messenger. It consisted of a very complete biography which, if it had ever been published, would have damaged his reputation beyond repair and banished him forever from public life."

"Was a threat of publication made?"

"I read it so."

"Read what?"

"A card, attached to the typescript."

I laid the salamander card on the table. "This card?"

"Yes, that's the one. Where did you get it?"

"In the general's bedroom. What happened to the biography?"

"He lodged it in his strongbox at the bank."

"Which you emptied yesterday. I want it."

"On a judge's order you may have it. Otherwise not."

"This card, what does it signify?"

"I don't know. The general mentioned something about Saint Martin's Day, but he wouldn't explain what it meant. I know only that in Spain pigs are killed on the Feast of Saint Martin."

"If you want to avoid your own Saint Martin's Day, I'll make a bargain with you. I'll forget the currency question. I'll send a man to your office with you now to list every paper you hold on the Pantaleone family. He will then seal them in your safe. Tomorrow I will go through them with you. Agreed?"

"I seem to have no choice. I agree."

"Good. My man will spend the night in your office."

"Why?"

"Protection. Politics is a risky business these days."

I meant it as an irony. I was the old-line professional patronizing a civilian. I should have known better. In this trade, in this country, you are always standing on a trapdoor with a hangman's noose around your neck.

The which being said, an explanation is needed. This republic of Italy is not a nation at all. We Italians are provinces, cities, countrysides, families, individuals—anything but a unity. Ask that fellow, that street cleaner, what he is. He will answer, "I am a Sard, a Calabrese, a Neapolitan." Never will he tell you he is an Italian. I myself am a Tuscan. I am paid to serve the nebulous public thing called the state, but my belonging is elsewhere—Florence and the Medici and the Arno and the pines on the graves of my ancestors.

Hence a kind of anarchy Anglo-Saxons can never understand. I can never say, "This is the enemy, destroy him!" I must say, "This is the enemy of the moment, but he comes from my country, his sister is married to my cousin and tomorrow we may need to be friends." I must comport myself so that the links are not broken, though the chain may be stretched almost to the breaking point.

Hence also a kind of order Anglo-Saxons can't understand. We have but one life, one opportunity to come to terms with it. We have to survive. So we try to negotiate. And if we are forced to accept a base bargain, we wait for a tomorrow when the contract may be annulled or improved by mutual consent. As you see, I know it all. So there is no excuse for the follies I began to commit that afternoon.

The first was my contemptuous bargain with Sergio Bandinelli, whom I judged to be a pliable, frightened man. I gave him for guardian one Giampiero Calvi, promising but young, who was to call headquarters every hour on the hour until I relieved him at nine the next morning. Then I called Lili Anders and told her that, in line of duty, I would call on her at eight thirty for a cocktail and take her out to dinner afterward. Finally, because I was—and am—too arrogant for my own good, I elected to play out my little testing game against the Director.

I had found out that Major General Leporello was here in Rome for conferences with senior service officers and was lodged at the Hassler. I telephoned him. The conversation was terse. "General, this is Colonel Matucci, SID."

"Yes?"

"A very urgent matter. I should like to see you."

"I am busy until six. I can spare you half an hour after that. Call me from the lobby. Suite ten."

"Thank you, sir."

"The name again?"

"Matucci. Section E."

I put down the telephone and waited. If I judged my man right, he would check back. Within three minutes my phone rang.

"Who is this, please?" said Leporello's voice.

"Matucci, Section E."

"This is Leporello. We have an appointment, I believe."

"Yes, sir. Suite ten at eighteen hundred hours."

"Please be punctual. Good-by."

I'd need some relaxation with Lili after half an hour with this hardhead. I made one more call, this time to a curious little office which provides information on the comings and goings of celebrities. My contact is a busty Dane. Her civil status is highly dubious, but her information is always accurate.

"Faubiani? Well, old Manzini's in town, so she's doing the rounds with him. Let's see . . . Tonight Fosco is displaying jewelry, and they will probably be there. It's a buffet supper at Fosco's, eight thirty until the champagne runs out. If you want a ticket, I can let you have mine. I only get envious when I look at all that expensive junk."

"You're an angel, Inger."

"When am I going to see you, Dante?"

"When I pick up the card at seven thirty. *Ciao, bambina!*"

After leaving two numbers with the night duty officer—Lili Anders's and my own—I was ready for grooming: a change of clothes, a trim, a shave, and a massage to tone up my sagging face muscles.

At six o'clock precisely I telephoned Major General Leporello from the front desk of the Hassler. He sent his aide to fetch me—a muscular young blood with red hair and freckles. I suspected that when he left me with the general he posted himself just outside the door. Leporello was a surprise. He was a tall man, blond and ruddy, more German than Latin. His chest was broad, his belly flat. His manner was brisk. He had no sense of humor at all. "Your identification, please." I gave it to him. "What do you wish to discuss, Colonel?"

"Matters arising out of the death of General Pantaleone."

"Such as?"

"This card, sir. It was found in the general's room. It was attached to a dossier which had just been delivered to him."

"What sort of dossier?"

"Incriminating documents of the general's past life."

"Blackmail?"

"We believe so."

"Where are they now?"

"In his lawyer's office, in custody of an officer of SID."

"What is this symbol?"

"A salamander."

"That's odd. During the war one of the most important of the partisan groups was led by a man called the Salamander."

"What was his real name? Did he use a card like this?"

"I don't know who he was. But I remember some talk of a calling card pinned to the chest of victims of the band."

"Did this group have Marxist connections?"

"Most groups in the North were reputed to have."

"Did you ever work with such groups, General?"

"I? Never. My loyalties were to the Crown. I disliked the Fascists, I loathed the Germans; but even for that I could not be a turncoat soldier. Today I am able to be both honest and proud."

"I am sure you are, sir. You are also a natural target for the terrorists of the Left. Which brings me to the real purpose of my visit—you are, sir, under surveillance by at least one network of foreign agents."

He gave me a thin smile. "That's hardly news, Colonel. I have always assumed surveillance—foreign and local."

"The news is, General, that this group regards you as a possible successor to General Pantaleone."

"In what capacity?"

"As leader in the event of a Right-wing coup."

"Which is nonsense, of course."

"Of course, sir. But it does make you vulnerable to blackmail or assassination."

I had thought to shake him, but he was hard and smooth as cemetery granite. "Blackmail, Colonel? Impossible. My life is an open book. As for attempts on my life, these have been foreseen and security measures arranged. I am more concerned by the suggestion that I might have political ambitions. I have none. I believe in hierarchy and order. I see myself only as a servant of duly constituted authority. Have you discussed this matter with your director?"

"I have."

"His opinion?"

"That no action is required by SID. I have, in fact, exceeded my brief by seeking this interview with you."

"Why did you seek it then?"

"We are members of the same corps, General, you and I. I felt that a point of carabinieri honor was involved. I decided to act on my own initiative and at my own risk. I am prepared to accept all consequences."

Leporello relaxed. He leaned back and surveyed me with grim approval. "You impress me, Colonel. If you need a friend, you have one in me. I shall instruct my staff that you may have instant access to me at any time."

"That is very generous, sir."

"Not at all. The security and stability of the republic is my business, and yours. Pantaleone was a dangerous fool. Today we need strong men who are prepared to risk themselves in public service. If ever you feel an inclination to join my personal staff, I should be happy to have you. And—ah, Colonel—I have no intention of discussing this meeting with your director."

"Thank you, sir," I said as he shook my hand and ushered me out, commending me to the care of his aide, who escorted me downstairs and saluted as I drove away.

In the gardens of the Pincio I stopped the car and sat for twenty minutes trying to make sense of Major General Leporello. I have an instinctive fear of characters who act as if they were first cousins to God Almighty. Their certainty of rectitude never ceases to amaze me. They are dogmatists all, and have no hesitation about rewriting the moral code to suit themselves. Their passion for order sets them beyond reason or pity. In short, I'm more afraid of them than of all the crooks I meet in my trade. They make me afraid of myself, too, because they provoke me to anger and misjudgment and savage reaction.

Still there was a tenuous profit to the interview. Leporello was tempting me with a promise of friendship into an alliance; an alliance suggested a strategy—to what end? What would be the next ambition of a man whose current job was controlling ant-heap cities and their millions of volatile humans? Eh! It was too late and too early for Dante Matucci to read the future. I started the car and drove through the dappled alleys of the gardens to drink cocktails with Lili Anders.

THE apartment had changed since my last visit. The portrait of Pantaleone was gone. Things had been rearranged to produce an air of femininity. Lili herself was changed; her hair more softly swept, her clothes more modish, her manner more confident. When I commented, she smiled and shrugged. "I am perhaps a little more my own woman. What will you drink?"

"Whiskey, please."

"You are changed, too. More human, less professional. How am I to call you, Colonel?"

"Dante. I'd like us to enjoy ourselves as friends tonight."

"That's hardly possible, is it? Because, Dante, in fact you own me. You direct me like a puppet. Your drink, master."

"Your health, Lili."

"Where are we dining?"

"We are guests at an exhibition and a champagne supper afterward. Fosco is displaying his new season's jewelry."

"That should be interesting. Do you like jewelry, Dante?"

"I do—even though I can't afford it."

"If you would like to see mine, I'll show it to you when we come back. I presume you will bring me back after the supper?"

"You're being rough with me, Lili."

"No. I want you to know that I understand our relationship. I promised value for money and protection."

"I'm not a whoremaster, Lili."

"Then what are you?"

"I am self-indulgent and I like pretty women. Also I'm tired and I want to laugh. I'm puzzled and I want to stop thinking. I'm scared and I don't really want to ask why."

"You, scared?"

"Yes. This is the age of the assassins, Lili—fanatics who want a new world. They'll tear down twenty centuries of civilization to achieve it. They don't see that when they're sitting in the ruins the old gang will come back—the technocrats to build the factories, the police to bully people into order, even the city rat-catchers like me. It's a madness, Lili, and I'm at the center of it. So are you. There's no escape for either of us. Now, please, may I have another drink?"

She gave it to me. Then she laid a cool hand on my cheek. "Even if you mean only half of it, I'll believe you."

I wasn't sure I believed myself; but I wanted to feel less like a pimp and more like a man who could face the sunlight without shame. I kissed her hand lightly. "Now, let's start again."

Twenty minutes later we were driving to Fosco's, and we joined the gathering, hand in hand, like lovers.

It was a gala occasion. The best titles in Rome staged a slow pavane around the showcases of Fosco's work. A master chef presided over the buffet. An army of waiters distributed champagne and canapés. It was a sophisticated social ballet, and Fosco directed it with charm and only a hint of contempt for the performers. He received us with vague courtesy and waved us into the concourse. We snared two glasses of champagne and a pair of catalogues and began our circuit of the exhibits. It was immediately clear that Fosco had made a killing. Half the items had been made to order or optioned in advance to great houses—Bulgari, Cartier, Buccellati, Tiffany. His designs were original, his craftsmanship superb. He labeled every exhibit as if it were a museum piece, including whenever he could the name and title of the person who had commissioned it. We were halfway around the room when Lili tugged at my sleeve and pointed to Number 63 in the catalogue. The description read:

> SALAMANDER. Brooch in the form of an heraldic beast. Emeralds in pavé. Crowned with brilliants and ornamented with Burma rubies. Adapted from a calligraphic design. Commissioned by Cavaliere di Gran Croce Bruno Manzini, Bologna.

It was not a gaudy jewel, but the craftsman had preserved the character and sweep of the calligraphy. There was no doubt that the design was identical with the one on the card. I drew Lili away from the showcase into the crush around the buffet. At the same moment Manzini entered the gallery with the Principessa Faubiani at his side. Fosco greeted them effusively and led them on a personal tour of the masterworks.

Somehow I must see Manzini before he left the gallery. I excused myself to Lili and made my way to the entrance, where a young man was hosting for Fosco. I flashed my card at him. "Carabinieri. Who is in charge of your security guards?"

"Over there, tall fellow with gray hair. There's trouble?"

"No, no. Just routine."

I drew the tall fellow into the shadows and showed him my card, too. "This is important. You will take me to Fosco's private office and escort there the gentleman to whom I'll give you a note. Then I'd like you to stay outside the door and let no one in while we're talking—clear?"

"Clear. There's no trouble, I hope."

"None. I've noted your security arrangements. First class."

He was happy then. In Fosco's office I scribbled my note.

> Regret intrusion but have urgent and official communication. Please accompany messenger to office.
>
> Matucci, SID

Manzini was with me in three minutes, cool and condescending. He demanded that I state my business and be done with it.

"Still General Pantaleone. Shortly before he died he received a communication—a dossier, in effect, of his past life."

"And what has that to do with me?"

"Attached to the dossier was this card. The design corresponds exactly with Number sixty-three in the Fosco catalogue."

"So what do you want from me, Colonel?"

"At this stage, an informal discussion. Now, if possible, sir."

"Quite impossible. It is a long story and I am occupied with friends. But tomorrow, at nine in the morning at the Grand Hotel, my dear Colonel, I'll do my best to enlighten you. Now, may I be excused?"

"One question, sir. What does the salamander signify?"

"Survival. It was my code name during the war."

"And the inscription?"

"Pantaleone was my half brother. Only he happened to be conceived on the right side of the blanket."

I stared at him openmouthed, like an idiot. He smiled at my discomfiture. "Please! I am not trying to make theater, only to show you that we do need time to be clear with each other. And now, Colonel, will you answer one question for me?"

"If I can, yes."

"Who killed Pantaleone?"

"The death certificate states that he died of cardiac arrest."

"But that's what kills us all. No other comment, Colonel?"

"None until tomorrow." Why didn't I hold him? Why didn't I hammer him with questions while I had him off-balance? Because this was a very special one, the best of the breed. He off-balance? Never for an instant. With him, I was the unsure novice groping for a handhold on a bare mountain.

Happy to leave, I carted Lili off to dinner at a place I knew in Trastevere, where the food was honest Tuscan, the wine honorable and the waiters proud to serve you. I have friends there: the cook whom I prized, and others whose talk, in front of the open fire in winter or under the arbor of vines in the summer, was as good as the food and drink. It was one place where I was myself—whoever that might be. I accepted everyone at face value. I used no one. I paid the score and was welcome in the house. Everyone needs a refuge. This was mine.

I tried to explain all this to Lili as we walked the last hundred meters through lanes hung with laundry. She seemed happy to listen, holding close to me as we stepped over spilled refuse while cats slunk back into the shadows. Sometimes, when the rare light fell on her face, she looked like a young girl. But I was not hunting now, I was simply glad not to be alone.

When we were settled at the table, she laid her hands on mine. "You look different now, Dante Matucci. At Fosco's you were tight, wary, like a fox. Now you are loose, free. You greet people like human beings. They, too, are glad to see you."

"This is Trastevere, my love. Across the river. These people refuse to belong to anyone but themselves."

"I like that. For tonight we, too, may do that. Please, may I have some wine?"

"I may get drunk and sing."

"I'll sing with you."

"And who will drive us back across the river?"

"Perhaps we won't go back—ever again."

It was a happy thought and we nursed it, from the antipasto to the dessert, to the tune of a guitar played by a plaintive fellow who sings there, sings the soul out of your body with the songs of the South. By one thirty in the morning we were vaguely drunk. The waiters had begun to wilt, so we wandered back to the car. Lili said drowsily, "Do you know, I really don't want to go home. Home is yesterday. I want to forget it."

"So let's drive out to a place I know. . . . But I have to call my duty officer first. I left your number with him."

"There's no escape, is there? You have to telephone—"

"Please, Lili."

"Please, just kiss me. . . ."

The evening of liberty ended with that kiss. Headquarters told me our agent, Calvi, had not made his hourly call from the lawyer's office; the time was ten minutes after two. I ordered one car of the mobile squadron to pick up Steffi, another one to meet me at Bandinelli's. I put Lili into a taxi. Then I drove like a madman across the sleeping city.

When I arrived at the office on the Via Sicilia, one squadron car was already there. The second, carrying Steffi, hurtled around the corner seconds later. I gave a few sharp directions to the squadron leaders: this was a high-security matter; no police, no press; two men to stand by the cars, one to stay with the porter, three to accompany Steffi and me. Then we rang the bell.

The porter, bleary-eyed, opened the door. We flashed our cards, left him grumbling and took the elevator to the fifth floor. Bandinelli's office was dark when I opened the door. I switched the lights on—to a curiously tranquil scene. The lawyer lay stretched on a leather settee. Our agent, Calvi, was seated in a chair behind the desk, head pillowed on his arms. Old Steffi sniffed the air and briefly examined the bodies. "Dead. Hydrocyanic-acid gas. Pistol or pressure pack."

I examined the safe. The seals were broken, the door was open—the Pantaleone papers were gone.

I picked up the phone and called the Director's private number. He answered with surprising promptness. I told him, "We're in trouble. Documents missing, and two bundles of dirty linen for immediate disposal—one of them ours. As soon as the situation is tidy, I'll report in person."

"I'll expect you for breakfast—the earlier the better."

Steffi cackled at me like an ancient parrot. "When everything's tidy! So now we're in the miracle business!"

Steffi was right as usual. If I reported to the police, the press would swarm. Finding the Pantaleone papers involved, they would ask about the general's hasty burial and handicap our search for the documents. We had, therefore, to get the bodies out. I sent Steffi down to question the porter in his cubbyhole—Steffie's talk would hypnotize a fighting cock.

The boys and I emptied Bandinelli's and Calvi's pockets, then bundled the bodies into the elevator and into the two squad cars. One drove Bandinelli to the casualty department of the Policlinico; the other deposited Calvi at the Hospital of the Blue Sisters. In each case the story was the same: the mobile squadron had found a man lying, apparently unconscious, in an alley. They were consigning him to the hospital while they pursued inquiries as to his identity. Dead on arrival? Dear me! Then hold him in the mortuary while we trace him.

Meanwhile I examined the last entries in Calvi's notes:

24.00 hrs. Telephoned duty officer HQ.

00.37 hrs. Bandinelli telephoned. He wished stop by office for late conference with two clients. A police matter, he said. He would not disturb me, but would use outer office. Since my instructions referred only to custody of safe, I had no authority to refuse access to his own office. I agreed.

01.00 hrs. Telephoned duty officer to report Bandinelli's request and my decision.

I called the duty officer. He confirmed the entries, which left me with a vital question: had Bandinelli come to the office under duress or as an accomplice who was liquidated when his usefulness was ended? Steffi, who came back at that point, was no help. The porter always went off duty at midnight; tenants had passkeys and came and went at all hours. "In fact anyone with a passkey could bring an army in here after midnight with no one the wiser," Steffi said.

"All right. So where was Bandinelli when he telephoned? Let's ring his house."

A surly majordomo finally answered. No, the lawyer wasn't there. Hadn't come home for dinner. The *signora?* She was in Naples.

Steffi grinned. "Which helps your little fiction about an unidentified body."

"But it doesn't tell me who killed him and took the documents."

"Does it matter, Colonel?"

"Steffi! What sort of question is that?"

"Look! This is a neat, simple, professional job. Do you want the killers or the people who paid them? This is not police work, friend; it's intelligence analysis. Start from the top and you halve the work and double your chances of solving it—believe me!"

"I do believe you, Steffi, but sometime in the next three hours I have to face the Director. What do I offer him?"

"Human sacrifice!" Steffi favored me with a gallows grin. "So why don't we make some coffee and discuss the candidates."

THE Director's apartment was the top floor of a sixteenth-century palace just off the Via della Scrofa. The revenues from the rest of the palace—dwellings and fashionable shops—would keep him in kingly state for a lifetime. His paintings and sculptures were a fortune in themselves, his library a minor treasure-house. The Director was resplendent in a brocaded dressing gown, attended by a wiry Sicilian who was both butler and bodyguard. At six in the morning, grubby, unshaven and very unsure of myself, I was in no mood to appreciate the dramatic effect. He offered me a cool welcome and an English breakfast—tea, toast, scrambled eggs and marmalade. I asked for coffee and pastry. He conceded the point with a smile and then proceeded to make a few of his own.

"You knew the Pantaleone papers were important, Colonel. Why did you not take immediate possession of them?"

"I needed a judicial order. I'd have had to appear against Bandinelli in the presence of a judge, which I thought unwise."

"So you made an arrangement which resulted in the death of our agent and of Bandinelli himself. Any excuse?"

"No excuse. I was trying to scare Bandinelli into further revelations. I thought the risk was minimal. I was wrong."

"Who else knows the facts at this moment?"

"Only SID. We had the place cleaned up by four this morning."

"And who has the Pantaleone papers? Right wing or Left?"

"Right, I think."

"Why?"

"The Left have a lot of dirt they haven't published yet. The Right have a lot of dirt they want to bury—I think last night was a funeral party."

"You don't convince me, Colonel."

"I'm not trying to, sir. I'm telling you what I believe. If you're thinking of Woodpecker, forget him. I had him pulled in at four this morning. I've worked on him for nearly two hours. I know his brief. Assassination is not part of it. Let's look at the other side of the coin. Bandinelli was far Right. He served Pantaleone. He could have sold out to a successor—"

"And been killed for his pains?"

"That, too."

"Name me a possible successor."

"Major General Marcantonio Leporello."

The Director set down his teacup with a clatter and sat staring at me with bleak and hostile eyes. At last he said quietly, "I presume you have evidence in support, Colonel?"

"Some. I interviewed the general yesterday at his hotel."

"You what?"

"I interviewed Leporello."

"In spite of my orders that no action was to be taken with that subject?"

"Yes, sir."

"And what did you tell him?"

"That he was under surveillance by a foreign network who had tipped him as political candidate for the Right. The whereabouts of the Pantaleone papers. And that I was acting against your orders."

"Oh! And what was his reaction to that?"

"He promised to keep the interview secret, and he offered me a job on his own staff."

"I'm tempted to make you immediately available, Matucci. You disobey orders, and that's dangerous."

"It was a risk. I think it paid dividends. I know who sent the card to Pantaleone. I've identified the Salamander."

That brought him up short. His piece of toast stopped halfway to his thin lips. "And do you propose to tell me who he is?"

"Yes, sir. He's the Cavaliere di Gran Croce Bruno Manzini. He tells me he's the bastard brother of General Pantaleone. I have an appointment with him at nine o'clock this morning."

"Leporello, your military superior. Manzini, one of the most powerful financiers in Italy. You're flying high, my friend."

"And you can shoot me down now, if you choose."

"What if I let you go on?"

"I want a free hand and access to the Leporello file."

"Can I trust you, Matucci?"

"You can, but you'd rather not."

"Do you trust me?"

"With reservations. I know what you are commissioned to do as director of SID. What I don't know is how you interpret your commission and to what secret ends you direct SID activities."

"Do you have any right to know?"

"Legally I suppose not. Personally? If you'd asked me that a week ago I'd have given a nice, complaisant answer. This morning it's different. I'm tired, I've lost a good man because I didn't think straight, and I don't want to be manipulated anymore. I want to know where I'm being directed and why. If I don't like it, I'll go back to police work."

The Director walked to the window and stood a long time looking out at the tumbled rooftops of Rome, gold and umber and crimson in the early light. When he turned, the light was at his back and the contours of his face were in shadow. He began to talk, quietly at first, then with mounting passion and eloquence.

"You are a presumptuous fellow, Colonel. Yet I can forgive you, because I also presume—on wealth and family and myself as a product of all our history. In a way I am yesterday's man; but then Italy is yesterday's country as well as today's. We build our prosperity on ruins and the genius of our ancient dead. Our law is a confusion of Justinian, the Church, Napoleon, Mussolini and the founding fathers of the United States. We shout for federal republican democracy—yet a man's country is whatever miserable village he was born in. We exist in a precarious balance, and when it tips ever so slightly we are plunged into civil strife and beg to be delivered. We tried one dictator, and we made a shambles of democracy. Now the people don't know what they want. I don't even know what they will tolerate.

"So I manipulate things to hold a balance as long as possible. I don't want dictatorship. I don't want Marxism. But I think the kind of democracy we have is too unstable to last. So, come one or the other, I'll try to make it as tolerable as I can. Politics, they say, is the art of the possible. Mediterranean politics is the art of the impossible, and I understand it better than most. You're worried about Leporello, but you have no evidence against him and I'm not going to antagonize him just when we may need him. I do confess your Salamander makes no sense to me at all just now. You may have your free hand to investigate, but—understand me, Matucci—when I move I am king on the board and you are a pawn. Take it or leave it."

I gave him the answer without a second's hesitation. "I'll take it. And I'll give you an honest report. If we don't agree, I'll fight you, but I'll do it in the open."

"If you ever fight me, Matucci, you'll have to lie like a whore and cheat like a cardsharp, just to save your skin. By the way, you can't meet Manzini looking like that. My valet will show you to the guest room and find you a razor and a clean shirt."

At eight o'clock on that same morning I joined Stefanelli as he strolled whistling down the Spanish Steps. The sun was bright, the air was crisp; every tread of the staircase blossomed with girls. I had been up all night, but I felt miraculously refreshed, and I could see the sap rising even in Steffi's withered trunk. At the foot of the steps we bought him a carnation for his buttonhole, then we turned into Babington's Tea Room, where he had promised to meet Solimbene for tea and English muffins. Solimbene was an amiable pedant who affected small eccentricities like velvet smoking jackets, and nourished a passion for English manners. We found him enthroned in a corner of the tearoom, clasping the hand of a waitress. He gave her up reluctantly for Steffi.

"My dear colleague! I have revelations for you!" He laid the salamander card on the table. "This is not heraldry at all, but calligraphy, a monkish art. At first I accepted a heraldic origin, and I chased salamanders across every escutcheon in Europe. Insanity! Finally I found this photograph, listed in our files under '*Curiosa* and *exotica*.' There is your salamander. Only it is not a coat of arms at all. It is merely an artist's conceit. It belongs to no known family."

"If it means nothing, why show it to us?" Stefanelli said.

"Oh, but it means a great deal—fraud, fakery and scandals. In the year 1910, dear colleague, there lived not a stone's throw from here a notable lady of fashion who called herself the Countess Salamandra. She entertained only the noble and the wealthy—among them a certain opera singer, who was shot and killed as he left her house one morning, presumably by a jealous rival. The lady fled to Nice. Police inquiries revealed that the Countess Salamandra was a young Scots lady named Anne Mackenzie, who, having fallen from grace in a noble bed, decided to enrich herself by the same means. She had this coat of arms forged for professional purposes."

"Is that all?"

"All?" Solimbene was outraged. "My dear Colonel. Miss Mackenzie was once governess to Count Pantaleone's daughters. Pregnant by him, she married—in August 1900—one Luca Salamandra, a circus performer, who, two days after the wedding, fell from a high wire and broke his neck. The child was born a week later and baptized Massimo Salamandra. I offer certificates of marriage and birth and baptism, all dated 1900. In October of the same year the Countess Salamandra began to prepare her entry into Roman society. It is a reasonable guess that she was financed by old Count Pantaleone."

"And what happened to the boy?"

"His mother took him with her to Nice. Yesterday, at the Central Registry in Rome, I found that in 1923 a young man named Massimo Salamandra changed his name to Bruno Manzini. Now, gentlemen, do I get my money?"

He could have tripled the fee. When you are playing against the house, it pays to have a spare ace in your sleeve. Even that doesn't help, of course, when the deck is stacked against you.

THE Cavaliere di Gran Croce Bruno Manzini received me in a suite large enough to house an infantry division. His morning face was benign. "You're looking peaked, Colonel. A late night?"

"A long one. I haven't been to bed yet."

"My dear fellow, let's save time then. How much do you know?"

"That your mother was one Anne Mackenzie. That, as you told me last night, you are the son of the old Count Pantaleone. That you were baptized Massimo Salamandra in Rome in 1900. That your mother adopted a spurious title and a coat of arms to match it. In 1923 you changed your name—"

"And how did you come by all this information?"

"Some luck, some heraldry and the Central Registry."

"What else can you tell me?"

"That depends, sir, on how much you are prepared to tell me."

"Anything you wish to know."

"Why were you blackmailing your brother?"

"Blackmail? My dear Matucci, I could have bought and sold him twenty times over. I was threatening him with public disgrace if he persisted in his crazy politics."

"Instead you killed him."

"I beg your pardon?"

"He died of an overdose of drugs—self-administered."

"A fact which was not made public. Why?"

"For fear of scandal which might lead to civil disorder."

"Now I could make the scandal."

"Will you?"

"No. It would defeat my purpose, which I take it is the same as yours. To avoid political disruption and civil violence."

"Next question then. If the dossier you sent your brother fell into other hands, what use could be made of it?"

"Now that he is dead, very little. Why do you ask?"

"Because all his papers were stolen last night from his lawyer's office. Bandinelli and one of our agents were murdered."

"There was no news of this in the press."

"Nor will there be, unless you choose to release it."

He stared at me in blank disbelief. "I can't believe that any intelligent man would put such a bomb in the hands of a stranger. I could blow up the country with it. You, a serving officer, have just admitted falsifying the records of a suicide and concealing two murders! What guarantee have you that I won't splash this news all over the place?"

"There are no guarantees in this dog's world. But I have to trust someone. Let's say I trust you because you despise the trade I'm in and make no secret of it. Now, can we go on?"

"You'll check my answers, of course?"

"As if I were the Grand Inquisitor himself."

"That's better. Please begin."

"What in the Pantaleone papers would be worth two lives?"

He pondered that. "In the family papers, very little. In my brother's personal papers? Well, as a soldier playing a political power game, he would have assembled dossiers on friends and enemies, and those might be valuable enough to the subjects, or to political rivals, to steal. But murder? Somehow I don't see it. There must be something else."

"For example?"

"Plans, more likely. The tactics and strategy of a coup. The political and military organization that must be ready to take over at a moment's notice. The list of participants, location of arms, and the disposition of available forces in sympathy with the plotters. Even your own service might murder for such things."

"In this case they didn't."

"So now, Matucci, we are at the heart of the artichoke. We have to decide whether we can trust each other. Whose move is next?"

"It's your turn, sir!"

"Before you arrived your director telephoned me."

I had that strange sensation of disembodiment that comes in moments of shock as I saw the trap opening under my unwary feet. Then I was back in my own skin, writhing at the irony of my situation. Manzini watched me gravely. "You are angry. You have a right to be. Your director is too clever for his own good and as vain as Lucifer. He wanted to display his cleverness to me and also, I think, to teach you a lesson for some delinquency."

"That's true, at least. Well, so now what?"

"Now I am going to give you information which your director does not yet possess. At eight o'clock yesterday evening I signed, on behalf of one of my companies, a procurement contract with the government. The contract calls for the urgent supply of great quantities of riot-control equipment. The specifications were drawn up by Major General Leporello, and the equipment will be used by troops under his command. You may care to hear what conclusions I draw from this."

"Please!"

"If I were a Fascist looking for a new leader, I'd be very ready to bargain with Marcantonio Leporello."

"Perhaps the bargain has already been struck."

"No, Colonel. Leporello would not commit himself until Pantaleone's papers were safe in his own hands."

"And he has them now?"

"I believe so."

"You are, it seems to me, rather more than a businessman."

"I'm a salamander, Colonel—a perennial survivor. You?"

"A servant of the state. Except that I'm not sure what the state is today, and I'm scared of what it may be tomorrow."

"That makes us allies."

"In a lopsided league."

"Does that frighten you?"

"Yes, that frightens me."

"Then let me offer you a small reassurance. I shall give you a name and an address. If you go there you will hear part of the truth about me. If it satisfies you, come to see me in Bologna."

On the back of a business card he wrote the name—Raquela Rabin; the address, a street near the Theater of Marcellus. We shook hands and he led me to the door. "Advice from an old campaigner, Colonel. Always walk close to the wall. I hope we meet again soon."

When I hit the street the church bells were tolling ten o'clock. All of a sudden I was maudlin tired, rocking on my feet. I drove in a perilous daze to Lili's apartment and almost fell into her arms when she opened the door. She asked no questions but led me into the bedroom and let me collapse into sleep.

That sleep was a journey to the underworld. I woke, sweating and trembling, with the sheets knotted about me like a shroud. The smell of my body offended me. It was the odor of dammed-up fear. I was marked now—by the Director as an intransigent, by Leporello as a man who must be bought or seduced, by Manzini as a collaborator, useful one moment, dispensable at the twitch of an eyebrow. I was in danger because I knew too much and could do too little.

Lili could be picked off, too. With Woodpecker's network broken, she'd be marked for liquidation. If her own people did not get her, the Director would arrest her, if only to teach me a lesson. I looked at my watch. Siesta-time. I lifted the bedside phone and called Stefanelli's house.

"Steffi? Matucci."

"Don't you ever sleep?"

"Steffi, the roof's falling in. Have you got a spare room? I have to store a very sensitive package."

"Miserable swine! I've had two hours of bad sleep and I'm still in my pajamas! Eh-eh-eh! Where do I collect it?"

"I'll bring it to you. Go back to sleep."

"Thank you for nothing, dear friend."

I had just put the phone down when Lili came in, frowning and solicitous. "I thought you were talking in your sleep. Earlier you were shouting and groaning."

"I had bad dreams. Lili, listen to me. It's condition red for you. I want to get you to Switzerland, but that needs time and planning. I'm taking you to a safe house. You stay there until I'm ready to move you. Yes or no?"

I saw the suspicion in her eyes. "If I say no . . . ?"

"You get killed by your own people or jailed by mine."

"I don't believe it. Last night—"

"That was a million years ago. While you and I were singing, two men were murdered—one of mine and Pantaleone's lawyer. I arrested Woodpecker at four this morning. You're compromised. I can't protect you for more than a few days."

"Why should you risk it at all?"

"To prove to myself I'm not a whoremaster. Will that do? You have fifteen minutes while I dress. Then you're on your own."

"Please! Hold me. I'm frightened."

"I want you frightened, Lili. I want you to do exactly as I tell you. Understand?" She nodded. "Pack an overnight bag. Take your jewelry, your checkbooks, cash—"

At that moment the doorbell chimed. I laid a finger on Lili's lips and whispered, "The housekeeper?"

"Out. Her day off."

I crept into the hallway. A letter had been thrust through the mail slot. I bent to pick it up and then drew back. No self-respecting postman would be on the streets at siesta-time. I went back into the bedroom.

"Lili, can you get me a spatula or something?"

While she rummaged in the kitchen, I dressed. Then, duly armed, I lifted the letter by sliding the spatula under it and gingerly laid it on the coffee table in the living room. The address was typed. The stamp was Italian. But it had not been stamped by a post office. I snapped at Lili to finish packing and telephoned a friend in the security section of the Post and Telegraph Office.

He gave me the cheerful news that a normal letter bomb contained enough explosive to kill the man who opened it and maim anyone else in the room. He promised to have an expert on the doorstep in thirty minutes. I told him I couldn't wait that long. He told me to call the police and put a man on guard until the expert arrived.

Lili locked the apartment after us, and then, avoiding the elevators, we walked down four flights of stairs. The street was lined on both sides with parked vehicles. My car was jammed beautifully between a Mercedes and a Fiat 600. I went back to the lobby and dialed Pronto Soccorso, the emergency service.

Five minutes later a squad car pulled up, and the crew came in at a run. The *brigadiere* was cool and efficient. The explosives squad would handle the letter as well as check my car for booby traps. Meantime, if I would give him a deposition . . . ? My card convinced him he could wait for that. I needed his car and his driver to deliver the lady and myself to the Excelsior Hotel.

In a few minutes we were dropped across from the hotel. We waited five minutes, window-shopping at Rizzoli's bookstore, then took a taxi to the Theater of Marcellus and, when I was satisfied we were not followed, walked through the maze of alleys to Steffi's house.

Steffi received us with characteristic flourish. He clucked over Lili, insisted on settling her into her room himself and then stormed downstairs to give me the rough edge of his tongue. "Matucci, you're a madman! That little baggage upstairs is dangerous! When the Director hears of this—and he will, sooner or later—you'll be cooked, screaming, like a lobster."

"Steffi, have you got any whiskey?"

"For you, hemlock and soda."

"Then pour me a big one. Now, who is Raquela Rabin?"

"Why do you want to know?"

"I have an introduction to her."

He sat down heavily, cupped his hands around his glass and stared into it, an old man ravaged by time and history. "Fifteen came back from Auschwitz, Colonel. Raquela Rabin was the only woman. In the ghetto, when you say that name you say it with respect. She did not have to go to the camp; she had powerful protectors. But when the trucks came she was here, standing in the *piazza,* waiting like a daughter of David. Everything that should not happen to a woman happened to her, but she is still sane and splendid as the evening star. You will be gentle with her. You will not mix her in this stinking business of ours, understand? And what she tells you, believe without question. I'll take you to her, but I want you humble, because this is a great woman. Tell me, who gave you this introduction?"

"Bruno Manzini."

"Why?"

"He said that if Raquela Rabin spoke well of him I might be prepared to trust him. I'm on the auction block, Steffi. The bids will be high and tempting, and I'm not sure I can resist them. A strong friend might lend me courage. I need that, Steffi. I don't know what to believe anymore. I don't even know who I am."

He brightened at that, as if I had told him the best news in the world. "So you don't know who you are? Who does? But sure as breathing, you'd better see what's being done to you."

"I see it. I don't understand it."

"Because you refuse to come to terms with yourself. You don't want to decide what you are—a patriot or a mercenary."

"Hard words from a friend!"

"True words, because I am your friend. Today you might have been killed. Tomorrow the risk is bigger. When you stake your life like this, what are you staking it for—or against?"

"Maybe for a dream, Steffi. I don't know. Maybe against a madness I smell in the streets. The land is the center of it somehow. The vines greening on the terraces, the white hills and the river with the mist on it. The people, too, are part of the dream; I see a woman bursting like a grape with love; I am served by a peasant who greets me and offers me wine and bread and salt as if I were his brother. These are the good things, Steffi, and this is home. I don't want it trampled by jackboots or desecrated by mindless mobs. . . . Now, let's leave it, eh?"

"I can leave it, friend. You can't. You're the man who knows the underside of politics, the cogs in the power machine. You have to decide how you will use that knowledge."

"I'm not paid to use it—only to collect it."

"But you filter it, too. You suppress, you emphasize, you collect. To what end?"

"Dammit, what do we all want? A quiet life. Some dignity in our living and dying."

"Not enough! Not half enough! Look—"

"Be quiet, old man!" Lili challenged him from the doorway, cold and angry. "Let him find his own answers in his own time."

"He has no time." Steffi was brusque and brutal. "He robbed himself when he gave it to you."

"I am here to give it back. May I sit down, please?"

She sat between us, holding herself erect. "You two are friends. I am the outsider. I accept to be here because I am afraid. But I am not a beggar, Dante. I can pay."

"You were not asked to pay."

"This morning you held my life in your hands. You did not bargain. Neither did your friend. So I will tell you what I did not tell last night. Massimo Pantaleone did not leave all his documents in the bank. He left microfilms and maps in the villa on Ponza. He took them there on our last visit—a week ago."

"But you didn't tell Woodpecker or any of your own people?"

"No. Because if Woodpecker had stolen the stuff, it would have finished me. Only Massimo and I could possibly have known the hiding place."

"Could you describe it to me?"

"No. I would have to take you there."

"I'll arrange it. You wait here, Lili. If there are any callers, don't answer. Steffi and I have a visit to make. We'll be back in an hour or so."

"I may never come back," said Steffi mournfully. "I may drown myself in the Tiber. I do not want to be alive when you try explaining this madness to the Director."

STEFFI DID not drown himself. He withdrew, quite deliberately, into his own yesterdays and forced me to withdraw with him, as if it were some rite I must undergo before I met Raquela Rabin. As we strolled through the alleys of the old ghetto he conjured ghosts out of every doorway, many of them friendly ghosts. But some were traitors and some were nightmare enemies.

"I would like to forget them all," said Steffi moodily. "But God keeps the key to memory in his own hands. Now I will present you to Raquela Rabin and then leave. You will come directly to the point with her and not stay too long. She is very frail."

She was frail indeed, white-haired, almost transparent. Only her eyes were alive, dark and lustrous, and strangely pitying. She sat listening in silence while I explained why I had come. I felt humbled, diminished—an ignorant neophyte in the presence of a woman who had seen and suffered everything. And when she spoke—she was very gentle with me—there was a quality of ageless wisdom in her tone that humbled me still further.

"Do you know why Bruno sent you to me?"

"No, madam."

"We were lovers for a long time. The love is still there. And he is still fighting those who took me to Auschwitz. He believes in forgiving, but not in forgetting. Strange . . ."

"Can I trust Bruno Manzini, madam?"

"To be what he is, yes. Which is a man who has built himself, cell by cell, from nothing. He is very strong, very faithful. Each year, on the anniversary of the Black Sabbath, he sends me a card. Get for me please the leather folder in that desk drawer."

When I gave it to her, she spread it open on her knees and handed me two cards—salamander cards like the one in Pantaleone's bedroom. Only the inscriptions were different.

HANS HELMUT ZIEGLER
São Paulo—3 January, 1968

EMANUELE SALATRI
London—18 August, 1971

"What do these mean, madam?"

"They are the names of men connected, each in his own way, with what happened to me and to others in 1943. I have fifteen so far. There are nine to come. Bruno Manzini traced them all, and sent each man a card and a dossier on his past."

"What do the dates mean?"

"The days on which they died."

"Who killed them?"

"They killed themselves."

"Are you happy with Bruno Manzini—a man who plays God?"

"He does not judge. Every man, he says, must be allowed to judge himself, but he must not be allowed to bury the evidence."

"And you agree, madam?"

"I do, Colonel. I hate no one now. But the terror has come again—in Vietnam, in Brazil, in Africa, here in Europe. Is not that why you have come to me—because you, too, are afraid?"

"Yes, madam, I am very much afraid."

"Then trust my Bruno, but not blindly, because then he would have no respect for you. Argue with him, fight him. You may even end as adversaries, but he will never, never betray you."

"Thank you, madam."

"Thank you for coming. I wish peace on your house and in your heart." I was grateful for the blessing, but I walked out into the sunlight a very pensive man.

I could understand Manzini and his conviction that tyrants should not be allowed to flourish; the Director and his willingness to settle for balance, however precarious; even Leporello and his fanatic belief that order at any price was cheaper than chaos. But I did not understand myself.

On the way back to Steffi's I stopped in a bar and telephoned Manzini to tell him I had seen Raquela Rabin and would like to see him. It was agreed I should go to Bologna as soon as I could.

Then I called the Director, and suppressed a sigh of relief when his aide told me he had been summoned to an urgent conference at the Ministry. No, no message I could leave him on an open line, except that there were new developments that would keep me out of contact for forty-eight hours. I knew I was only putting off the bad day; but if I could lay my hands on those files at Ponza, I might still cheat the headsman.

I was faced now with a problem in space and time. To get to the island of Ponza means a road journey south from Rome and a three- or four-hour sea trip by ferry from Anzio, Formia or Naples. But I must at all costs avoid public transport. If the Director should have reason to send out a panic call for me, I would be as conspicuous as a wart on the Mona Lisa. Also, whoever had the stolen papers would know by now that they were incomplete, and might come looking for Lili Anders at the villa she had shared with Pantaleone. I needed help in a hurry.

By the time I got back to Steffi's, it was five thirty. I put through a priority call to Colonel Carl Malinowski at NATO headquarters in Naples. Malinowski is an agreeable American I'd managed to help out of an embarrassing situation involving his girl friend and a Russian agent. He owed me a favor. I needed it now, in the shape of the big Baglietto, the motor cruiser which he used for drinking parties and seduction and which could do twenty-five knots in any reasonable sea.

Malinowski was happy to oblige. He had a new girl friend who would appreciate the outing. If we cared to come to Naples tonight, he would feed us dinner and offer us a bed. Two hours later Lili and I were heading south in an unidentifiable hired car.

Major Carl Malinowski of the United States Marines was all brawn and muscle, with ham fists and a big laugh. He was a tonic for our spirits. His apartment was a bachelor's paradise, with a view across the Bay of Naples, a bewildering liquor cupboard, and piped music in every room. His new girl was a Swede, culled from the summer crop of tourists and blooming after the transplant. He took one look at Lili and shouted his approval to the neighborhood.

"*Bella! Bellissima!* Dante, my boy, your taste's improving. Helga, why don't you get Lili settled while Dante and I build some drinks." He clamped an iron fist on my shoulder. "Tell me now, Colonel, is this business or pleasure?"

"Business, Carl. We've got to get to Ponza and back, fast."

"In this weather it's three hours each way—more if the wind freshens. How long do you want to stay?"

"Two hours should do it."

"Okay. We leave at six in the morning. Expecting trouble?"

"An outside chance."

"What's with you and Lili-belle?"

"Some business, some pleasure. Too much of one, not enough of the other."

"I get you. So tonight we drink and make merry!"

We did. We dined like kings on caviar, steak and Neapolitan ice cream. We drank wine and brandy. We told bawdy stories. And sometime after midnight we paired off and went to bed.

It was a good night for Lili and me. We pleased each other. We were glad, we were grateful and, for a while, not solitary. We slept deeply and we did not dream at all.

I have told it badly. I might have used the same words for a dozen encounters, because I am a man who has been fortunate in his women. But this time there was a difference, a sense of consequence if not yet of commitment. There was another difference, too. I was disposed to be sentimental afterward, while Lili would have none of it.

She told me so bluntly, as we stood on the Baglietto's deck and watched the green cone on Ischia fade against the dawn.

"*Caro,* sometimes you treat me as if I had no brains at all. I know what's at stake. If the material at the villa is important, it puts power into your hands. You think it will also buy me a free passage out of Italy."

"I hope it will."

"I don't need you to get me out of Italy, Dante. I could hire any fisherman on Ponza to run me into Corsica tomorrow."

"What are you trying to say, Lili?"

"That you need me, as much as you need the Pantaleone records, for a bargaining card. Let me go, and you rob yourself of your ace in the hole. I understand that. But you insult me when you try to dress the thing up. Your friend Steffi was right. You refuse to come to terms with yourself. Now can we go inside, please? I'm cold."

It was cold. The wind was freshening from the northwest, whipping up an uncomfortable sea, and Malinowski was driving the boat hard. We settled ourselves in the Baglietto's saloon and I tried with some desperation to salvage the argument. "Let's have it clear, Lili. I made a treaty with you. So far I've honored it. You're free and protected. Now you want to change it. You want me to turn a blind eye while you make a run for Corsica."

"No! I want you to be sure what kind of treaty you are making with other people, and what it will do to you in the end."

"And why the hell should you care?"

"Poor Dante! So many women and you've learned so little!"

"At least I don't have any illusions."

"Let's not argue. You write the script, you say the words, you pull the strings, and when the play's over, Lili, the puppet, is packed up in her box. Just so we know, my love."

"So that's the way you read it. Let's go up on the bridge."

"I'd like to be alone for a while."

"This is business, Lili."

"At your service, Colonel."

Malinowski welcomed us and spread out a map of Ponza. The villa was on its eastern shore, noted in the *Pilot* as a landmark for mariners: "a large square building of gray stone, due east of which the pillars and arches of a Roman ruin are clearly visible. In winds W to NW the southern inlet offers fair shelter to small vessels."

I asked Lili, "If we put in there, can we get to the villa from the beach?"

"Yes. There's a rough path that goes up to the ruins."

"The villa itself. Any servants?"

"No. Out of season it's closed up. But we don't have to go near the villa. What we want is in the ruins."

"Can you overlook the ruins from the house?"

"Only the top of them. Our domain is walled all the way round. The ruins are outside the walls, on government land."

"Better still. How close in can you anchor, Carl?"

"Let's see . . . for safety, a cable's length."

"Which will be visible from the house?"

"On the approach, yes. When we're anchored, probably not. I don't understand your problem though. The shoreline's public terrain. Anyone can land from the sea."

"I'm not worried about trespassing, Carl. Lili owns the villa anyway. Let's say I'm concerned with hostile intruders."

"Those, Colonel, we can take care of nicely." He opened a cupboard and brought out an automatic rifle. "While you and Lili-belle go ashore, I watch for hostile intruders. Okay?"

"No. I can't have an American officer involved in an Italian domestic drama. So, if you don't mind, I'll take the gun."

"Just as you like. Switch on the radio, will you? I'd like to catch the news and the weather."

The news was the usual mixture, until the terse postscript: an Arab had been shot dead outside the Libyan embassy. He was the Roman representative of Al-Fatah, the Palestine guerrilla organization. The police assumed it was a political crime, probably organized by Israeli agents. The item made my hair stand up; this was a personal disaster. I was the SID expert on Arab-Israeli affairs. The Director *would* be pressing panic buttons and combing the country for me. If I could deliver the Pantaleone papers and Lili Anders before he found me, I might just escape the rack and thumbscrew. But if I got back empty-handed, he would rend me limb from limb and feed me to the lions in the zoo.

We reached Ponza in a driving rain, visibility terrible. At least any watchers in the villa would see nothing either. Lili and I draped ourselves in oilskins, Carl handed me the rifle and we drove the dinghy to the beach.

The path which led to the ruins was steep. We scrambled up on hands and knees. Breathless and irritable, I was convinced that either Pantaleone was mad to have hidden the documents in such a place or Lili had deliberately led me on a fool's errand. I said as much. She took me by the hand and led me through a moldering archway into a vault which had somehow withstood the ravages of the centuries. The outer walls were stone, but the inner ones were brick. The floor was paved with marble, cracked and sagging but mostly intact. Lili threw back the hood of her oilskins and surveyed the shadowy interior.

The brickwork of the walls revealed nothing. I tested the floor for hollow spaces. Again nothing. Lili grinned. She moved to a small sunken patch of floor where the rain driving in through the archway had created a puddle. She knelt down and with her bare hands eased up a piece of marble about the size of my palm. "Like a bath plug, eh, Dante? You didn't walk in the puddle, but even if you had, the floor would have sounded solid. Massimo was not as stupid as he looked."

She plunged her fingers into the aperture and drew out a long aluminum tube, sealed at both ends with black adhesive tape. "It is exactly as we left it. The maps and microfilms are inside."

"There's nothing else?"

"Nothing." She replaced the marble piece.

"Let's go. You carry the tube."

"Not even a thank you for puppet Lili?"

"Thank you, puppet Lili. Follow me out of here. Then on the beach track you go first."

I released the safety catch on the rifle and stopped to scan the narrow vista framed by the archway. All I could see was the rise of the land and the base of the wall surrounding the villa. So far, so good. I moved closer to the entrance so that the vista widened and the top of the wall became visible. Then I heard a shout, amplified and distorted by a bullhorn. "You, in there! Come out with your hands up. This is the carabinieri."

I snatched the tube from Lili. "Stay close. Say nothing." And holding the rifle and the tube high above my head, I walked through the archway with Lili at my heels. Twenty yards away, just outside my last field of vision, there were five men. Four were in uniform and armed with submachine guns. The fifth, with the bullhorn, was in civilian clothes. I recognized him immediately: the freckle-faced redhead I'd seen at the Hassler, aide to General Leporello. He recognized me, too, and the expression on his face gave me a singular pleasure.

The troops began to close in, guns cocked. I let them come to within five meters before I halted them in my best parade-ground style. Then I said, "I will identify myself in proper form. I am Dante Matucci, colonel in the Service of Defense Information. The person with me is Lili Anders, in my custody and assisting me in highly secret investigations. Now we shall lower our hands, and the officer in command will approach to check my documents and explain the situation."

The shaken young man found voice and gave me a tentative salute. "Captain Matteo Roditi, aide to Major General Leporello. Your papers, please, sir?" He made a great play of reading them, then handed them back. "Thank you, sir. The situation, sir, is as follows. I am under orders from General Leporello to maintain surveillance of the Villa Pantaleone and its environs, and to inhibit any attempt to remove property from the premises. In pursuance of these orders I am empowered to call upon the assistance of local units."

"May I see those orders, please, Captain?"

"Certainly, sir."

I took a little longer than I needed to study them. Then I quizzed him, loud enough for the local boys to hear. "It would appear, Captain, that you have misread these orders."

"Sir?"

"The orders refer exclusively to, and I quote, 'the villa and the domain dependent thereon which is called the Villa Pantaleone.' You will note that the land on which we are now standing and the ruins at my back are outside the domain and are, in fact, public property. Therefore you have exceeded your orders. You have placed a senior officer of SID and the person in his custody at considerable risk. One incautious move by your troops might have caused a fatal accident. You do see that."

"Respectfully, I submit the danger was minimal."

"No doubt that submission will be considered at the proper time and place. Anything else, Captain?"

"No, sir."

"My compliments to General Leporello. I shall telephone him on my return to Rome. Dismiss! Come, Miss Anders."

It is hard to make it down a slippery path in the rain, carrying a rifle and a long tube of documents. In point of fact, we slid the last thirty feet and floundered into the dinghy like seals.

By the time we reached the Baglietto, I was sweating from every pore and Lili was retching. Helga hauled us aboard; Carl had the anchor up and was charging seaward before I had poured our first brandy. Lili lay on the settee while I forced the liquor between her chattering teeth. She stared at me as if I were a stranger. "They were going to kill us!"

"They didn't, Lili. And they can't touch us now."

"Not now. But tomorrow, the day after . . ."

"Finish your drink. Relax now . . . relax."

"I don't know you at all, Dante. Your face changes all the time. I can't tell which one is yours."

"I'm a bad actor, that's all. Trust me, *bambina.*"

"I have to. There's no one else."

She lay quiet then, and the surge of the sea made her dozy. I stripped the seals from the metal tube. I found a set of overlay maps on transparent paper, each labeled with the name of a city and references to standard ordnance maps, and half a dozen metal capsules, each containing a spool of microfilm. The maps showed the positions of police posts, military installations, communications centers, traffic control points, military and civilian airfields. The microfilms were impossible to decipher without projection equipment. However, with the boat's chart enlarger I could see that they consisted of documents, letters, lists of figures and of names. I had no doubt these supplied motive enough for the murders in the Via Sicilia. They were, in fact, the blueprints of a *colpo di stato.* It would need an expert to interpret them—and a very wise statesman to decide how to use them. I went up on the bridge to talk to Carl.

"How much fuel have you got? Enough to get us to Ostia?"

"Ostia! That wasn't on the schedule at all! Why?"

"Because I've just identified a murderer, and we could have been murdered ourselves. I've got to get to Rome fast."

"So we go to Ostia. Take five while I lay me a course."

While he was playing with his slide rule I sent a coded message to the Director by ship-to-shore radio. I'd need a car and armed escort from Ostia, an emergency conference immediately on our arrival at Rome, and a guard for Lili Anders. Forty minutes later I had the Director's answer. "Communication acknowledged. Arrangements agreed."

We have code words for thanks and commendations. He didn't use them. Under the circumstances I could hardly blame him.

THE Director was extremely civil, if a little frosty at first, but he thawed like ice in whiskey when I handed over the maps and the microfilms. He lodged Lili Anders, with protection, at the Grand Hotel and took me to dinner at his apartment. He commended me for my imagination, my finesse, my courage in risking my career and perhaps my life to conclude an important investigation. He saw good sense in my suspicions of Leporello, although he was not yet ready to pass judgment. He sat with me through a screening of the microfilms, and he read the maps. At the end of the session, which lasted until midnight, he ordered fresh coffee, brought out his best brandy and offered me the rewards of virtue.

"This Lili Anders—I agree with your estimate," he said. "She has done us a service. She is no longer a security risk. She could be an embarrassment. Let's get her out of the country—tomorrow."

"Very good, sir."

"As to your own future, Matucci, how much leave have you accumulated?"

"About four months."

"I'd like you to take it, now. After you return I propose to detach you for extended studies with agencies abroad. You will have the best possible introductions, a flexible schedule, and your pay and allowances will be supplemented by a generous grant from the funds of this service. How does that sound?"

"Like an obituary notice."

The Director smiled and spread his elegant hands in a gesture of deprecation. "My dear Matucci! You will not be dead, just buried for a while enjoying yourself till resurrection day."

"No alternatives?"

"There are always alternatives. I could retain you on the Leporello investigation, in which case you would be a prime target for assassination. Or I could return you to your own corps of carabinieri, under the direct authority of General Leporello. He knows you for a nuisance. He may consider you a threat."

"I see what you mean."

"You see everything except the core of the apple."

"Which is?"

"You know too much. You lack the authority and—forgive me—the experience to make use of the knowledge."

"And . . . ?"

"And you would be very unwilling to make a deal with political conspirators, however high they stood."

"Exactly."

"So, because I respect you and want to be in a position to recall you at an appropriate time, I immobilize you. I offer you as a propitiatory victim to powerful people—and so buy myself time to deal with them."

"I couldn't ask for a more stylish funeral."

"Excellent. Some more brandy? As of this moment you are on vacation. You will escort Lili Anders to Zurich tomorrow morning.

The service has no further interest in her, provided she does not attempt to reenter the republic. Your flight has been booked. A reservation has been made for you at the Hotel Baur au Lac. You yourself will remain outside Italy for at least a month. It's all a little rushed, but I am sure you will find the financial arrangements more than generous. . . . Questions?"

"No. Just a minor worry. I'd hate to spend a long vacation waiting for a bullet in the back. I'd much rather stay on duty where there's a certain amount of protection."

"The whole purpose of this tactic is to demonstrate that you are no longer a threat to Leporello or anyone else, and that action against you would violate your very useful neutrality. . . . There is a danger period, however: from the moment you leave this house until you take off for Zurich. So I've assigned a two-man team to cover you. They've already packed your clothes and delivered the suitcases to the Grand Hotel, where your room adjoins Miss Anders's. You will leave the hotel together at eight thirty. Now . . . two air tickets, ten thousand Swiss francs and an order on the Union Bank in Zurich for another twenty thousand. That's a bonus, with my personal thanks. Your salary will be credited in the normal way to your bank account. . . . That's all, I think. My car is waiting for you. I wish you a pleasant vacation. *Sogni d'oro,* Matucci—golden dreams."

We parted with a handshake, firm and fraternal. I was escorted from his door to the Grand Hotel like a visiting potentate.

It was after midnight. The foyer was deserted. Two Sicilian bodyguards installed me in my bedroom, checking inside cupboards and under beds and pointing out that the key to the *signora*'s room was on my side of the communicating door. Then they bade me good night and retired like lackeys from the presence of a prince.

Perhaps they were right. I was the Director's man, bought and paid for. His brand was on my head, his money in my pocket, his gift sleeping next door. Still, give the devil his due, he was a rare specimen. Never once had he suggested that I was making a slave's bargain. He knew it, of course. So did I. Which is why I could not go to Lili, but instead lay dressed and wakeful, scheming revolt.

At dawn I abandoned the futile exercise and went to Lili Anders. The Director had told her nothing, so at six o'clock in the morning I was forced to explain the whole complicated play. She was so delighted to be going to her liberty in Switzerland, and to be going with me, that I had no heart to tell her the price. From the moment I left Italy I would be, in effect, an exile.

Our exit from Italy was impressive. Limousine, VIP lounge at Fiumicino airport, escorts all the way to our first-class seats. Airborne then, and in the care of the Swiss, we held hands and made foolish jokes and toasted each other with champagne.

At the Baur au Lac we were accommodated in a three-room suite, complete with flowers, fruit, liquor, a welcome note from the management and a telegram from the Director. SECOND SAMUEL SEVEN ONE, it said. I deciphered his joke, from the Bible on my bedside table: "The Lord gave him rest from all his enemies."

By that evening the joke was becoming too bitter. I had to make an end of it and tell Lili the truth.

The moment of telling had a curious quality about it. We had decided to dine in the suite. I was mixing drinks, feeling very domestic, remote, as if I were recovering from a long illness. I heard myself speak as if I were listening to another man.

"Everything the Director says is true and yet it all adds up to a lie. He conjures you into a world that doesn't exist and makes you believe it—shows you another self and makes you believe it's you. 'You lack authority, Matucci. You lack experience. You are not dead, just buried for a while.' But I knew, the moment I stepped on that plane, I was dead; because he has all my files now and he can reprocess history in any way he chooses. Suppose he wants to conquer, to play Fouché to Leporello's Napoleon and like that opportunist chief of police betray and succeed his superior? I've given him all the weapons he needs, and he paid me for them—with this long holiday."

"Why did you accept it, Dante? Because I was part of it?"

"No. I believe he'd have let you go anyway, might have worked to set you against me—he spins the web so fine. I don't know . . .

but last night, working with him on the documents, I enjoyed him and respected him—because he respected me. So when he gave me his reasons for my stepping out, I had to respect those, too. But after I had agreed, he had to show me how clever he was; how he was so certain of my consent that he had arranged everything in advance—even to the roses in your bedroom. Suddenly I was not a man anymore, I was—"

"A puppet, my love. It's a bitter experience, isn't it?"

"The joke of the century! Dante Matucci, the clown puppet! That's his final triumph, don't you see? He's probably spread the news all over the service."

"I'd like to see how it ends."

"This *is* the end, Lili. Don't you understand that?"

"It's the end he wrote. I think there's a better one."

"I'd love to hear it."

"The puppet becomes a man, scrapes off the clown's paint and rides out to confront his enemy."

"It's a fairy tale, Lili."

"No! It's a truth. Remember that salamander card? 'One fine tomorrow, brother.' Telephone Bruno Manzini, my love. Now."

The idea was seductive. But I was still gun-shy and suspicious. True, there was Raquela Rabin, his proof of good faith. Manzini had invited my trust. But if he betrayed me, then I was truly lost beyond redemption. The jurisdiction of money is universal.

I argued this with Lili—the new Lili who had flowered overnight into another woman, serene, mature, wholly confident.

"What have you to lose?" she said. "Nothing. What have you to gain? At best a powerful friend; at least an alliance of interest that you can dissolve at will. Most important of all, you will have begun to fight."

To put the call through to Bologna was easy. To get Manzini on the line was only less difficult than having a Sunday chat with the pope. Finally I took a risk and used the magical name of the service. It worked. I told him the story of Ponza, of the records I had delivered to the Director, of my current situation.

There was a moment's silence, then a series of brusque questions.

"Have you yourself examined the records?" Manzini began.

"Yes."

"Important?"

"As you suggested in Rome."

"Do you know what will happen to them now?"

"Only what might happen. There are several possibilities."

"Which you can no longer control."

"Precisely."

"Do you need assistance, financial or otherwise?"

"I need the man Raquela Rabin recommended, provided, of course, he is still available."

"He is. He will be at the Dolder Grand in Zurich tomorrow evening. Are you in good health?"

"Our mutual friend assures me I have nothing to fear."

"He would know, of course."

"Yes. But he never tells all he knows."

"Remember it, my friend. Walk close to the wall."

"Thank you, Cavaliere. . . . Good night."

When I put down the phone I was trembling. I was truly afraid now. The old man's parting words had demolished the last frail illusion of security. I was a stranger in a foreign land, a member of a legal underworld, suspect everywhere and nowhere loved. I could be shot down on any street corner with no fuss. In that moment I tasted the full, fine Florentine flavor of the Director's revenge. Lili held me close while she whispered over and over, "One fine tomorrow, brother . . ."

Tomorrow was a gift of God: no wind, no cloud, the lake dazzling under the spring sun, snow on the uplands, the lower meadows ankle-deep in spring grass. I hired a car and we drove into Graubünden, aimless and happy as a honeymoon pair. Lili sang, clowned, played word games and love games and built dream houses. And for the first time I really saw her: the honey color of her hair, the high Slavic cheekbones flushed with wind and excitement, the little flecks of gold in her eyes, the half smile that haunted the corners of her mouth, even the first faint touch of time in the texture of her skin. She was no girl, this Lili. She had lived too strangely for too long. But I was no boy either; and I was tired of baby talk and lovers' lies.

We lunched in a mountain inn on cheese soufflé and an effervescent wine. We talked of the future and Lili assessed her own without resentment.

"I am on file now. Any policeman can harass me like a streetwalker. So I have to be careful. If I live modestly and soberly, I may be able to live in peace in Switzerland for a long while. If I married, it would be different. I would have a new civil status and a new life. So I have to think of that . . . but not yet. I have enough money for two years of simple living. And I can sell the villa on Ponza. Massimo told me he had provided for me, but even if his will is found I can base nothing on it, as I can never return to Italy. Still, I am very lucky. Lucky in you, too, my love. I did not believe you would have so much concern for me."

"I didn't believe I'd ever need a woman in this way. To be calm, to prove nothing, just to be glad she's in the room. What would you say if I asked you to spend this month with me?"

"I would say yes, but I would also say let it be as it is now—one hour, one day at a time."

"One day at a time. Good."

"And when you go away, as you must, and find yourself lonely, come back. You must be very free now. You have to begin to know the man who lives in your skin."

"I'm afraid of him, Lili."

"So one day you must confront him in the mirror. After that, please God, you will be able to be happy."

"I hope so. But there is something that must be said, Lili. If a day should come when you have to choose between me and yourself, consider your own interest first. I would want that."

"I don't understand."

"Listen, *bambina!* We are not lodged here by people who want us to be happy. We are to become so tied to each other that a threat to one could be used as pressure on the other. The Director may be convinced he has bought me, but he also buys insurance against my cheating on the contract. You see?"

"I do. And I want you to cheat him. Tell me—you never name this man, the Director. Why?"

"A rule of the game that has become second nature. But there is another reason. This is a very attractive man. He can seduce you with a smile, a handshake, a show of confidence and infinite good sense. That talent was bred into him through twenty generations. I envy it, and I am afraid of it. So I force myself to think of him not as a man, but as a function, like the pope or the president. That way I can cope with him."

"Perhaps the day will come when you will be able to name the two in one breath—the man who lives in your skin, and the other of whom you are still afraid."

"Am I so great a coward, Lili?"

"There is one fear that makes each of us a coward."

"And what is yours?"

"The little room, the light shining in my eyes, the questions and the blows that come from nowhere. You saved me from that, and there is nothing I would not do to repay you."

"We're both rewarded, *cara*. Today is enough. We should go back now. It's an hour and a half to Zurich."

THAT evening Bruno Manzini received me in his opulent suite at the Dolder Grand. His greeting was warm, but from the moment I entered he was reading me by stance and attitude and intonation. "You are changed, Colonel."

"How so, Cavaliere?"

"You are more loose, more forthcoming. I would guess you had found yourself a good woman and a new crop of courage."

"Both true."

"A drink?"

"Whiskey, please."

He served me himself, and I noticed that he drank very lightly. He raised his glass in a toast. "Health, money and love—"

"And time to enjoy them, sir."

"That above all, Colonel. Now, tell me all that has happened since we met in Rome."

I told him all—up to and including my arrival in Zurich with Lili Anders and the relationship which had begun to mature between us. As I did so his eyes never left my face. There was a long silence before he began the questions. "You are convinced that Major General Leporello has allied himself with the neo-Fascists?"

"I am convinced that he is a candidate for such an alliance."

"You infer, then, that he ordered the murders of the lawyer, Bandinelli, and your agent, Calvi, and the theft of the Pantaleone papers."

"There is a case to be investigated. Leporello knew, from me, where the papers were. Whoever had the papers would have seen instantly that they were incomplete, and he would take steps to trace the remainder. It was Leporello's aide who was on Ponza."

"What is the ground of dispute between you and your director?"

"I asked for an investigation of Leporello. He deferred it. I disobeyed a direct order and made contact with Leporello."

"In effect then you may be responsible for two murders and the theft of vital documents."

"I believe I am responsible."

"So the Director is justified in having taken you off the case."

"If he did it on disciplinary grounds, yes."

"You suggest he had other reasons?"

"He stated them clearly: I lacked the authority and experience to deal with a complex political situation, and I was a convenient victim who would buy him time."

"Good reasons or bad?"

"Eminently sound."

"So what is your quarrel with him?"

"I have no quarrel, no valid objection. But I said it to his face and I say it still. I do not trust him. He said to me, 'I don't want dictatorship. I don't want Marxism. I'm sure the kind of democracy we have is too unstable to last. But, come one or the other, I'll try to make it as tolerable as I can.'"

"A laudable ambition, surely?"

"That depends on the interpretation. He added, 'I am king on the board and you are a pawn.'"

"You would prefer to be king, no doubt?"

"I would like to be a servant of an open society."

"But you joined a closed service, more subject than any to the corruption of secrecy. Why?"

"Because I think I have a talent for investigation."

"And a taste for influence without responsibility?"

"No. I like responsibility."

"And you resent the fact that you can no longer exercise it?"

"Yes. But what I resent most is that the man who can, at a whim, make me less than I am can also, if he chooses, bury, manipulate or trade information that may determine the political future of this country. My country, and yours."

"Can you be bought, Colonel?"

"I was, forty-eight hours ago."

"Can you be frightened?"

"I am frightened now. I know too much. And I'm isolated."

"And who would want to eliminate you?"

"The Director for one. Leporello for another. Or—and this is the real nightmare—both, working together. Acting in concert they could be very formidable very quickly."

"And what did you think I could do about this?"

"Advise me how to use what I know to prevent a *colpo di stato.*"

"What knowledge do you have, Matucci?"

"I know every name on the Pantaleone microfilms. I could reproduce every document, every map. I have a photographic memory, Cavaliere."

"Does the Director know that?"

"Yes."

"Then he told you the truth. You are a natural victim."

"And you, Cavaliere?"

"I, too, told you the truth. We are natural allies. But you will have to accept that it will be—what did you call it?—a lopsided league. I have everything you lack—influence, money, friends. Also I'm old and obstinate. I hold the advantage."

"I understand that and accept it."

"There is one more condition. This Lili Anders is a danger to you, an embarrassment for me, since she was my brother's mistress. Pay her off and forget her."

"I can't do that, Cavaliere."

"I insist on it, if we are to work together."

"You offer me the same stale bargain as the Director. Submit and be safe. The market's closed." I rose. "And if you'll excuse me—"

"Sit down, man! The game is over."

"I beg your pardon."

"I offered you a shabby contract, my friend. Had you consented, I would have sold you myself to the assassins. Now, ring the bell, please. I think we are ready to dine."

THE man who sat with me at dinner that night was a phenomenon. He was in his seventies, yet he bubbled like champagne. He talked books, women, painting, money, fashion, religion, wine and the growing of roses. He enjoyed. He savored. Between the fruit and the cheese he opened a new line of talk.

"We are all inheritors, Matucci, and we can no more shed our past than we can slough off our skins. You and I, for instance, have begun a friendship. But you will never understand me unless you remember that I was born in an attic above Zia Rosa's brothel, on the Feast of the Assumption of the Virgin, which is the day the acrobats came to town. You are curious? . . . I'm glad. I will tell you of my birthday.

"On that feast day in 1900, Matucci, my mother was in labor in that attic, with Zia Rosa's sister Angela—later my nurse—as midwife. Down in the *piazza*—and this I know, because Angela was watching—Luca Salamandra, the high-wire walker, was about to begin his pilgrimage across the sky. Dressed all in black, with plastered hair and curled mustaches, he climbed to the little platform on top of the pole and saluted the cheering crowds. He stepped onto the wire. The crowd fell silent. He moved slowly, testing the tension of the cable. Then halfway across he flipped into a somersault and landed upright on the swaying cable. He was, perhaps, five meters from the end of the wire when he stopped, staring straight into Angela's eyes. She remembers him smiling at her, beginning to walk toward her. . . . At which precise moment, Matucci, my mother screamed and I poked my reluctant head into the world and Luca Salamandra toppled into eternity.

"Ten days later a woman in deep mourning, with an elderly companion, presented herself at the registry office to deposit a set of notarized documents. The first was a certificate of marriage between Anne Mary Mackenzie and Luca Salamandra. The second was the surgeon's certificate of the death of Luca Salamandra. The third was a notification of the birth of Massimo Luca Salamandra. This extraordinary collection of documents was the result of a long discussion between Anne Mary Mackenzie and Zia Rosa, followed by three hours' hard bargaining among Angela, Zia Rosa and Aldo the Calligrapher, an elderly forger of legendary skill. The registry clerk accepted the documents without question, with the result that Anne Mary Mackenzie became a respectable Roman widow, and I was endowed with a spurious legitimacy.

"That is my story, Matucci. It is also a parable. I was sired by a nobleman, fathered by a dead acrobat. I am, and always have been, a contradiction. And you, now, are the man on the tightrope. You want to save yourself and serve a very divided country and a very contentious people. You will need steady nerves, because you, too, will see monsters borning—and if you slip once, you are dead. I hope you understand that."

"I do. But where do we begin?"

"You are under orders not to return to Italy for a month. We use that month to take out some insurance of our own. Tomorrow morning at nine you and Lili Anders will check out of the Baur au Lac. A limousine will take you to a house in Liechtenstein which belongs to one of my companies. A converted hunting lodge, quite comfortable. There you will record everything you know of the Pantaleone affair, the microfilms, the maps—everything. This material will be copied and lodged in banks inside and outside Italy. During this same month you will receive other material from me which will prepare you for your return to Italy. We shall, of course, remain in close personal contact. You will have two of my staff on constant call as guards and couriers."

"And when I go back to Italy?"

"I shall offer you substantial fees as a consultant on economic intelligence. Of course, I shall make it my business to secure your director's approval."

"Are you sure he will give it?"

"Why not? It will give him another possible means of compromising you. He will take it that you are, as he hopes, a venal man, easily bought and silenced. Under this cover you will continue to investigate Leporello's connection with the new Fascist movement. Does that make sense to you?"

"With one reservation. I have seen the Director write similar scripts. I do not believe he will buy this one."

"Nor I. But he will try to make us believe he has bought it. The real problem is rather different; we have to keep you alive."

THE hunting lodge was built at the neck of a high valley, accessible only by a single road which ended at a massive pine gate slung between pillars of hewn stone. Inside the gate a paved driveway wound through tall trees to the lodge itself, a long, sandstone building, raftered with logs and roofed with zinc on timber.

Outside it looked unwelcoming, ready to withstand invasion or avalanche. Inside it was warm, with firelight gleaming on paneled walls and polished copper and peasant pottery. The house was kept by an elderly Tirolese and his wife, and there were two other staff: Heinz, a taciturn fellow from Graubünden canton who was a deadly shot with a rifle, and Domenico, a swarthy young Varesino accomplished in pistol and karate. One of them was always on duty. Each evening the gates were locked and a complicated series of alarms was set. There was a telephone in the house, but we were warned not to use it. We could walk freely within the estate, but only with Heinz or Domenico in attendance.

For the first few days I felt caged and restless; but Lili scolded me into relaxation and a simple routine of work. Each morning I settled down to the task of reconstructing from memory the material in the microfilms. It was an exhausting job on which I could concentrate for only about four hours a day. The rest of the time I spent annotating the dispatches which arrived each day by mail from Bruno Manzini.

All the dispatches were posted from Chiasso, which is the frontier town of the Swiss canton of Ticino. The information was codified and covered everything from the organization and control of labor unions to the financial structure and principal directors of large companies; from investment holdings by foreign organizations to the private histories of prominent functionaries and a schedule of their visits to Greece and Spain; from the makeup of Marxist cells to the finances of the Vatican. I had been in the intelligence trade for a long time, but much of this was new even to me. I was impressed with the organization that must have collected it all, and, as I read, was more and more in awe at the complexity of Italian life. The tension was so high, the balance of forces so precarious, that no one could ignore the daily threat of disaster.

I understood vividly the frustration of the revolutionary who wanted to sweep the whole mess away and begin again. I understood the despair of the young who wanted to drop out. I understood the seductive illusion of a dictator who could impose order and unity with a wave of his scepter.

More slowly, I began to see the meaning of Bruno Manzini's belief that we were all prisoners of our genes and our history, and that our future was written by scribes long perished. And I was oppressed. What right had I to try to affect a single line of that future?

In those desert days Lili was an oasis of comfort. She refused to be put out by my snappishness. She lavished tenderness on me and shamed me back into sanity. "I know how you feel, my love. You and I will pass, and the horror of the world will still remain. But think of this—while we are still fighting, we hold it back, if only for a little while. If everyone gave up the fight, the barbarians would take over for another thousand years. Even if we are ignorant and misguided, the cause is still good. You must never let yourself forget that."

And our love was good; but it was haunted, too, by the thought that all too soon it must end. I was the cord that tied her to the past; the cord must be snapped before she could be wholly free.

There was no hope for either of us in a daydream future, and the thought of lonely tomorrows weighed on us both. Our days and nights were the more precious to us.

We had been at the lodge about two weeks when Bruno Manzini came to visit us. He took my notes and retired, joining us only for a drink before dinner.

"I've studied your notes, Matucci. Excellent! But very disturbing. Have you made any sense out of the stuff I've sent you?"

"Some, yes. I'd like to discuss it with you after dinner."

"That's why I'm here. We will shut you out, young lady, but you are going to forgive me in advance; because the more you know, the more you are at risk." He put his arm around Lili and toasted her with old-fashioned gallantry, then launched into a cascade of reminiscences that swept us from soup to coffee.

Afterward, when we were alone, with the brandy warming in our hands, he said, "Things are bad, Matucci. Take this business last week of Bessarione. The police say he blew himself up while attempting to sabotage a power pylon. The Left say he was framed and assassinated by the Right. I knew him—a wealthy romantic and a very good publisher. What's the truth? Who knows? At least it should be open to public debate. Instead, we arrest journalists and students in the old Fascist dragnet: 'Spreading news calculated to disturb public order.' Result? More division. More unrest. The Fascists blame the Marxists, the Marxists blame the Fascists. In the middle are the people—they can't get educated because we don't build enough schools, and when they're sick they're lined up three-deep in hospital wards. They can't get to work and back because of bus strikes, and they live in a dunghill when the garbage collectors are on strike.

"Even the markets are beginning to panic. If I told you how much money went out of the country last week, you'd weep, Matucci. And now I'm on notice to rush my deliveries of riot equipment. What I cannot make I am to buy, borrow or steal. So how does it add up? The Marxists can, and maybe will, disrupt the country, but they are not ready to mount a military coup. The Right could, given enough support from the Center and from the Church.

"Your notes confirm all this, Matucci. But they tell more; my half brother planned better than I knew. His strategy is valid, and—I've kept this till last—Leporello has made his deal. He has stepped into Pantaleone's shoes."

"And the Director?"

"Has joined him. They had a meeting last weekend at Prince Baldassare's villa."

"How do you know this?'

"I was there, too. The Director invited me because they wanted me to join the club. I agreed, of course. A natural union, when you come to think of it. Heavy industry, textiles, newspapers, banking, and a stable government pledged to law and order."

"Why had they never asked you before?"

"Pantaleone wouldn't hear of it then. And they needed him more than me. But now they knew all about my connection with my brother, so the time was ripe for a civilized arrangement. Don't you think so?"

"I think, Bruno Manzini, that I am going quietly mad."

"Not yet, please, Matucci. I need you very sane. I joined to be inside the conspiracy. I want this precious junta broken and brought down. I believe between us we can do it, by convicting Leporello of murder and the Director of conspiracy with a murderer. Could you do that?"

"I'd be willing to try. But I think we need a new script."

"We'll discuss that in a moment. Do you have any conditions?"

"Only that I conduct the affair in my own way, without interference. And with help from you as I need it. But I have one request, that's all."

"Name it."

"From the moment we leave this place I want Lili Anders protected. If I succeed in the job, I want amnesty for her, from the President, so she may reenter Italy if she chooses. Can you guarantee that?"

"No. But I'd break my back to procure it."

"That's all, then. Now let's talk about the script."

"My dear Colonel, did we not agree, in Zurich, on that?"

"We did. But the circumstances are different. Your being inside the club colors any public relationship I have with you."

"May I suggest that the colors make a better camouflage?"

"You may suggest what you like. I need proof."

"Let me try to give it to you. During the weekend at the Villa Baldassare your name was mentioned several times. The Director, with his usual delicacy, said you were a nuisance. Leporello used the words 'grave risk.' The Director said you were immobilized. Leporello said he required the risk eliminated."

"To which you replied?"

"That as a very intelligent senior officer you had probably taken certain precautions, such as lodging documents in a bank for publication in the event of your death. I suggested that an untimely accident might demoralize your colleagues in the service. I then ventured a small fiction and said that after your arrival in Switzerland you telephoned me and asked whether I could find a place for you in my organization, saying that you had been badly treated and were thinking of resigning your commission. I told the Director I had invited you here to discuss the matter and that it might be a good idea if I offered you temporary employment while he still retained you under his authority. In sum, I persuaded him that you were safer alive than dead, for the moment. Leporello did not agree. The Director overrode him—for how long I don't know. However, the arrangement depends on your consent. You may prefer to conduct this operation in secret and without any overt connection with me."

"If I work underground, I am constantly on the run. I prefer to work openly as your employee, but I might expose you to risk."

"I've faced that already. So tomorrow I telephone the Director that I want to employ you on trial and ask his permission to bring you back to Italy with me."

"So soon?"

"The answer's in your own notes. There is very little time."

"I haven't finished the notes yet."

"Finish them at my house near Bologna. I'll be lodging you."

"What do I tell Lili?"

"Whatever she needs to keep her happy. I'll instruct her on the security arrangements, you handle the love passages."

"Talking of love passages, Cavaliere—what is your exact relationship with the Principessa Faubiani?"

"And how the devil does that concern you?"

"I have to ask, Cavaliere. I've known several good men talked to death in bed."

He stared at me for a long, hostile moment. Then he smiled. "Let's say that I'm a wealthy patron who has visitor's privileges. But I take your point, Matucci. The lady does gossip. Perhaps I should introduce you and let you judge for yourself. I also have other relationships. Do you propose to intrude on them all?"

"If my life is involved, yes."

"We do snarl at each other! Well, I need an argument occasionally to keep me honest. Good night, friend!"

Later I told Lili, as she and I lay in the dark, the promises I had exacted to keep her safe and claim amnesty for her.

"No!" she exclaimed, to my surprise. "Don't you see? You tie me to the past. And to yourself in a way I do not want. When you come to me again—if you come—you will visit me in my house, drink my wine, eat at my table. I will not be empty-handed as I am now. I need that, my love. And you must be free, too, to choose other women. You'll be doing work you can't do with a divided mind. Now, please, let's not be tense and desperate."

SOMEWHERE, in the small dark hours, the alarm went off—an ear-shattering noise of bells and sirens. I ran to the window. The grounds blazed with floodlights, and I saw Heinz and Domenico loping toward the pinewoods. We threw on dressing gowns and hurried downstairs, where we found Manzini, erect and calm, staring into the night. It was impossible to speak against the noise until, in about twenty minutes, Domenico hurried back and switched off the system and reset it.

"We got him, Cavaliere," he reported. "Up on the northern boundary. Heinz killed him with the first shot."

"Who was he?"

"Italian, I think. No papers, no identifying marks. He had grenades, plastic explosive, fuses and a Walther pistol."

"How did he get in?"

"He had to come over the mountain on foot. We might be able to trace his route when the sun comes up."

"Not worth the trouble. Bury him."

When Domenico had gone, Manzini poured three glasses of brandy and passed one to each of us. His hand was steady as he raised his glass in salute. "Like the old partisan days, Matucci, which you are too young to remember."

He meant it as a battle cry. To me it sounded like an epitaph.

two

WE DID not go directly into Italy, but drove by way of Salzburg, where Manzini wanted to discuss a lumber contract with an Austrian mill, and then down through the Brenner Pass and on to Mestre, where one of his companies was building a dry dock for small tankers. It was a tedious journey. Because of heavy snowfalls north and south of the Alps, the roads were a mess of churned snow and dangerous ice.

Manzini talked business. "You will stay for a few days at my place outside Bologna, Matucci. Then I suggest you establish yourself in my Milan apartment. You will need a bank account, credit facilities, and a cover story for your activities in my employ."

"I'll also need a list of safe houses and two or three sets of papers. The best forgeries."

"I know the best forger in the business."

"Yes. Carlo Metaponte, who engraved your salamander. He's on our files. Usable if you can control him."

"I can control him. Matucci, will you try to be generous with me? Your father was an old-line Socialist, exiled to Lipari. Mine was an old-line aristocrat who exploited the poor. But when you were thirteen years old, I was making petrol bombs in a barn. When you were fourteen, I was hung by my thumbs in a Gestapo cell in Milan. What I fought for then, you are trying to preserve now—a liberty, however precarious and imperfect. I cannot risk what you risk because I have only the tag end of a life. But I savor every second of it. This is—how can I call it?—a plea that we should enjoy this fight. Go down, if we must; survive, if we can, singing and shouting. Can you understand that?"

"I can. I do. I'm grateful, Cavaliere."

"Please! I am Bruno now. And you are Dante. *Bene?*"

"*Bene, grazie!*"

"And I want you to develop some style, my Dante. New uniforms. New suits, too, the best fashion. And don't be mean with money; spread it like sauce on spaghetti. Good! That's the first time I've heard you laugh like a happy man!"

But he must still play the conjurer. Tonight, he announced, we would stay, not in Mestre but across the water in Venice, at the Gritti Palace—and the Director would join us for dinner. After all the charm he had spent on me, I had to take this trick with grace.

"You have to confront him sometime. Better with me than alone. Better in his own city, where he feels most a prince. You will be courteous, reserved, but not insensible of his magnanimity. He will goad you, but you will fight back. He will ask you about Lili Anders. You will shrug her off, a ripe peach tasted and thrown away. When you want to leave, say you have to meet a woman in Harry's Bar. You do, in fact. Ask the barman for Gisela Pestalozzi. She will be on your list of safe houses. You will say that the Salamander sent you. Clear?"

"Clear. Except how you manage it all."

"It's a game, Dante. One of the few I can still play well."

Domenico drove us to Venice in the early dark. He parked the car, and we took a gondola to the Gritti, where we were welcomed like medieval cardinals and lodged in adjoining suites.

At dinner the Director received me like the prodigal son. "My dear Matucci! Delighted! Filthy weather, isn't it?"

I agreed it was; but Venice was still Venice after all.

Manzini asked him if he had invested in a little project he had recommended, and snorted when the Director replied he'd bought a Picasso instead. "You should have waited for the Pantaleone collection to come on the market," he said.

"If you are interested in painting, Matucci," the Director said, "take my advice. Collect the young ones. If you have a good eye, you can't fail to pick at least one in ten, and you'll still make a profit. Wouldn't you say, Bruno?"

"I want him interested in my profits first. That's the quickest way he'll make them for himself. He has already made some intelligent suggestions. If he can put them into action, I'll be prepared to bid very high for him."

"Provided, my dear Bruno, that the service is prepared to waive claims on his valuable talents. Still, I'm glad to see him have this opportunity. I owe you some thanks, Matucci. You behaved well in a difficult situation. We've made a few changes at headquarters since you left."

"Oh?"

"Gonzaga takes the Middle East desk. We've retired Stefanelli from forensics. He was getting too old and crotchety. . . . Ah, the menu! . . . What do you recommend, Bruno?"

"My dear fellow, I never recommend food, horses or women. By the way, have you recovered the Pantaleone will?"

"No. Which reminds me, Matucci. We were lucky about the lawyer, Bandinelli. It appears his wife was having an affair with a young singer. She was only too pleased to consent to a quiet funeral."

"I'm afraid I didn't handle that situation very well, sir."

"You were under a big strain. Let's order, shall we?"

I was glad of the respite and the small talk that came with the food. They were well matched, these two: the Director so entrenched in history that you had only to change his costume to set him back among the Council of Ten—the rulers of medieval Venice; Manzini, the technocrat, straddling past, present and future like a colossus in a business suit. I was content to listen. Then, without warning, the Director tossed a question to me. "Matucci, what happened to the Anders woman?"

"I took your advice, sir."

"Where is she now?"

"She was talking of going to Klosters for a while. And I think she has marriage in mind."

"Any prospects?"

"Not with me, I assure you. Which reminds me, if you gentlemen will excuse me, I have an appointment with another lady."

"Before you go, Matucci . . . this dual employment of yours. I'm glad to oblige my friend Bruno here. But you will be discreet about it among your service colleagues, won't you? You do understand?"

"Perfectly, sir. I'm very grateful. Good night, gentlemen."

"It's a dirty night," said Manzini. "Don't fall into the canal."

I TOOK the warning seriously. I went up to my room, put on a topcoat and slipped a pistol into my pocket. I spent a moment in the lobby buying postage stamps and then stepped out into the alley. The alley opens into a *piazza*. To get to Harry's Bar you turn right and cross a bridge into the Calle Larga 22 Marzo, which brings you slap against the façade of the church of San Moisè. Even by day it is a quiet route. That night, in fog, with every window shuttered, it was like a city of the dead.

I paused and heard a murmur of voices from the left; boatmen, probably. I began to walk, holding to the wall for direction, listening for footsteps. Nothing except the wash of the canal and the wail of foghorns. When I turned out of the *piazza* I thought I heard a faint *slap-slap* of rubber soles on the cobbles, but the sound was too muted to be sure. I walked on faster, though, toward the bridge. Then, from behind me, I heard a long, high whistle. I flattened myself against the wall, took out the pistol and slipped off the safety catch. Behind me was one man. Ahead, where the canal cut across the alley, there would be two. Before I reached the bridge they would close the trap and kill me inside it.

I began to ease myself slowly along the wall, feeling for a doorway. I heard a few swift, running steps. I saw a faint movement near the bridge, which might have been a man, but could just as easily have been a swirl of mist. Then my fingers slid off the wall

TABACC

and groped in emptiness. It was an open archway into a courtyard. Thanks be to God! Now they would have to come for me. I slid down on one knee and peered out cautiously. It was perhaps ten seconds before they began to move, two hugging the wall on my side, the third moving down the opposite side of the alley. This was the one I must take first. Mercifully he made a run that brought him into range, but I could not see him clearly. I had to guess that he was between a barred window and the deeper shadow of a doorway. I fired. He did not fire back. He turned and ran. The others ran, too. I fired two more shots, wild into the mist. Then, because shutters were opening, I bolted for the shelter of Harry's Bar.

Luckily the bar was busy. My breathless entrance attracted no attention. I ordered a large drink, carried it to the telephone booth and called Manzini at the Gritti. "Thanks for the warning," I said. "I nearly did fall into the canal."

"What happened?"

"A well-laid trap. Three men. I fired shots. They got away."

"Where are you now?"

"Where you sent me. I haven't met the lady yet."

"Come to my room when you get back."

"How's our mutual friend?"

"Smug as a cat. I think I'll stir him up a little."

When I asked the barman about Gisela Pestalozzi, he grinned. "She's expensive, but she's got the best girls in town."

"How will I know her?"

"She sits in the far corner. Big redhead in her mid-forties. Wears lots of bangles, big earrings. You can't miss her."

I took my drink over to Gisela's corner and sipped it slowly. A few minutes later she came in, scattering greetings and perfume, and sat down beside me. She wore neck chains enough to moor the *Galileo*. Her hair was titian red, her lips geranium and her voice like pebbles in a gravel grinder. She ignored me for a full half minute, then announced, "This is my place, young man. You must be new here."

"And you must be Gisela? The Salamander sent me."

"Eh!" She collapsed like a vast balloon. "What do you need?"

"A safe house."

"For how long?"

"I don't know yet. Weeks, months."

"With or without?"

"With or without what?"

"A woman, of course. What else?"

"Without."

"Two rooms, kitchen and bath. Fully furnished, light, heat and telephone. Near Saint Mark's. Two hundred thousand lire a month. Suit you?"

"It's a murderous price."

"It's safe. Private entrance. No porter and two other exits."

"Where do I get the key?"

"From me. With a month in advance and a month's deposit."

"I'll think about it. How do I find you?"

"The Salamander has my number. Now move over, lover! This is working hours."

"*Ciao,* Gisela! We'll be seeing each other."

And that was it, pointless and unreal like everything else that was happening to me. I left my drink on the table and paid a sleepy boatman one thousand lire to deliver me two hundred meters down the canal. From the Gritti, I called Stefanelli. "Steffi, this is Matucci." In ten seconds it was clear I was not a welcome caller.

"I remember the name. Yes?"

"I'm in Venice, Steffi."

"Happy you. Happy Venice."

"Steffi, stop clowning. This is serious. Listen, please!"

"No! You listen. You sold out, little brother! You took a long leave, and now you're on the payroll of private industry."

"Where did you hear all this?"

"From the great talking horse himself on the day he retired me. I quote: 'Why don't you emulate your colleague Matucci and direct your talents to civilian occupation? I venture to suggest that Matucci will end a very rich man.' Do you want to hear any more?"

"No, thanks. But do me one favor, Steffi. Go talk to Raquela Rabin and ask her what we discussed when I saw her. Then, if you want, you can call me all the names in the book when I ring you again. Good night, Steffi."

After that I went up to Manzini's suite. I was surprised to see the Director still with him. The atmosphere was tense. Manzini plunged straight in. "What happened, Matucci?"

I made it clear that someone had set me up like a clay pigeon and that I wasn't happy about it. Manzini cut me off. "I have told your director what happened at the lodge. And our suspicion that both attempts were officially inspired."

"And I am shocked at the suggestion." He looked it, too. I caught a hint of real unease under the Director's sardonic mask.

"It had to be you or Leporello," I said. "You both knew where I was. Knowing the trade, it's not illogical, is it?"

"From my point of view, Matucci, it's madness. I have a vested interest in keeping you alive."

"I will not work with fools," said Manzini flatly. "You will talk sense into that upstart Leporello."

"Please, Bruno," said the Director softly. "No tantrums. I will deal with it." He rose. "Sleep well, Matucci."

When he had gone, Manzini surveyed me with ironic amusement. "Well, my Dante, what did you make of that?"

"I think he's telling the truth."

"I know he is. He's worried. If he can't control Leporello now, he'll never be able to afterward. All profit, Dante! When thieves fall out, it's gold in the pockets of the godly." And he sat there chuckling like a spider who had just made a meal of a gadfly.

THERE were lions at the gates, supporting an illegible escutcheon. The gates were of black iron, scrolled, and twice the height of a man. A graveled drive wound through an avenue of cypresses and opened into a fantasy of flower beds, beyond which a stairway of white marble led to the villa, a small jewel, light and beautiful even under the steady drenching rain.

This was Pedognana, country seat of the Cavaliere di Gran Croce Bruno Manzini, and he displayed it to me with pride.

"Home, my Dante! The one place where I am truly myself. My

mother bought it in the good years and sold it in the bad ones. When I made my first real money I bought it back. The battered arms over the gate are the ones my mother invented for herself. I defaced the salamander in the partisan days, because this was my headquarters until the Germans arrested me. Come inside."

In the pillared entrance, under a resplendent dome, the household was assembled to greet the master. Manzini saluted them all by name, and I had to repeat each salutation. By the time the ceremony was over I felt myself in the nineteenth century.

The housekeeper bustled me upstairs to a room whose splendor overwhelmed me—the blazing fire, the bookcase full of leather-bound tomes. Suddenly it was all too much, and I wondered irrationally whether this were not a Manzini tactic—to stifle me with grandeur and bind me like a serf to his service. Or was it another of his ways of testing me?

Later that evening, with maps and documents spread all over the table, we sketched the first plan of campaign. I marveled again that so old a man could be so precise and so ruthless.

"State the purpose of the exercise, Colonel."

"To convict Major General Leporello of conspiracy to murder the lawyer, Bandinelli, and the agent, Calvi. To discredit the Director by showing him joined in the conspiracy."

"And where do you begin?"

"With three facts: Leporello knew the location of the Pantaleone papers and my arrangements to have Calvi guard them; his aide, Captain Roditi, appeared on Ponza with orders to claim the other documents; later the Director joined Leporello in a plot to establish military rule."

"Given those facts, where do you probe first?"

"At the weakest point. Captain Roditi."

"Next?"

"Leporello. We can build a dossier on him easily enough, but it will take time. What is your impression of him?"

"Cold, ambitious, more than a little paranoid. But put him on that balcony in the Piazza Venezia and many people would go mad for him. I'd like you to examine him in social circumstances. He's based in Milan, so we'd better install you in the apartment there as soon as possible. Which raises another question, Dante *mio*. Women!"

"Oh?"

"I suggest you put yourself in the marriage market."

"You must be joking!"

"Not at all. You're a good candidate for any woman's guest list. Use that. Now, your cover story. You are appointed as my personal adviser on all aspects of industrial security. You have free access to all plants and offices. You will be supplied with a company credit card and a car. When I am absent from the country, you will report to me in a code which I shall supply to you. My secretary will inform you of my movements. My banker arrives at ten tomorrow morning to open your account and establish a credit rating backed by me. Now, what else is on the list?"

"Personnel."

"Employ whomever you wish. But check with me before you use any of my staff. Next?"

"You've written here: 'The Church.'"

"Oh, yes. This is a delicate one, Matucci. Mother Church is up to her neck in Italian politics. She's a very old and very shrewd lady, and she has friends of the Left and Right as well as Center. Sometimes it's hard to distinguish them. If you find you're treading on a cassock, tread lightly until you know who's wearing it. Are you religious, by the way?"

"I was baptized, communicated and confirmed. Why?"

"It helps to know what a man thinks about dying—"

"I think about it as little as possible. I find that helps."

"My age makes a difference. I've lived the discord, but I think I hear a harmony. I hear it plainest in the old words and the old signs of grace. Maybe it's an illusion, but I'd rather die with it than without it. . . . I really must get you to a good tailor! That suit was cut by a pork butcher."

In the morning the banker came; in the afternoon a tailor, who measured me for more clothes than my father had worn in a lifetime. In the evening I called Steffi.

"So, I apologize," he said.

"Don't mention it. How would you like to work for me? Good salary, expenses, a little travel."

"I'll have to ask my wife."

"She can't wait to get you out of the house and you know it."

"Now, that's a great truth, little brother. How soon?"

"A week. Ten days at most."

"How much?"

"Your service salary."

"You've bought me."

"Good. One more thing. Do I have any friends left?"

"Still a few. Need something?"

"Yes. Any background you can get on Matteo Roditi, captain of carabinieri, aide to Major General Leporello."

"Should be easy enough."

"Thanks, Steffi. Soon, eh?"

"Shalom."

I felt happier after that, and I typed a short note to Lili, who was staying at a small hotel in the Bernese Oberland. The note would be carried across the border by a courier and posted inside Switzerland. There is no official censorship of mails in Italy, but letters do get opened. I could not say very much because Lili might still be under surveillance and someone might go through her things. And it's hard to be passionate when you sign a letter Uncle Pavel. Still, she would know I was well and would be able to answer through Manzini's private Chiasso address.

For the next week I worked like a galley slave on notes and mnemonics, and had daily conferences with Manzini. He was a rough old pirate, but I was beginning to love him. He had so much talent, so much drive, that he made me feel like a clod. No detail was too small for his attention: the names I should use on my false papers, the decoration of the apartment in Milan, the clubs at which he might present me, whether I should play tennis or take a few lessons in golf, and even the make of car I should drive. He instructed me in the workings of the stock market, in the histories of the great families and the careers of the modern adventurers.

He showed me where the money was—American, German, Swiss—and how the oil war was fought. "Think always in the frame of history, Dante," he would say over and over.

Then, abruptly, he would change the subject and take me out on a tour of the estate, reminiscing about his youth and about his father. "He was happy to profit from politics but refused to engage himself in it, being content with a public affirmation of loyalty to the Crown and a private manipulation of conflicting parties to the sole interest of Pantaleone. . . . I see you smile, my friend. You're right. I'm very like him. He was a good businessman, too. My mother fought him to make a settlement on me, and that was the foundation of what I have today. Have you no land of your own, Dante?"

"None."

"Then buy yourself a plot, however small. Plow and plant and love it. Every man needs earth he can call his own."

"Perhaps, after this is over . . ."

The rest of the thought remained unspoken, but we both understood the big *perhaps*. If things went wrong, I should have all the earth I needed: two meters long, a meter and a half deep—a grave in the churchyard.

THE apartment in Milan was the penthouse of a new building built by Manzini. There was a terrace on three sides, planted with shrubs. The only access was by private elevator, whose entrance and interior could be scanned by closed-circuit television from inside the apartment. The servants had one key to the elevator. I had another. The doors of the apartment were equipped with double locks and chain bolts, and the windows with steel shutters. There were two independent alarm systems, each connected by telephone circuit to the headquarters of the mobile squadron.

Everything in the place was new and designed for a rich and social bachelor: deep leather furniture, a well-stocked bar, stereo and television, books, old and new. There were a typewriter, a Xerox copier, a tape machine, notepaper with my name on it and visiting cards. Concealed behind the bookshelves was a safe with an electronic locking device and an alarm. The telephone index on my desk listed not only tradesmen, doctor and dentist, but all the numbers I might need within Manzini's organization. He turned it all over to me with a smile of satisfaction. "There, my dear Dante. Now you have nothing to do but work and divert yourself profitably. Let me introduce you to the servants."

There were two of them, twin brothers from Sardinia named Pietro and Paolo. They had served a prison term for banditry. Manzini had hired them for a season on his yacht, and then offered them permanent jobs. They were fiercely loyal and discreet.

We toasted the enterprise and blessed the house with a glass of champagne, and then Manzini did a touching thing. He put his hands on my shoulders and embraced me, cheek to cheek, as if we were brothers. Then he took from around his neck a thin gold chain which he slipped over my head. "It's the Saint Christopher I had all through the war. You don't have to believe. Just wear him for me, eh?" An instant later he was walking out the door, his old ironic self. "Good luck!"

The old man's spirit gave me the will to be up and doing. I telephoned Steffi to get to Milan fast. He said he had pulled the file on Captain Matteo Roditi, but there was nothing in it. So I'd have to start digging for myself.

There is a club in Milan called the Duca di Gallodoro that I used whenever I came to Milan. It was one of the few places where the food was reasonably good, the drinks were honest, and it was close enough to headquarters for carabinieri officers to drop in for a drink. It was about ten thirty when I arrived. I perched myself in my favorite corner and made small talk with Gianni, the barman, who was kind enough to notice my new clothes and pay me what he thought was a compliment.

"Eh! Beautiful! English cloth, virgin lamb's wool. And the cut—perfect! What is this, Colonel—a legacy or a rich widow?"

"My life's savings, Gianni. I'm on leave. I thought I owed myself a present. What's going on in town?"

"The same, only more so. Strikes, students marching, police on every corner. People are scared. They're buttoning their pockets and staying home. All this violence! Maybe we need a new *duce* to pull things into line."

"Maybe."

"This new fellow's shaking things up, though. What's his name? Lep-something. That's it—Leporello. I hear your boys talking about him. They say he doesn't care how many heads get broken, so long as we have a quiet city. He's training new riot squads, they tell me. You must know him. Big fellow. The boys call him Old Iron Jaw."

"Good name. Do you know any of his staff?"

"Sure. Some of them come in here. Never on duty, though. He's stopped all that. Hullo, isn't this a friend of yours?"

He sidled up to the bar, all six feet six and two hundred and sixty pounds of him: Giorgione, Big George, Major Marinello. When he saw me his sad spaniel eyes brightened a little. "Matucci! Good to see you. What are you doing in this town?"

"I'm on leave. Let me buy you a drink."

"Thanks, I need it. Old Iron Jaw's been snapping at my heels."

"Big changes, eh?"

"Changes? I tell you, Matucci, this Leporello is a one-hundred-percent armor-plated bastard. He's bringing in brains, he says, computer boys and statisticians, even psychiatrists! But that's not all. He's building up a private group of musclemen. Something funny's going on. I wish I knew what. Ever see that Roditi fellow he's got running around?"

"I've met him. I don't know him."

"Well, he's a weird one. Big shot, big secrets. No friends, except among the new bunch. I wouldn't trust him far."

"Does he ever come here?"

"No, no! This is girl territory. Nothing here for our Roditi."

"*Finocchio,* eh? Is Leporello that way, too?"

"I wouldn't say so. He's married, got two kids. Goes to lunch with the cardinal archbishop. Very proper! Say, what's your big interest anyway?" He set down his glass and swiveled himself around to face me. "Come on, Matucci, give, eh?"

"How would you like to take a walk, Giorgione? Come on to my place; it's not far. It's quiet there, and the drinks are free."

"All right. But it won't get you off the hook. I want—"

"Shut up, or I'll make you pay for the drinks."

The walk gave me time to think. For all his vast bulk and shambling ways, Giorgione was as cunning as a badger. He was one of the mainstays of the division that dealt with fraud and corrupt practices. If I wanted his help, I had to give him enough of the truth to keep him happy and discreet. The apartment helped. He smelled money and power, and he had a healthy respect for both. So, when I judged Giorgione ready and relaxed, I gave him the story.

"For the record, Giorgione, I'm on leave. Four months. I'm working for a big company as security adviser. This place goes with the job. Everything else is off the record."

"Listen, Matucci, I didn't mean to—"

"I know you didn't. And you may be able to help me. I'm still with SID, active. All this is a cover for a job that's maximum security and dangerous. I've also been asked to check out Roditi while I'm here, without upsetting General Leporello. If Roditi is a homosexual, we don't want him in a sensitive post. If he's a disruptive influence, that's another good reason for moving him out. So I have to move carefully, but because of this other business I can't waste time. If you can help me, fine! If not, there's no harm done, provided you sit quiet, as I know you will. That's it, Giorgione . . . check?"

"Check. What do you want to know about this fellow?"

"The full sheet, Giorgione. What's his relationship with Leporello, and what, if anything, does he have to do with the musclemen? Any immediate thoughts?"

"Some, yes. Roditi's a bit of a muscleman himself. Works out every day in the gymnasium—weight lifting, judo, karate. Then he's doing some kind of recruiting job around the country, inside the corps, that is. They seem to be setting up some kind of commando group—real thugs, from what I hear."

"Where do they train?"

"That's one of the big secrets. I'll smell around a bit."

"Where does Roditi live?"

"I don't know that either, but it must be on file. I'll get Rita to dig it out. You remember Rita, you and she—"

"Please, Giorgione, don't tell her I'm in town! Now, you think Roditi's a *finocchio*. Any evidence?"

"Not really. But no girl friends and all this body-building stuff—it points that way, doesn't it?"

"How does Leporello treat him?"

"Oh, very formally, but like a man of confidence. You know the sort of thing. 'If you need any further direction, Captain Roditi will make himself available. . . . Captain Roditi will call you to arrange a conference. . . .' I know he visits Leporello's home."

"Where's that?"

"On the road to Linate Airport. Big villa with a high wall."

"Does Leporello have any women working in his office?"

"Three. Nothing for you there, Matucci. The secretary's a dragon and the two typists are straight from the nunnery."

"What about Leporello's wife?"

"Never seen her."

"Does his wife travel with him?"

"No. But Roditi did, by God! Yes, he did."

"It doesn't prove anything, Giorgione. What's the general feeling in the corps about Leporello?"

"Uneasy. Except the top group, the hard-nose, everything-by-the-book boys, they like Leporello. And he's good, very good. A lot of the things he's done are real improvements."

"But you don't much like him yourself, I take it?"

"I hate his guts. But that's natural. I'm good enough at my job, but I'm no great ornament to the service. And Leporello makes me feel it all the time. Hey! It's late! My wife will kill me! How do I get this stuff to you?"

"Phone me here. If I'm out, leave a message with the servants. Name a place and time, and I'll meet you or call you back."

He left me both pleased and worried. Roditi was unpopular, with a dubious reputation. Leporello was a hard-nose with an unhappy staff. There would be plenty of enthusiastic helpers to dig up the dirt. But the news about the strong-arm squads was disquieting. It was a new threat to privacy and personal rights. Italian law was already heavily loaded in favor of the state and against the individual. A man could be held almost indefinitely on a trumped-up charge. Our interrogation methods were brutal, and our prison system a public shame. I understood Manzini's anxious conviction that the twenty-third hour was already past and the minute hand was climbing to midnight.

I was restless now, itchy for action, so I flipped through my notebook in search of a night owl I could call. I settled on Patrizia Pompa, a lady of singular beauty who made a handsome living decorating the apartments of rich Milanese. To my knowledge, she never went to bed before three in the morning. I called her. She sounded faintly hostile. "Who the hell is this?"

"Dante Matucci, sweetheart. Did I interrupt something?"

"Nothing important. What do you want at this hour?"

"Information—and a little company."

"What sort of information?"

"Clubs for the gay boys. Know any?"

"A couple. Why?"

"I'm looking for a man."

"I didn't think you'd be looking there for a girl, lover."

"He's a nasty man. I think he killed a friend of mine."

"Oh! Then try the Alcibiade. It's open till four."

"Care to come along and hold my hand?"

"Why not? I'll be ready in twenty minutes."

I picked her up in the red Mercedes that Manzini had provided. When she saw my new rig she chuckled. "You didn't do all this on a colonel's salary, Matucci. Who's keeping you?"

"Sweetheart, you embarrass me."

"You'll be more embarrassed where you're going."

"About where we're going, listen, darling, and get the story straight. I'm an old friend and you're showing me the town. This is serious. If you get any telephone calls afterward, stick to this story and don't play games. It could be dangerous."

"With a friend like you, Matucci, I need extra life insurance."

The Alcibiade was plush and expensively decorated. It was designed in a complete circle, with a bar on one side of the small round dance floor and a curved stage on the other. The stage, when we went in, was occupied by three youths in baggy gold pants and turned-up slippers, one playing a sitar and another tooting soulfully on a pipe while the third executed some kind of slow dance. The drinks cost an arm and a leg, but they were served in crystal goblets, with fresh canapés.

Patrizia purred. "Lover, I'm glad you brought me. Can you see your man?"

"Not yet. Wait till the act's over and the lights go up."

We waited a small eternity. The lights, when they were turned on, were dim, but they were bright enough to show me Captain Matteo Roditi seated with two other young men at a table on the edge of the dance floor. I whispered to Patrizia, "I've seen him."

"What do you want to do?"

"Talk to him, alone. Better you're not seen with me. It doesn't look it, but it's dangerous. Order another drink and make your own arrangements."

I pressed some notes into her hand and then wandered to Roditi's table. They did not notice me until I stood over them. "Captain Roditi, isn't it?"

He didn't recognize me for a moment, then he leaped to his feet. "Colonel Matucci! Forgive me, I didn't recognize you."

"Relax, Captain, we're not on parade now."

"What are you doing in Milan, sir?"

"Enjoying some leave."

"Forgive me, but I heard you were retired from the service."

"It's under discussion. I'm still on the active list. Won't you introduce me to your friends?"

"Oh, I'm sorry, sir. Franco Gozzoli, Giuseppe Balbo—Colonel Matucci."

"Are you gentlemen in the service, too?"

He was quick, but not quick enough to intercept their swift looks of inquiry. "No, sir, no. They're both in business here."

"What sort of business?"

"Oh—er—architectural draftsmen."

"How very interesting. Please sit down, gentlemen. Do you come here often, Captain?"

"Occasionally. It's a change. You, sir?"

"Oh, I just dropped in for a drink—cruising, you might say."

"Indeed?" He reacted instantly to the word, and a hint of conspiracy crept into his smile. "Will you be here long?"

"A few weeks. Come and have a drink one evening."

"I'd like that, sir."

"Good. I'll call you at headquarters. Please give my compliments to General Leporello. Tell him I hope to see him soon."

"I'll do that, sir, with pleasure."

"Good night, Roditi. Enjoy yourself."

I saw Patrizia Pompa deep in conversation as I walked past the bar. She gave me a farewell twitch of the fingers, letting me know it was too early for her to go home.

It was three in the morning when I got back to the apartment. I was desperately tired, but slept restlessly.

AT MIDDAY Steffi arrived, chirpy as a cricket. He brought me blessings from his wife, who, he claimed, was happy to be rid of him. He listened in silence while I told him what had happened to me since our last meeting. Then, sober and subdued, he gave me his own version of events in Rome.

"Look, a simple thing! When I arrived at the airport this morning the computer system had broken down. The airline officials went into hiding. And five thousand passengers didn't know whether they were coming or going. We don't form a queue like the English. We shout and scream just for the merry hell of it. But there could have been a riot. For what? A blown fuse that cost maybe a hundred lire. That's the terror of it, Matucci. Nobody blames the fuse. Everybody wants a scapegoat to kick because the plane's late. They're daubing slogans on the bridges of Rome now: DEATH TO THE FASCISTS and DOWN WITH THE MARXISTS. And where I live, it's ZIONIST PIG. . . . I wonder if you understand what you're fighting."

"I wish I didn't, Steffi. This is a dangerous project. I don't want you too close to me. You work from the Europa Hotel. We're investigating murder at this moment, so it's old-fashioned detective work I want from you. On Leporello and Roditi first. I want to know what they eat for breakfast and what brand of toothpaste they use. If you've got any friendly colleagues at Milan headquarters, use them; but be careful."

"I should give you the same advice, little brother. The Director has a man writing a black book on you."

"I'm writing a black book of my own, Steffi."

"The big question for the big money—who gets into print first? One more item: Woodpecker has sold out his whole network. Lili Anders figures prominently in the transcript."

"The Swiss don't extradite for political offenses."

"They do for criminal acts."

"There's nothing criminal in her dossier."

"There wasn't when you last looked at it. There may be now."

"Steffi, you make me feel like Job."

"So, bless the Lord for your afflictions and pray for His mercies. Also, don't underrate the Director. He wants you alive—but buried up to your neck in a mess. Get me a drink and I'll give you a few good words for a change."

"The words first, you old vulture."

"Remember the letter bomb that was posted in Lili Anders's flat? Well, the police reported that the prints on it belong to Marco Vitucci, age twenty-eight, wanted for larceny and robbery with violence. He also uses the name Giuseppe Balbo—"

"Say that one again."

"Giuseppe Balbo."

"One Giuseppe Balbo was with Roditi last night at the Alcibiade! If it's the same one, what a beautiful beginning! Steffi, the soup's beginning to cook!"

"So, please may I have my whiskey?"

We talked it all over. We arranged codes, meeting places, a schedule of telephone contacts; then Steffi left to rest his aged bones and plot his own campaign of investigation. And he left me disturbed, in spite of the lead to Roditi.

Because once again I had lapsed into dangerous inattention, concentrating on only one issue and ignoring a whole complex of threats behind it. The black book was an ingenious perversion. The trick was to take a man's dossier and, by editing, emphasis and interpretation, distort it into a criminal caricature. For "bachelor" read "not interested in women," for "likes card games" read "known gambler," and you have the art in a nutshell. It's a filthy game, but it works.

I knew the game because I had played it myself. And I knew what an easy victim I was, a secret agent working always on the outer margin of the law. Lili Anders likewise. One telephone call from the Director to his counterpart in Switzerland, and she would be helpless as a leaf in a winter storm.

I had just finished transcribing Steffi's information onto tape when the telephone rang. It was Major General Leporello, brisk and cordial. "Welcome to Milan, Colonel. Captain Roditi delivered your message. I should be delighted to see you."

"I simply wanted to pay my respects, sir," I said. "I know how busy you are."

"Dinner on Thursday. How would that be?"

"Fine, sir. I'm free on that night."

"My house at eight thirty. I'll send you directions. Informal—a family foursome. Is there someone you would care to bring?"

"No, sir."

"Leave it to my wife, then—she's the party girl. You and I can have a private chat over the coffee. By the way, have you thought about my offer?"

"Yes, sir, I have."

"Let's talk about it again. Until Thursday, then."

I had expected some approach, but this was out of all proportion. Two weeks ago he wanted me dead; now he wanted me to dinner. This was not necessarily a contradiction. I was chewing on that sour thought when a courier arrived with messages from Manzini.

One was a note requesting me to dine with him this night at the Bankers' Club, in order, as he put it, "to meet money and see whether it smells or not." The other was a letter from Lili:

My dear,

I am sitting on my balcony, bathed in sunshine, with a marvelous vista of snow-covered peaks and valley farms like dolls' houses. I am enjoying it all, my dear, in a way I would never have thought possible. I walk. I read. I chat with the other guests, pleasant people. There are a honeymoon couple who make me envious sometimes, an elderly American professor who is writing a book, and a very dashing fellow from Lugano, an engineer here on a construction job, who keeps offering me whirlwind tours in his Maserati.

I worry sometimes, because I am still so transient and insecure; but my lawyer, Herr Neumann, reassures me. He says that I may be able to apply for political asylum. He has taken a lot of depositions and is seeking advice from colleagues in Zurich.

And you, my Dante, how are you? I love you and I miss you, but I dare not let myself depend on the loving, and I must get used to the missing. As I write, I am jealous of every woman you meet. I wonder if you are jealous of my engineer. I'd like to think so. Take care, my dear. Think gently of me.

One fine tomorrow, perhaps I'll be

Yours, Lili

I read it three times, then tore it and burned the shreds in the ashtray. I was jealous, and I had no right to be. If I wasn't in love, I was as near to it as I had ever been in my life. I couldn't risk the distraction. There were too many dangerous tomorrows to survive, and Lili's shining day might never come.

THE Bankers' Club in Milan is only a whit less venerable than the Chess Club in Rome. It is, however, much more impressive because the focus of its power is clearer, and all its members are fluent in a single, international language—money. It is a religious language reserved to priests and acolytes—and as such, precise, flexible, subtle, and quite unintelligible to the profane populace. I was curious to know why Manzini had chosen so sacrosanct a place to present me to his world. I asked him as we sat over cocktails.

"Here everyone has money, Dante. Money imposes discretion. Discretion conduces to free speech. Here, therefore, there is free speech—quite a lot of it, in fact. There are six of us who meet for dinner once a month. We talk about everything under the sun. Any of us may bring a guest, provided he guarantees him as a safe man with a secret. Two of the men I particularly want you to meet. One is Ludovisi from the Banca Centrale. The other is Monsignore Frantisek, from the Vatican, one of the shrewdest bankers in the business. They can both be very useful to you."

"How?"

"They can tell you quicker than anybody where the big money is going and why. There's another reason, too. Ludovisi is the brother-in-law of your director." He chuckled and held up his hand. "No, don't be alarmed. They love each other like cat and dog. Ludovisi is suing for divorce. He blames his wife's family for the failure of the marriage. The rest of the men? Well, they're agreeable and well informed. One's a Liberal, others are Christian Democrats of varying shades. Paolini's an out-and-out Fascist, but on a personal basis he's so agreeable you can almost forgive him."

"And what do you expect me to do?"

"Whatever you like. Talk, listen, argue. Now, tell me, what have you been doing?"

He heard me out in silence and then gave a long, low whistle of satisfaction. "Good! Good! What do you propose to do now?"

"Wait until I get more evidence. I may lose Balbo, but if I hand him to the police now, I might lose Roditi and Leporello."

He frowned over that. "I hate the thought of losing a key witness. But premature action is a risk. Those riot squads worry me, though —and I do wonder why Leporello's asked you to dinner. He's in high favor with the businessmen just now. He gave a talk here last week on order and progress—very well received. Let's go in, shall we? The others should be here by now. We'll take soundings and see if there's any news floating around."

We were eight people at a round table so there was no question of precedence. Protocol was honored by an opening grace from Monsignore Frantisek. Ludovisi was the wit of the group, a lean, gray-eyed dandy. The others, except for Paolini, were typical of their breed, eloquent about everything to do with money, agreeably cynical about any other human concern. Paolini I found an enigma. He radiated charm, but his mind was closed to every logic but his own.

"Look what happened in Greece," he said. "A few years ago you could hardly raise a dollar for investment. Now they've got some law and order, the money pours in. And the government controls the terms. That's a much better situation than we've got."

"Correction, old friend," the monsignor cut in with a tart reminder. "The colonels suspended law and imposed order."

"It's a proper distinction," said Manzini mildly, "but I wonder if it makes any difference to the man in the street. We've got so many laws we can't enforce that we end up with government by regulation. Did anybody hear Leporello's speech last week?"

"I did," said Paolini. "I thought he made excellent sense."

There was tepid agreement from everyone except Ludovisi, who groaned. "He was one long cliché! 'Liberty is not license; provocative elements; strong security measures.' Paolini, do you know this fellow personally?"

"I do. And I think he's the kind of man we need, resolute, clear-headed, absolutely incorruptible."

"Has anyone else met this paragon?"

I caught a faint signal from Manzini. "I have," I said.

The monsignor's eyebrows went up. "And your opinion of him?"

"I'd rather not make a judgment of him as a man. I will say I think he's embarked on a highly dangerous policy."

"What policy is that?"

"Surely you gentlemen know. He's recruiting special riot squads. It's a secret operation, and that worries me. Where the recruits are coming from worries me even more."

"Where do they come from, Matucci?"

"Resorts of known criminals and social delinquents."

"That's a serious statement." Paolini was visibly shocked.

"I know. I make it here in privacy. I shall be presenting evidence to General Leporello himself on Thursday."

"It sounds like the death squads in Brazil," said Ludovisi grimly. "A familiar pattern: pull the rowdies off the streets and set them breaking heads under legal sanction. If you're right, I'd say we were in for a very bloody mess."

"I think we're making a morbid prejudgment." Paolini was too bland to be true. "Why don't we change the subject? No offense, Matucci, but you don't know my colleagues. If you spread alarm like that, you'll rattle the market for a month. Eh, Bruno?"

"I hope not." Manzini chuckled like a happy child. "I'm coming into the market myself tomorrow. The English have just come out with an electron welder that will join two plates of steel—twenty-centimeter steel—in a single welding pass. I want to buy rights in it and finance a local manufacturer. Any of you interested? You'll come in, won't you, Monsignore? Just what His Holiness needs to repair the rifts in the Church."

They all laughed at that, and the tension relaxed.

As we moved from the dining room to take coffee in the salon, Ludovisi laid a hand on my arm. "That was bad news, Matucci. Do you know where it's pointing?"

"Yes."

"How do you know?"

"I work for SID as well as for Manzini."

"Then you know my brother-in-law."

"Yes."

"Where does he stand in this matter? Before you answer—I don't like him. I think he's both devious and dangerous."

"As a serving officer, I couldn't comment. As a guest in your club, I would say that I agree with you."

"Thank you. Here's my card. If ever I can help, call me."

"Thank you, but I doubt you can help me with this mess."

"You keep an open mind. I'll keep an open door. Agreed?"

At eleven thirty the guests dispersed, but Manzini held me for a final coffee. There were dark circles under his eyes. "That dinner tonight . . . Truly, I could go out and cut my wrists in a bathtub! You shoved a live grenade under their noses and only two had sense enough to see it. The others didn't want to see it. Have you thought, friend, that if you die one night in a back street, you'll be dying for men like these?"

"You must have thought about it, too."

"I have, many times. When the Gestapo had me in jail, Dante, my half brother came to see me. He was Captain Pantaleone then, very chic, very general staff. He offered me a bargain. If I'd give him the list of the Salamander network, the Gestapo would release me and I could live out the war at the Pantaleone villa in Frascati. I was sick and tired, and I didn't spit in his eye like a hero. What I did was to tell him the story of my birth, and another story—of how his father, and mine, had had one of my mother's lovers murdered for threatening to tell the world whose son I was. I thought I was signing my death warrant, which would have suited me well at that moment. Instead I was handed back to the interrogators to be worked on for another month. Then, without warning, I was put into a car and driven to Frascati—house arrest at the villa. One day my half brother told me why he had procured my release: he wanted to discharge his father's obligations to me! I'm afraid I did spit in his eye then; though, looking back, I think he meant at least half of it. That was the half that took me to his funeral. The other half? Well, you know what he was doing—the other half is what made me send him the salamander card. You see what I mean, Dante—motives for martyrdom are sometimes clear and simple, and sometimes they're very confused."

EARLY next morning Giorgione woke me up with good news. He had discovered the location of a camp that could be where the riot squads were training. It was in Camerata, a small town in the mountains north of Bergamo, about an hour's drive from Milan. He had other information, too. Captain Roditi lived in a new apartment house with rents much higher than he could afford on a captain's pay. So either he had private income, or someone was subsidizing him.

After breakfast I rang Roditi's office to set our date for drinks. His sergeant told me Roditi would be in Turin with General Leporello until Thursday. By ten o'clock Steffi and I were on the expressway heading for Bergamo.

I explained my plan to Steffi. I still had my SID identification, which would procure me entrance to any maximum-security installation. The risk was that the commanding officer could insist on his right to check the document back to its origin before admitting me. I thought I could bluff my way through that. Nevertheless, I proposed to drop Steffi off in Bergamo with instructions to telephone Manzini if I were detained beyond a reasonable time.

Steffi was not enthusiastic. "You're crazy, Matucci. If they do check, you're up to your neck in trouble. What reason are you going to give them for this visit?"

"The best. I'm looking for a man named Marco Vitucci, wanted on charges of subversion and murder. We feel he may have slipped through the screening into a sensitive organization. Of course I won't find Vitucci. But if I do find Balbo, we're in big profit."

"Enough to buy you a beautiful tombstone, little brother."

"Relax, Steffi. I'll be back in a couple of hours. *Ciao*."

From Bergamo the road to Camerata wound upward along the flanks of the Lombard hills. I drove into the town and stopped several times to ask directions. No one knew where the camp was. Security was obviously effective. Finally, I had to call on the local police and produce my card for the *brigadiere*, who drew me a map on a sheet of yellow paper. Even then I nearly missed the turnoff, a rutty road into a narrow pass which was closed off at the end by a stockade of logs surmounted by a watchtower with a searchlight and a machine gun.

Two husky guards halted me. I told them I wanted to see the commandant. One of them took my card and went to his box to telephone. I waited five minutes, and then they waved me through.

The place was grim: twin rows of log huts with a broad parade ground in between, and beyond, a vast basin, obviously the training area. I parked my car outside the commandant's office and went inside. A desk sergeant took my card, and it was five more minutes before I was presented to a bullet-headed major who looked as though he could straighten horseshoes with his bare hands. His desk was a mess of papers and he was quite self-conscious about it, fumbling with this sheet and that, as if he weren't sure what was written on them.

His greeting was uneasily cool. "Major Zenobio at your service, Colonel. I'm afraid I had no notice of your visit."

"There were good reasons, Major. General Leporello left for Turin early this morning. I was still waiting for information from Rome, and I left as soon as it came. I am required to report to the general on his return. In fact, we're dining together tomorrow evening. If you feel the need to check that, please call his secretary immediately. I'd like to get down to business."

"And your business is?" His tone was one degree less frigid.

"I'm looking for a man. The police want him for attempted murder. We want him because he is a known subversive."

"And you hope to find him here, Colonel?"

"There's a certain logic in the idea. Your recruiting methods are, shall we say, unorthodox. Even social delinquents are acceptable, provided they can be retrained to certain essential skills. Correct? And the project is secret. A man who wanted to go underground might well present himself for enlistment."

"The project *is* secret. So how would your man know about it?"

"Ah, that's one of the matters I have to discuss with the general. It affects an officer who has been less than discreet. Take it for granted that the man would know and could present himself. Now, we're not interested in the police side, but an active Marxist agent inside this kind of group—well! You do see my point?"

"Too clearly, Colonel. What's the name of your man?"

"Marco Vitucci."

"Let's take a look at the roster."

"In a moment. What other records do you keep on your troops?"

"Each man has a record card, which contains his personal details, a photograph, thumbprint and a list of distinguishing marks."

"Good. Now let's have a look at the roster."

It took him three minutes to find it under the mess on his desk. It took only a minute to establish that in a list of four hundred men there was no Marco Vitucci.

"Well, we do have one other alias." I thumbed through my notebook. "Here it is—Barone, Turi." That landed me among the B's. There was no Barone either; but I did light on the name Balbo,

Giuseppe, and I pointed it out to the major. "Balbo, eh? Nothing to do with the case, of course. I was just wondering if he's any relation to General Balbo, who marched with the *Duce*?"

The major smiled for the first time. "I doubt it. But let's take a look." He opened a filing cabinet and handed me a card. The identification was clear. This was the same man I had met with Roditi in the Alcibiade. If the thumbprint tallied with the one on the police files, I had all I needed. I gave the card back to the major, who tossed it onto the littered desk.

"No connection, I'm afraid. The old general was a Ferrarese. This one comes from Gaeta. I wonder if I could ask you one favor. Could I have a cup of coffee?"

"Certainly." He yelled for the sergeant, and when there was no answer he went through the door at a run, and I heard him shouting across the parade ground. I slipped the Balbo card in my pocket and followed him. "Don't bother, please, Major. I'll be on my way. Just a reminder—this visit is strictly confidential."

"Of course, Colonel. Have a good journey."

He was glad to see me go, but not half so glad as I was to hear the gates of the stockade slam behind me. I drove fast and dangerously back to Bergamo, snatched up a plaintive Steffi and shot back to Milan. The prints on the Balbo card did match the prints from Rome. We made four copies and locked the original in the safe. Then we had Pietro bring champagne to celebrate this first real rape of the ungodly. It was a jubilant hour. But at four in the afternoon, sober but sleepy, we still did not know what to do with our evidence.

Steffi summed it up irritably. "Well, now! We could put one Giuseppe Balbo in prison for life. You don't want that. You want him here, singing like a lovebird, telling you all he knows about Roditi, the letter bomb and the murders of Bandinelli and Calvi. Then you want Roditi here, singing another song about General Leporello. And when you've got it all down, who's going to want to believe you? And much more important, who's going to do anything about it? Matucci, little brother, big woodenhead, you have to answer all those questions!"

"I know, Steffi, I know! I have to create doubt, confusion and panic among them. How far is it to Chiasso?"

"Less than fifty kilometers. Why?"

I grabbed the telephone and dialed Bruno Manzini's private number. When he was on the line I said, "I want a courier, Bruno. To drive to Chiasso and post some letters. They have to be delivered in Milan with tomorrow's mail. And I need to see you, here at the apartment. It's very urgent."

He always ran true to form. The courier would be with me in fifteen minutes. He himself would join me at six. Steffi was looking at me as if I were a lunatic as I unlocked the safe, took out the Balbo card, rubbed it clean with a new handkerchief and laid it on the desk. Then I rang for Paolo and asked for a pair of his clean white gloves.

"So, tell me, Matucci!" Steffi finally burst out. "Or do I just stand here and watch you make like Sherlock Holmes?"

"Step one. We make two fresh copies of this document, without our fingerprints all over the copy paper. Step two. We clip Balbo's thumbprint off each copy. Step three. I type two identical notes to accompany the thumbprints. Step four. Said notes and thumbprints are posted from Chiasso."

"And what will be in the notes?"

"Two names: Bandinelli, Calvi. A place: Via Sicilia, Rome. And the date on which they died."

"And who gets the notes?"

"General Leporello and Captain Roditi—at their homes."

"And how long will it take them to check the print?

"Forty-eight hours at least."

"And how long to tie it all back to you through a stolen card?"

"Another twenty-four. Maybe a little longer."

"Then what, little brother?"

"Then there is the beautiful scene, Steffi. I think we'll get Fellini to film it. I, Dante, am standing solitary and noble in the middle of the Olympic Stadium. The stands are full. All the spectators look exactly like the Director. They all have guns and they're all pointing at me. What happens after that, I'm not sure."

"I'm sure, Matucci. I'm going home to Mother."

"Not tonight you're not. At ten o'clock we are going to visit the apartment of Captain Matteo Roditi. How does that sound?"

"Like madness. Like old-fashioned dancing madness!"

WHEN Manzini heard of my day's exploits he was coldly and eloquently angry. "Matucci, you shock me! You have at least some sense of politics. So this children's game you have played today is an incredible and inexcusable folly."

"Now, listen—"

"No! You hear me first! You have set in motion a whole train of events for which we are unprepared. Have you learned nothing? This is high politics. We are talking of revolution, barricades in the streets, gunfire and bombs! Yet you behave like some fly-brained agent from a comic book! Truly I despair!"

"You despair too quickly. First point. Locked in that safe is a document which can tie Roditi and Leporello to a conspiracy to murder. Next point. We agreed on a policy of doubt and confusion. I have begun to create it."

"Prematurely. Without foresight!"

"We are dealing with conjurers, sir. People who can make files disappear and silence politicians and buy perjurers—if we give them time. I'm trying to deny them time. You can sit with them, the movement, in the Bankers' Club and plan. I have to fight the street battles. I'm the opportunist because I have to be. . . . Eh! This is madness! Let's drop it!"

He stared at me for a long moment, bleak-faced and hostile; then he nodded slowly. "You are right and I am right. And we are both wrong. Let's see what we can salvage."

"No. Let's see what we can build."

A small reluctant smile twitched at the corners of his mouth. "You're a real woodenhead, Matucci. What am I to do with you?"

"Wear me, like a hairshirt, and give me some advice. We establish a case that involves Balbo as an assassin, and Roditi and Leporello as conspirators. But how do we present our case? And how do we tie the Director into it? He's got a perfect position. He can excuse anything he has done on grounds that he was infiltrating a conspiracy that threatened the security of the state. He knows so many secrets that everyone's afraid of him."

"I'm not afraid of him, Dante."

"No. But neither have you the lever that will topple him."

"You, my Dante, may without knowing have provided both lever and fulcrum."

"I don't understand."

"I know you don't. And that is what makes me angry with you. In the heat of a new situation you slip out of gear. You lose sight of the main show. You chase the marsh light and forget the fires burning on the hills behind you. Remember what happened at the lodge? In Venice? The same thing is happening now. This is why you are at the mercy of such a man as the Director. You have every talent he has, and some he lacks, but you cannot or you will not focus them. So, always until now, you have been a tool of other men's designs. I'm sorry if I offend you, but I have so much regard for you that I cannot bear that you do this to yourself. . . . Let me show you what I mean. Two things you missed, and the consequence to you. First, when you left my brother's house on the morning after his death, you left the old servant weeping, and asked him to record telephone calls for you. He did that, but you never went back to him, never spoke to him again. I did. I went there to see to the wants of an old man who had known my father. Because he was afraid, he told me that he had lied to you. He was not awake when my brother came home from the Chess Club; he was drunk and snoring. He had lied because he thought he would be blamed for not having put on the alarms; they were off when he woke in the morning. . . .

"No, please don't interrupt. Let me embarrass you a moment longer. The night after my brother's funeral I had his body removed from the vault. An autopsy was performed in a private clinic. My brother had indeed taken barbiturates, but not enough to kill him. He was killed by an injection of air into the femoral artery. The mark of the syringe was clearly visible. You see what happened, Dante? You connived with the Director to hush up a suicide; by his will and your own blindness you were made an accomplice in murder."

"Why didn't you tell me this before?"

For a full minute he said absolutely nothing. When he did speak, his voice was frosty, remote, like the first chill wind of autumn. "To teach you a lesson, Matucci. Trust no one. Not even me. Don't believe that the old Adam is dead until you've screwed down the coffin and seen the gravedigger stamp the last sod on top of him."

He was right, of course. We are an illogical people, sometimes mistrusting our mothers but believing happily the most unprovable propositions. The old man was always right.

Our visit to Roditi's apartment began auspiciously. There was a party on the sixth floor; the lobby was busy with guests and the porter had lost count of the arrivals. Steffi and I rode with the partygoers as far as the fifth floor and stepped out into a deserted corridor. We rang the bell of Roditi's apartment. There was no answer, so I opened the door with a picklock.

The interior of the apartment was a surprise. It was as impersonal and spotless as a hotel room. The furniture, Danish modern, glowed with recent polishing. The only pictures, arranged in a severe symmetry, were of soldiers in historic costumes. There were a cabinet for drinks and a stereo player with a few records of popular songs. The desk was bare, with a clean blotter and a leather cup full of ball-point pens and freshly sharpened pencils. Kitchen, dining room and living room revealed nothing of any interest. We moved on to the bedroom. Roditi had ten suits and four uniforms, all made by an expensive tailor. His shirts were handmade and monogrammed. He was prolific in shoes, ties, scarves and costly accessories. It was all unnaturally tidy—and like the rest of the place, as neutral as a showroom.

Then, in the right-hand drawer of the dressing table, face down, I found a photograph in a silver frame. It was a professional portrait of a woman in her early thirties, inscribed in a bold, round hand: "To my dearest Matteo, for memory and for promise, Elena." Beside the photograph lay a bundle of letters, more than thirty of them, written in the same hand, signed with the same name. I passed them one by one to Steffi. They were love letters, lyrical, tender, and uninhibited in their celebration of passionate nights and days. I have thumbed through many letters in my time, but these moved me deeply, and I was filled with shame at my invasion of this unknown woman's privacy. There were no dates, but from the text it was clear that the last had been written no more than a week ago. Elena was married, unhappily, to an older man. Roditi, whatever else he was, was obviously a warm and thoughtful lover. There was no reproach in any of the letters, only yearning and gratitude and a vivid, sensual poetry.

Even old Steffi was awed. "Eh, Matucci! If you and I could move a woman like that . . ."

"It doesn't make sense, Steffi. A fellow like Roditi—"

"Now hold it, Matucci. Maybe you have to rethink this fellow. You've seen him once, at the Alcibiade, and you've heard he's a physical-culture buff. That's all you've got. Hand me that photograph a minute." He slid it out of the frame and copied the photographer's notation from the back: A. Donati, Bologna, 673125. "Tomorrow I'll trace that print. Let's take one letter from the middle of the bundle and get out of here. I feel like a criminal."

"Which is exactly what you are, Steffi. But you bring me back the lady's name tomorrow and I'll pin a medal on you."

We left the apartment as pristine as we found it. In the lobby the porter was watching television. We could have been trailing a bloodied corpse and he would not have blinked an eye.

It was a little after eleven. The night was balmy and the streets were still lively with strollers and traffic. Steffi was tired, so I dropped him at his hotel. I was too restless to sleep. Bruno Manzini had taught me a rough lesson. My thinking stopped short of the point. My judgments were hasty. My actions were precipitate and dangerous. The Director, seeing this, had made me a facile actor in his sardonic dramas. Lili, too, saw my weaknesses, and would not commit herself to me until I had mastered them, if indeed I ever could.

The prospect of my solitary apartment daunted me, so I headed for the old Duca di Gallodoro, where I could share my loneliness at least. They greeted me warmly and gave me a table in a shadowy corner, where I sat morosely over a drink watching the shuffle of the dancers. I had been there for perhaps twenty minutes when I noticed two men come in and sit a few tables away from me. One was a big fellow with the battered face of a pugilist; the other was small, dark and dapper, with ferret eyes.

The small one I knew. Everyone in the corps knew him, at least by name and reputation. They called him the Surgeon, because, they said, he would cut the brain out of a living man and dissect it for the last morsel of information. The suspect who had jumped or been pushed from a window had been under his studious care. The big fellow was obviously his bodyguard—and probably his assistant butcher. I sat back farther into the shadows lest he see me and I be forced to acknowledge him.

A few moments later the band stopped playing and the dancers drifted back to their tables. Then the lights went out, and there were five seconds of darkness until a spot splashed in the center of the dance floor and revealed a singer in a splendor of fishnet and sequins. She looked better than she sang, but the audience loved her, called her back for two repeats and sang the last chorus with her.

When the houselights went up again, I glanced across at the Surgeon. He was lying slumped across the table. His bodyguard was sprawled sideways on the banquette. Both had been shot in the head by a small-caliber pistol. I tossed some money on the table and made for the exit. I was halfway there before I heard a woman's scream and the commotion that followed it.

THE killing of the Surgeon made headlines in the morning press. The police announced a nationwide hunt for the assassins and appealed for information from the public, especially from anyone who had left the Duca di Gallodoro before the police arrived.

Manzini, who had telephoned me at breakfast to invite me on a tour of his factories, was gloomy. "A fellow like that is better dead, but fifty others are waiting to step into his shoes. So nothing is solved. The factions are polarized further, each suspicious of the next. Watch the tensions rise, Dante, the unrest and the fear. And tyrants look so much more attractive to a scared people. I've just had a call from Rome. The government is considering a new regulation that will give the police even wider powers of search and arrest. They talk of ninety-two hours' preventive detention on mere suspicion. That's madness! It puts us back forty years."

He was still dispirited when we had lunch with some of his plant managers. Afterward, when we got into the car, he said, "Come now, I'll show you something a little more cheerful."

Ten miles or so out of the city we turned off the main road into a private parkland, all lawns and gardens, where twenty bungalows were grouped around a central building that looked rather like a clubhouse.

"A sop to my pirate's conscience, Dante. It's a home for mongoloid children who can't be cared for by their families. Institutional care of any kind is so often only destructive. Here we try to reproduce a family situation. Each house has six to ten children under the care of a married couple. The central building contains classrooms, a clinic, a recreation hall and staff quarters. And every week we learn something, some small revelation that makes it even more worthwhile."

To me, the greatest revelation was the old man himself. The staff adored him. With the children he was like a happy grandfather. He hugged them, squatted on the floor and played games with them. He swung one tiny mite on his shoulders and carried him around, while half a dozen others tugged at his coattails. There was nothing organized about the chanted chorus of welcome or farewell. He came and went as the patriarch of a frail family which without him would have remained ungathered and forgotten. The odd thing was that he seemed to need to justify it—and to me of all people.

"To me it's pure joy, Dante. I go back to the anthill changed, if only a little. I know that life is not all vendetta, and woe to the vanquished. The mystery is that we must still fight to keep room even for so small a loving. If we didn't, they would hand those babies of mine over to the brutes of the world for anatomical experiments."

He spoke to me in a new vein as we drove back to town. "We are going back into the jungle now—you to see Leporello. You cannot afford illusions, Dante."

"What illusions, Bruno?"

"That the Salamander will survive. I have a heart condition which will kill me, probably sooner than later. If I go before this is finished, you will be alone. What then?"

"I could go back to SID, an obedient servant. Or take the job Leporello will offer me tonight. Or emigrate to Australia."

"There are no other possibilities?"

"Yes. There is one. Write me into your will, Bruno. Leave me the engraver's plate from which you print your cards. I'll set up in business as the Salamander. Who knows? I might write a new legend!"

He laughed. I laughed, too—at the wondrous spectacle of Dante Matucci, perched on his dunghill and crowing defiance at all the dark powers of this sunlit Latin world.

I GAVE great care to the manner in which I dressed for Leporello's dinner. I must cut just the right figure. The general should know where the bidding started. Pietro flicked the last speck of fluff from my impeccable lapels, and swept me out into the car he had just polished to mirror brightness.

I drove carefully, because there were police and carabinieri at every intersection. The murder of the Surgeon was no small matter in this city of a million and a half people, restive under the twin threats of violence and repression. Two carabinieri checked my papers at the gates of Leporello's villa. There were two plainclothesmen inside the grounds. One of them opened the door of my car and delivered me to the front door, where a maid took charge and led me into the living room.

Leporello was alone. His handshake was firm and welcoming. A servant offered drinks. We toasted each other. Leporello made a joking reference to the security men. I said I thought them a wise precaution. Then the ladies came in—and it was as if the roof had fallen on my head. The woman in Roditi's photograph was the wife of General Leporello.

I stammered a greeting and bent over her hand in a panic of embarrassment. It is one thing to look into a woman's cleavage when you know she has put it on show for you. It is quite another to look into her eyes when you have read her love letters.

Fortunately the other lady provided a diversion. Laura Balestra was a lively blonde with big, bedroom eyes, a little-girl smile and a talent for chitchat. She loved dressy men. She hated stuffy soldiers. She had just come back from Austria, where she had almost fallen in love with a ski instructor. Didn't I love Elena's dress and wasn't this a beautiful villa? I was so grateful for her chattering I wanted to kiss her. Then she turned to Leporello and left me to my hostess.

Elena Leporello was a beautiful woman, with large, lustrous dark eyes and dark, straight tresses drawn back over her ears and braided behind the head. I wondered how a ramrod like the general had managed to marry her. She was wondering about me, too. "You're older than I expected, Colonel."

"I try hard to conceal it, madam."

"I didn't mean that. My husband likes to surround himself with very young officers."

"Oh? I've only met one member of the staff, Captain Roditi."

"Do you know him well?"

"Hardly at all. We've met only three times, very briefly."

"He's rather exceptional. He's been with my husband for seven years. My husband tells me you're to join his staff."

"The general has suggested it."

"You don't like the idea?"

"I have some reservations I'll be discussing with him."

"You're very discreet."

"In my business I have to be discreet."

"Oh, yes. You're something in intelligence, aren't you?"

"That's right."

"Do you like your work?"

"Not always. It destroys one's illusions too quickly."

"Do you have any left, Colonel?"

"Some. And you?"

"Ask me some other time."

Dinner was announced at that moment. If I guessed my lady right, she was playing a reckless game of spite-my-husband. At table she found a dozen subtle ways of flattering me and denigrating Leporello as he expressed his earnest wish to have me on his staff. I had the impression that he was afraid of her, and that she, knowing it, was prepared to push him to the limit of endurance. Tiring of their game, I began to devise one of my own. "By the way, General, did you know someone tried to kill me in Venice?"

He was a good actor. He choked on his wine, silenced the women's excited exclamations with a gesture and demanded a full account of the affair.

I shrugged it off. "Well, I'd just dined with the Director and Cavaliere Manzini. I was on my way to Harry's Bar to meet a girl, and three men waylaid me in an alley. I fired some shots, and they ran away."

"This worries me, Colonel. This kind of violence is becoming epidemic. You heard what happened in Milan last night?"

"I was there, General."

He was not acting now. He gaped at me, fish-eyed. I explained with elaborate discretion. "You won't find my name in your reports because I slipped out before the panic started—to avoid embarrassing questions."

"And you saw nothing?"

"Only the bodies when the lights went up. It was obviously a professional job. I wouldn't push the inquiries too hard."

"That's an odd thing to say, Colonel."

"Not really, General. Both sides stand to gain. The Left have their victim, and you're rid of a discreditable nuisance."

Elena Leporello was quick to see the point and turn it against us both. "That sounds like a loaded proposition, Colonel."

"Not at all. It's a statement of fact—unless you want me to say that your husband approved of sadism in police interrogations. However, I agree it's not a thing one shouts in public."

Leporello brightened and nodded a vigorous approval. "Very proper, Matucci. Our public image is very important at this time."

"And what do you think of the image, Colonel?" Elena was persistent. "I get the impression it's rather tarnished just now."

"In some respects. But your husband's reputation is growing."

"His reputation for what, Colonel?"

"Firm policy, decisive action. I was at the Bankers' Club the other night, General. Your speech had made a big impression. These riot squads you are training—"

"Where did you hear about those, Colonel?"

"They're talked about in every bar in town, General."

"It's supposed to be a secret project."

"I assure you it isn't anymore."

"Could you name me any places where you've heard this talk?"

"The Duca di Gallodoro, the Hilton bar, the Alcibiade . . ."

The general developed a sudden interest in the strawberry flan. Laura Balestra quizzed me pertly. "The Alcibiade? And what were you doing there, Colonel?"

"Just looking."

"Did you find what you were looking for?"

"Yes. I found a man I've been chasing for weeks."

"I didn't think you could find a man in that place."

"Indeed, yes. I was there. Captain Roditi was there."

"Matteo?" Elena addressed the question to Leporello.

"Don't ask me, my dear," said the general, smiling. "I wasn't there. . . . Now, if you don't mind, the colonel and I will take coffee in the library."

No sooner were we alone than his manner changed. He was every inch the soldier again, curt, decisive. "Matucci, why do you hesitate to join me?"

"Two reasons to begin with: I want to finish my leave, and I want to test myself in civilian employment with Bruno Manzini."

"Manzini's a dangerous rogue. He has blackmailed people into suicide. Before you leave this evening I shall give you copies of two dossiers to study and return to me. You will come to your own conclusions."

"You seem sure mine will agree with yours."

"We'll see. If you join me, you may finish your leave first."

"That's very fair."

"Now, as to the post itself. You would be required to set up a completely new section, subject only to me, for political intelligence in the widest sense. If certain events take place, your position would be one of considerable power. Interested?"

"So far, very. Can you specify the events, General?"

"I can, when I am sure of your political affiliation."

"Which should be of what nature, General?"

"I need a very conservative man."

"That could be a contradiction in terms. Intelligence deals both with the actual and the possible. I could quote the Director—"

"Would it help if I told you that the Director has become a very conservative man?"

"I already know that, sir."

"What do you know?"

"The meeting was held at the Villa Baldassare, was it not?"

"How the devil—"

"I told you I dined with the Director and Manzini."

"What did they tell you?"

"Let's say I was made aware of certain situations. For instance, that there had been a discussion as to whether I should be eliminated. There were two votes against, one for killing me—your vote, General. So you see, I'm rather puzzled by your offer."

I had thought to shake him. But as soldier and strategist he was impregnable. He reproved me quietly. "Why? You know the trade. We're all at risk. I voted yes. Then I changed my mind."

"Why?"

"I have always regarded the Director as a useful but fickle ally. After that meeting I concluded I needed a rival, and an ultimate substitute for him. You, my dear Colonel. Simple, isn't it?"

"Too simple. Everyone carries life insurance except me. Manzini has wealth and influence. The Director has a presidential appointment. You have the rank of general in the carabinieri. Me? I'm out on the limb of the cherry tree."

"Join me and you will have my personal protection, Colonel."

"I was thinking of the Surgeon. He's dead."

"I wasn't protecting him. You said it yourself: the man was a discreditable nuisance. More brandy?"

"Thank you. Do you mind if I ask a few questions?"

"Please!"

"This aide of yours, Captain Roditi. Explain him to me."

I had touched him on the raw. He was suddenly tense and threatening. "I think you should explain yourself, Colonel."

"You want me to join you. But I am not prepared to come in blind. Roditi, I hear, is a court favorite. He is resented. Because of him you are resented, too. I want to know why."

He considered that. Finally he said, "Roditi is dispensable. You come, he goes, if that's what you want."

"What was he doing at the Alcibiade?"

"He recruits there."

"I'm curious to know why you're using these types."

"We need men without ties, with no ambition beyond money and the companionship of their own kind. They, too, will be dispensable, like mercenaries."

"General, if you were I, would you accept that answer?"

"If I were you, I should not expect to have all the words spelled out for me."

"Fair comment, General. However, you offer me patronage. I have to know where the power lies, and the weakness, too."

"I'm listening."

"Your marriage is obviously unhappy. You must be very lonely."

"I am. I confess that these are desert days for me, Matucci."

"So you lean on Roditi?"

"More than I should, perhaps. He's become like a son to me. But I need someone much stronger, much wiser. You, my friend."

"But you're still not prepared to trust me. Please, General, let's not play games. There's a dossier on you at SID. The Director knows what's in it. I don't, because he has always reserved it to himself. You want to set me up against him, but I'm impotent unless I know what weapons he can use against you. Why don't you think about that? If you still want me, we can talk again."

"You might decide not to join me after all."

"And you might decide to withdraw your protection. In which case I could end like the Surgeon. If that happened, there is a data bank in Switzerland which would immediately circulate a lot of information to the press and other interested parties."

"Blackmail, Colonel?"

"No, General. Simply insurance. Look, I didn't ask for this job. If you're unhappy with my terms, let's forget it."

"Let's define them more clearly."

"Full disclosure on both sides?"

"Very well. I'll be in touch with you again in a few days. Meantime, you can study the two dossiers and judge Manzini's role. More brandy?"

"No, thank you. I should get home. It's been a long day."

"Not too unprofitable, I hope?"

"Far from it, General. I think we've come a long way."

"Good. By the way, would you mind dropping Laura in town?"

"Not at all. I'd be delighted."

"She's a cheerful soul—and unattached. A word to the wise, eh?"

Cheerful she was, and she chattered like a featherbrain in the car. "You know, you were very naughty, Dante. You're the first man I've ever seen who could handle Elena when she had her claws out for Leporello. You don't really want to work for him, do you? With all those *finocchi* he has around him? Did you see Elena's face when you dropped that hot brick about Roditi at the Alcibiade? My dear man, everybody knows they're lovers—even the general. Matteo has to be the father of their five-year-old twins. . . . Why? Oh, come on, Matucci! Why do you think the old boy uses Matteo to do all his dirty work? Look, I know Elena! I'll make a bet with you. If she doesn't call you in the next twenty-four hours, I'll give you a night in bed myself."

"No bet. You're already invited. There's champagne and—"

"And Elena will hate me ever after. She's wild for you."

"You told me she was wild for Roditi."

"Oh, that's special. The others—and there have been a lot—are her revenge on her husband. If you join him, she'll get you to bed if she has to scream murder to do it."

"She sounds like a candidate for the madhouse!"

"Who wouldn't be, married to a middle-aged homo with delusions of grandeur? Now, tell me about *your* love life, Colonel."

As it turned out, three glasses of champagne put Laura out cold. I tucked her into bed, stuck a get-well note to the bathroom mirror and closed the door on her.

It was now one in the morning in Milan, where, if her citizens are to be believed, money will buy you anything, day or night. My needs were essentially simple: an atomizer and a one-eyed notary, deaf and dumb and very greedy. Even with my contacts it took me an hour to find him and a hundred thousand lire to coax him out of his house.

At three fifteen, armed and accompanied by said notary, I presented myself at the apartment of Captain Roditi. The captain was out. I entered, closed the notary in the bedroom to doze awhile, made myself a cup of coffee and settled down to wait. At three forty-five, not quite sober, Roditi came home. I pushed him against the wall while I patted him for concealed weapons. Then I sat him in the Danish armchair and perched myself on the desk, with the pistol and the atomizer beside me.

"Captain, you may be tempted to think I am playing games. I am not. If you don't give me truthful answers, I shall spray hydrocyanic-acid gas in your face, and you will be dead in four seconds. If you cooperate, I may offer you a way out of the mess you're in now. Clear?"

"Yes."

"In your bedroom there is a photograph of a woman and a bundle of love letters from someone called Elena. Who is Elena?"

"She's the wife of General Leporello."

"How long have you been lovers?"

"About six years."

"Are you the father of her children?"

"I believe so."

"Does the general know of your association?"

"Yes."

"And condones it?"

"Yes. It gives him a hold over both of us."

"Explain that."

"He is the legal father of the children. His name is on the registration of birth. He could remove them from Elena's custody."

"And what is his hold over you?"

"I have procured for him. I am therefore in legal jeopardy."

"Inside or outside the service?"

"Both. I have an apartment, near the cathedral, which he uses. I pay the people and make sure there's no trouble afterward."

"How do you do that?"

"Threats mostly. Action, if necessary."

"You have people beaten up, that sort of thing?"

"Yes."

"Do you know Major Zenobio, the commandant at Camerata?"

"Yes."

"Have you heard from him today?"

"There was a message to call him. I haven't done it yet."

"Did you get a letter from Chiasso today?"

"Yes."

"Did the general get one?"

"Yes."

"What did you do about them?"

"I sent them to forensics to have the fingerprint and the typewriting checked."

"Did you know whose print it was?"

"It could have belonged to Balbo."

"Did he kill Bandinelli and Calvi?"

"Yes."

"Did he plant a letter bomb in the apartment of one Lili Anders?"

"Yes."

"Who gave the orders?"

"I did."

"Who gave you your orders?"

"The general."

"Where are the Pantaleone papers?"

"I gave them to Leporello."

"Where are they now?"

"I don't know. Possibly at his house."

"Where is Giuseppe Balbo?"

"I think he's dead. The general told me to take him to the Alcibiade tonight and make sure we left at two forty-five."

"Who was going to do the job?"

"I don't know. He didn't tell me."

"Did you ever think he may want to get rid of you one day?"

"Yes."

"Did you never take out any insurance?"

"Yes. I had the other apartment bugged. Elena has one set of tapes and photographs. I have another in a safe-deposit box at the Banca Centrale."

"I'll need the key to that box and an authorization for access."

"Very well."

"How do you feel about Elena now?"

"I love her. Why else do you think I've stayed in this rotten business?"

"Because you didn't want to get out. If Leporello brings off his coup, you'll be a very big man."

"What are you going to do now?"

"Not I, Roditi, you! You're going to write a deposition. There's a man in your bedroom who will notarize the document. Then we'll talk about what's next. Now, I'll dictate. You write."

It took us half an hour. I then sent the notary on his drowsy way, had Roditi write a letter to his bank, stuffed the documents into my breast pocket and settled down to chat. Roditi was sallow and trembling, so I let him have a whiskey while I laid out the deal.

"You're going absent without leave, Roditi. You'll pack a bag. I'll drive you to a safe place in the country, and you'll stay there until I've built the last brick into my case against Leporello. You'll be interrogated. You'll make more depositions. But at least you won't be in jail, waiting for some cellmate to put a skewer in your back. Then, before the case breaks, you'll have twenty-four hours to get out of the country with Elena and the children. It's the best I can do. Take it or leave it."

"It's no good. It won't work."

"Have you got a better idea?"

"Yes. Leave me free until you've finished your case. I can feed you information. Things are going to happen fast now, Matucci."

"What sort of things?"

"I can't tell you yet. But I will as soon as I know."

"I'm sorry. I don't like it. Pack your bag now."

"I'm not going."

"Then you're going to tell me why."

"All right. You've been followed all evening. While your car was at the general's house, they fixed a bleeper on it."

"Which means they know where I am now?"

"Yes."

"So that's why it was all so easy, eh? They cut me down as I walk out the front door! Or they've taped the car with plastic explosive, and when I switch on the ignition it blows me sky-high. Now, which is it?"

"I don't know. I swear I don't know."

"Then let's find out." I dialed the SID office in Milan and spoke to the duty officer, quoting my identification number. "I am questioning a suspect. My car is parked outside the building. Red Mercedes with a Milan license. It has been bugged, and may be planted with an explosive device. It is also possible there may be an attempt to assassinate me as I go out. The suspect is an officer of carabinieri, so I'd rather not have them brought in. I don't care about the car, but I'll need another vehicle to use. When you're ready, send a man up to this apartment. Code word, Dragon. Hurry, please. Oh, for safety, check me back on this number as soon as I hang up."

He checked and told me the boys would be with me in thirty

minutes. A lot could happen in that time. I switched off the lights and looked out the window. It was already happening. Three police cars were parked outside the building, another was pulling in. The plot was clear: arrest and ninety-two hours' detention on any charge in the book. I could think of two that would stick—breaking and entering, and withholding information on the killing of the Surgeon. By the time I got out, if ever, the deposition would have disappeared into thin air.

I hauled Roditi to his feet, thrust a wadded handkerchief into his mouth, poked my gun into his kidneys and prodded him up four flights of stairs to the roof. I locked the roof door from the outside; then I faced Roditi against it and chopped him hard on the back of the skull. He went down like a sack. I dragged him into the shelter of the water tanks and took the gag out of his mouth so he wouldn't choke. He had a lot more talking to do, if ever I could get out of this very neat trap.

A cautious circuit of the roof showed me that I could get across to the next two roofs and escape through the third building. But it would be impossible to take Roditi with me. So I left him, and a few minutes later I found myself in a deserted office building. There I waited until morning, wondering what had happened to Roditi and whether anyone had bothered to check the rooftop. When the workers began to arrive, I walked out into the crowded, sunlit streets and took a taxi to Steffi's hotel.

Steffi in crisis was a treasure. While I bathed and shaved he went out and made copies of the depositions on a coin-in-the-slot duplicator. He deposited the original document in the Milan office of his bank for safekeeping. After that he took one of the copies to Manzini and presented it to him with my compliments. The pair of them then came to the hotel for breakfast, chatting as if they had known each other all their lives.

Breakfast, however, was a sober meal. Manzini telephoned the editor of his newspaper, and came back with two stories which would be featured in the afternoon editions. One dealt with a gun battle in which Giuseppe Balbo, a suspect in the murders at the

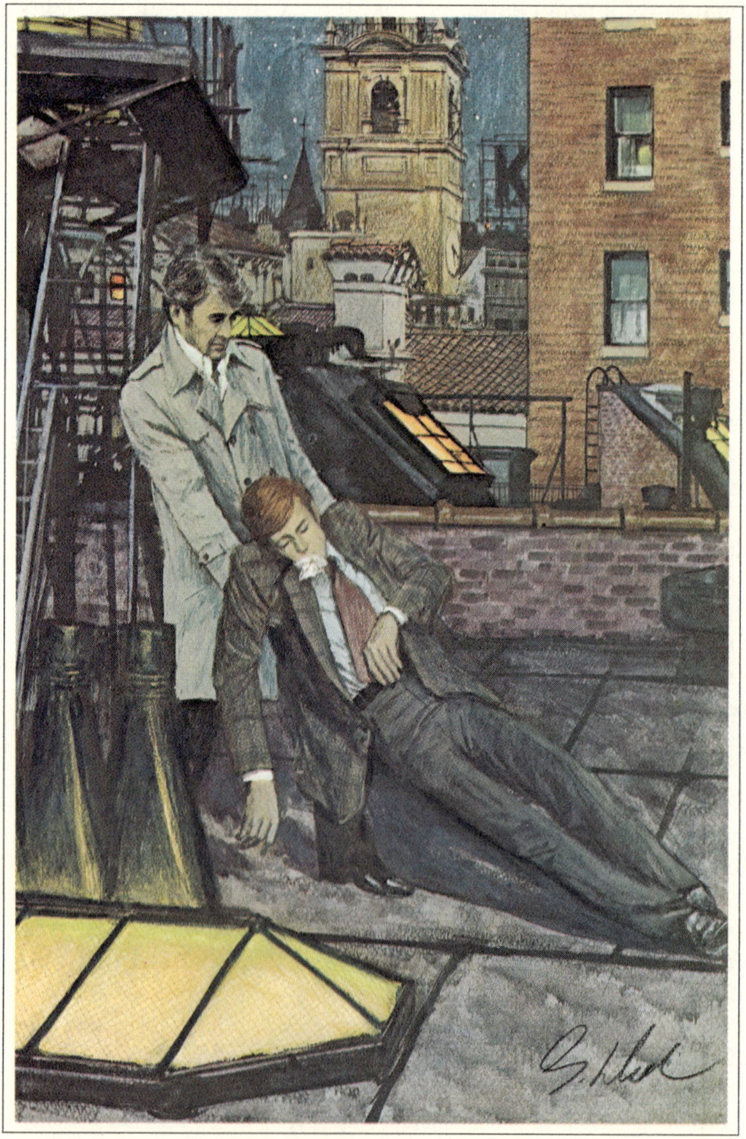
K

Duca di Gallodoro, had been killed while resisting arrest. The other was an account of a mysterious occurrence in a fashionable apartment building. Answering an anonymous telephone call, the police had visited the apartment of Captain Matteo Roditi, personal aide to Major General Leporello. The apartment was empty and in disorder. The captain, at press time, was still missing. The police had detained one man who was known to have visited the apartment in the early hours of the morning. They were seeking Dante Matucci, member of a government agency, whose car was parked outside the building and whose fingerprints were found in the apartment. There was a photograph of me.

"And that, gentlemen," said Manzini flatly, "disposes of our case. Balbo is dead. Roditi is dead or in protective custody. His deposition is worthless, because they will get out of your notary a signed counter-deposition proving duress. You, my Dante, are now a man on the run."

"You're forgetting something, Bruno. I have a key and Roditi's authorization to open his safe-deposit box at the Banca Centrale. If he was telling me the truth, what's in that box can finish Leporello."

Manzini was not cheered. "How do you plan to get to that box? You'd have to present identification, and an hour from now your description will be all over Milan. Which also means we've got to get you out of here fast."

"You have that authorization signed by Roditi to work with. You have a very good calligrapher in Carlo Metaponte, who did your salamander card. And you have your friend Ludovisi right in the Banca Centrale. Well, Bruno . . . ?"

"It depends on Ludovisi, doesn't it? I'll try him. Give me that authorization and the key. Now, Matucci, what are we going to do with you?"

"I'll have to go underground. I'll need the false papers which are in the safe at the apartment."

"I'll get them. Meantime, where do we put you?"

"Could you keep me at Pedognana for a couple of days?"

"Not in the house. I think we might have a visit from the carabinieri. On the estate, certainly, if you don't mind a little peasant living. What about Stefanelli here?"

"I'll stay in town, Cavaliere. This oaf needs an old hand more than he admits."

I thanked Steffi. "When I call, I'm Rabin. It should be a lucky name for us all."

Manzini ignored this. "What if Ludovisi won't play?"

"Then there's one last hope—Leporello's wife."

"When she reads that report, she'll think you killed or kidnapped Roditi."

"The report came from her husband. I don't think she'd believe him if he told her the day of the week."

"It's an awful gamble."

"I know a worse one," said Steffi somberly. "Leporello for *duce* and his bullyboys keeping order with truncheons."

I SPENT four days at Pedognana, lodged in the attic of the farm manager's house. The carabinieri prowled the estate all one afternoon; I was in a barn loft acquiring a dose of hay fever. On the fourth day Manzini arrived with my false papers and clothes to fit my new identity as one Aldo Carnera, a traveling salesman with a Manzini company. If anyone checked, the name and personal details were on file there.

He brought discouraging news, too. Ludovisi was in New York on his way to Mexico, and he was not expected back for ten days. Manzini was fretful. All his careful plans for me were now in ruins, and because of me he had fallen into some discredit with the movement. He was excluded from its inner councils. The Director had sent him a caustic note suggesting that he might confine his activities for now to financial contribution.

We dined together that night, and I tried to coax him into his anecdotal mood, but he refused to be drawn out until I mentioned the two dossiers Leporello had given to me, which I had not yet read. But I remembered the names: Hans Helmut Ziegler and Emanuele Salatri. He mused over them for a moment and then cast off his ill humor like a cloak.

"Eh! What is the past for, if not to renew our hope in the future? The Ziegler file. That story began in 1930. I was in Saõ Paulo then, spending my first big money. One night in a gambling club I was standing next to a Brazilian about my own age. By midnight he was cleaned out. He looked so disconsolate that I invited him to share a stake with me—just for luck—and we won. We walked away, arm in arm, friends for life. He is now one of the biggest bankers in Brazil, Paulo Pinto. When he got his first directorship he sent me a souvenir of that night—an emerald. I had it set in a brooch for Raquela Rabin.

"The second part of the story is much later. Hans Helmut Ziegler was the Gestapo man who worked me over in prison. After the war he disappeared. In 1965 my old friend Pinto sent me his daughter's wedding photograph. The man she had married was Hans Helmut Ziegler. It took me two years' work and twenty thousand dollars to build the dossier on him. I sent it to him with a salamander card. He drove himself over a cliff at high speed. When Pinto read the dossier, he thought the Israelis had killed him. He called in the Brazilian police, and they sent the dossier to Interpol. Eventually it was tracked to me, by way of the Italian authorities—which is, I suppose, how it came into Leporello's hands.

"That ought to be the end of the story, my Dante, but it isn't. In the days before the Black Sabbath the Jews of Rome believed they had a deal with the Germans to ransom themselves. A fund was set up to which everyone contributed gold, jewelry, whatever they had. But the Germans took the collection and the people as well. Raquela had given her emerald brooch to one of the collectors, a man called Emanuele Salatri. He vanished with the loot. In 1969 there was an auction of jewelry in Zurich. Among the pieces in the catalogue was that brooch. I traced it to a prosperous gem dealer in London, one Emanuele Salatri. I sent him a dossier and a card. He blew his brains out. Again the dossier was traced to me. Again I had committed no crime.

"Old history! Am I wrong to dig it up? I have thought so many times. Always though, I come back to the same question: why should the villains flourish while the victims still suffer the effects of their villainies? This is your question now, Matucci. It is possible that Leporello could wade through a whole ocean of crimes and still become a good ruler. But even if he did, should we still suffer him? Even if he came now in sackcloth and ashes, should we in one breath forgive him his crimes and consecrate him to power? I cannot see it."

IT WAS late when we went to bed that night. And I didn't sleep. I sat up, desperately lonely, and wrote to Lili; not from Uncle Pavel this time, but from Dante Matucci, fugitive.

My dearest Lili,

This letter is from your puppet-man, who has discovered, late and painfully, how little he can control his own destiny. I tore up your last letter because I wanted to put you out of my mind until all this business was finished. It was no use. I cannot bear the empty room in my heart. I am jealous that you may have found someone to take my place in yours. I love you, Lili. There now! It is said. Will you marry me? Don't answer until you are sure; because when you are sure and I am free, I shall follow you to the last frontiers.

Things have gone badly for us, but there is still hope of a good outcome. Tomorrow I go back into the underworld, a man on the run looking for something left by a man I think is dead. If I find it, all will be well. If not, I'm likely to turn up in Switzerland sooner than you expect.

I am afraid, but not too afraid, because I am learning slowly to live with the man who lives in my skin. And I am learning from the Salamander the art of survival. . . . You will smile, but I never thought I could survive so long without a woman's company. Perhaps the truth is that my woman is never so far absent that I am without her utterly.

Strange how the words of that poet namesake of mine come back: 'She who makes my mind a paradise.' Old Dante said some very good things in his day. A pity he didn't write more about the body. That's very lonely just now.

Always yours,
Dante

I have the letter still, because it was returned to me in circumstances which belong later in this record.

I GOT in touch with Gisela Pestalozzi in Venice. The safe apartment was a little gem: with a front entrance on a quiet alley, a rear one from which you could step straight into a boat, and an attic window from which you could climb over the rooftops. I paid two months' rent in cash.

Then I began the approach to Elena Leporello. She was my last chance. If I lost on her, I might as well head for the Alps at once. Telephoning her in Milan was risky, but to write a note or have Steffi accost her in the street would be much more so. I decided to telephone. A maid answered.

"May I speak with the general, please?" I asked.

"The general is not home. I suggest you try headquarters."

"This is headquarters. Is the *signora* at home?" I waited a very long moment, and when Elena came on the line I talked fast and eloquently.

"Please, madam, do not hang up until I have finished. This is Dante Matucci. There is an order out for my arrest. I have been in hiding for several days. I do not know whether Captain Roditi is alive or dead. Can you tell me, please?"

"I can't tell you, not at this moment."

"The reports give the impression that I either kidnapped him or murdered him. Neither is true. If he is alive, I must find him. Are you willing to talk to me?"

"Yes."

"When?"

"Any day between ten and six."

"Thank you. Now listen, carefully. At ten thirty tomorrow morning go to the Ambrosian Library. Say you want to look at Petrarch's Virgil. A friend of mine will contact you then and bring you to me in your own car. Are you being watched?"

"I don't know."

"If you think you are, don't keep the appointment. The same arrangement will stand for three days. My friend will ask, 'Are you

Raquela Rabin?' You will answer, 'Yes!' Then do whatever he asks. Expect to be out of town all afternoon."

"I understand that. Thank you. Good-by."

So far, so good; but how far is far when you are dealing with a woman practiced in intrigue? I called Steffi to tell him about my plan to get Roditi's tapes and photographs from Elena.

"Matucci, little brother," Steffi said dolefully, "hear what an old married man has to tell you. This woman is sick. Worse, she knows it and loves it. She needs a husband she can kick around and humiliate. If he's a big shot, so much the better. She needs—and has got—a lover of the same kind. Now you come waltzing to her party all done up like a wedding cake. You're new, you're male. She has to prove she can make you eat out of her hand, too. She's got something you want—even if it's not what she'd like you to want—and she's going to make you sit up and beg. And beg, and beg. And if you won't, she'll turn you in, just to show you who holds the whip."

"She has got something I want. How do I get it?"

"A woman like that, with a dirty story and pictures to match, isn't going to keep it to her lonely self. She has to tell it. Figure who shares it with her. Crack that source, and threaten Elena you'll tell her husband."

Laura Balestra, I thought. She might well know where the stuff was. But Elena would not react to such a threat by handing the stuff to me. "No, I don't buy that," I said. "You get Elena to Venice, buy her a sandwich in St. Mark's Square and leave when I turn up. Wait for me at the safe house."

At two o'clock the next afternoon, dressed in slacks and a green pullover and carrying the papers of Aldo Carnera, I walked to St. Mark's Square. Steffi saw me coming and left.

Elena gave me a frosty welcome. "I hope, Colonel, there is some sense in this sordid little drama."

"I hope so, too, madam. Have you heard from Captain Roditi?"

"Not a word."

"Does your husband know where he is?"

"No. He knows, from the notary, that you forced Matteo to

write a false and incriminating document, then had him killed or kidnapped."

"Has your husband seen the document?"

"He hasn't said so."

"Would you like to see it?"

"Please."

I handed her a copy of Roditi's confession and watched her closely as she read it. The color drained from her face. She trembled violently and I thought for a moment she was going to faint. By the time she had finished she was in control of herself again, and the sudden mastery of her emotions was frightening to see. She faced me, cold-eyed and contemptuous.

"That's a tissue of lies, Colonel, monstrous, horrible lies. Dictated by you—the notary heard you from the bedroom."

"Are you sure it's false? You and Roditi were not lovers?"

"Of course not."

"I read your letters, madam. I saw your signed photograph."

"There are no letters, Colonel."

"You mean they were removed on your husband's orders. Not all. I have one in my pocket now. The photograph was taken by Donati in Bologna. He made a copy for me. Let me tell you something else. Roditi was a friend of Giuseppe Balbo, who was killed by the police a few nights ago. I met them together at the Alcibiade. No, madam, I'm not lying. You are. Why? Are you afraid of your husband?"

"No, Colonel."

"Roditi told me you have photographs and tapes which prove against your husband all the charges in that document. He said they were your only insurance against your husband."

"I have no such material. And I need no insurance."

"Why? Because Roditi's dead? Or your husband's giving up his little games? What about you? What sort of woman are you?"

"I'll tell you the sort of woman I am, Colonel. If my husband is clever enough to handle this mess, he's clever enough to climb to the top of the tree. I want to be there, too. If he can't make it . . . Well, there's always another day for me."

"You can settle your future now, madam. There's a policeman over there, and two carabinieri in front of the cathedral. Call them. Tell them who I am and have me arrested."

"No, my dear Colonel, I'm not sure yet how clever you are and whether you're a match for my husband. It's a game, don't you see? I'm the privileged spectator. I could even enjoy an hour in bed with you now. No? Another time, perhaps. Which reminds me, did you hear about Laura?"

"Hear what?"

"She drove her car into a tree last night. She drinks too much, you know. She may live, but as no more than a vegetable. Pity! She was such a pretty girl. Good-by, Colonel."

She offered me her hand. I could not take it. I watched her walk away, head high, hips swinging, jaunty as any girl on the beat. The pigeons rose in clouds as she passed, and the waiter, counting my change, sighed at the waste of so much woman.

IT WAS all defeat and disaster. Steffi summed it up.

"Checkmate, little brother. Your last hope—and it's a slim one—is the safe-deposit box. I wish I could help you. I can't. I'm going home. Call if you need me. But take some advice. Leave this to Manzini, and you cut out to Switzerland. You're in a trap. I'm fond of you, Matucci, God knows why, and I don't want to see you lopped off before you grow up."

I called Manzini, and he, too, advised Switzerland. He sounded tired and spiritless, and I wondered about his health. When I put down the phone I found myself in the grip of a violent reaction. I slammed about Gisela's apartment in a frenzy of frustration. It was incredible that with so much evidence we could do nothing. It was monstrous that an individual could manipulate an arm of the law to make it an instrument of crime. It shamed me that an unprincipled man could turn me into a fugitive while his wife sat laughing. To hell with it! I would not be forced to flee like a criminal. I would stay!

How I was going to stay was another matter. I needed to think that one out over a meal and a bottle of wine, and I was not going to sit here afraid to poke my nose outside the door. I strolled out and found a simple place where the food smelled good. The night was balmy, so I sat outside. I ordered a risotto and a dish of seafood and a bottle of red wine. I was settling down to enjoy it when two carabinieri picked me up like an orange from a basket and carted me off to headquarters.

They took me straight to the commandant. He looked at my papers, and I assured him that I was indeed the Aldo Carnera, traveling salesman, described in them. Was I charged with some offense? He assured me I was not. It was simply a question of the green pullover. Had I been in St. Mark's Square that afternoon? I had. Ah! That was it.

I begged to know what was so special about a green pullover. He admitted that he could see nothing special in it. However, a woman who declined to give her name had telephoned them; she had identified a man wearing such a garment as one Dante Matucci, wanted for questioning in Milan. She had seen his photograph in the papers.

The commandant brought out a photograph of me and a set of fingerprints from the SID files. I smiled and he smiled, and we agreed it was the luck of the game. I asked whether I might make a telephone call. He produced an order stating that if Colonel Matucci were apprehended, he should be held incommunicado. He was going to telephone Milan now. He hated to do this to a senior colleague. He begged me to make myself comfortable until he returned.

A wink being as good as a nod, I used the telephone on his desk and dialed Manzini. He was out. His servant took the message. At least the old man would know what had happened.

The commandant was gone a long time. He came back looking grave and preoccupied. I was now, he said, formally under arrest. I must surrender all my belongings, for which he would issue a receipt. His orders were to detain me overnight, and to send me, in the morning, to Milan.

A *brigadiere* escorted me to the detention cell. A turnkey locked me in. About fifteen minutes later the *brigadiere* returned, accompanied by a guard and a man in a white coat carrying a kidney dish covered with a towel. He introduced himself as the police surgeon and asked me to roll up my sleeve for a sedative. I winced at the prick of the needle and began counting one, two, three . . .

Then all the lights went out.

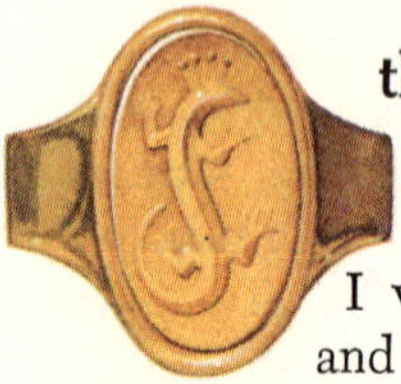

three

I WOKE—or dreamed I woke—in absolute darkness and absolute silence. I was—or dreamed I was—floating in undetermined space in a timeless continuum. I was not sad; I was not happy; I was not in pain; I simply was. At first that was enough. Then I began to be uneasy, faintly at first, then more and more acutely. Something was absent. I could not define what it was. My mind was a swirl of mist and I was groping, without hands, into nowhere.

The mist dispersed slowly in drifts and eddies. I began to collect the scattered parts of myself. My thumb encountered my fingertips. My tongue met my palate. My eyelids blinked. Somewhere out in the fog my feet brushed one against the other. Then the parts became a whole, and I was aware that my body and I were still together. I was there, naked and lying on a hard, flat surface.

Then panic engulfed me. I was buried alive. I was blind. I was deaf. I was dumb. When I cried out, no sound would issue from my parched, constricted throat. I broke out into a sweat of terror. Slowly the panic subsided until, mercifully, it was no longer a madness. Now at least I knew I had a mind and must, somehow, begin to use it.

First I directed my fingers to explore my environment. The slab on which I lay felt like marble. It terminated a few centimeters on either side of my body; above and all around was empty space. Below it my fingers encountered a floor, rough to the touch and colder than my slab. How far it stretched I did not know. Enough that I had found a foothold in reality.

Now I must make a search of my inward self, testing for time holds and memory pegs. This was more difficult. At last one memory held: a woman walking through a cloud of pigeons, a man in a green pullover sitting at a table watching her. I could go on from that. I could go back from it. I found myself weeping quietly in the dark. The tears were good. They fell like oil on the panic waters. When they were spent, I knew that I was still a man. I knew what had happened to me and what would happen very soon.

Of all the intricate instruments of torture men have devised, none is so potent as darkness and silence. My namesake, Dante Alighieri, wrote a poem about hell which is one of the world's classics. I stand to witness that he didn't know what he was talking about. Hell is a dark and silent room. Damnation means to be locked inside it—alone.

I can tell you what happens because it happened to me. It was the subtlest vengeance any man could contrive against another. . . . You say to yourself, I know who I am. I know what they are trying to do to me. I will not let them. I will live inside my skull and hold fast to the facts I know. I know they will have to give me food, or at least water.

Someone will come, if only to gloat; else why take all this trouble to torment me when it would have been so simple to put a bullet in my head.

Nobody comes. You discover in your first circuit of the walls that they have left three plastic demijohns of water, enough to keep you alive for a long, long time. You discover, too, that the world inside your skull won't stay in focus. You grasp for one memory and find another. You hallucinate constantly. If they came, you would not know whether they were real or not.

This is the trick of it, you see. They do come, but you do not know. They scoop you up from the floor and pump barbiturates into you to continue the hallucination. They drip enough glucose into your veins to keep you alive, and they feed you with enough new fears to derange you. I learned later that I was there fifteen days. When they brought me out I was blind for a while, and dumb and ataxic, shambling like an animal, bearded, and filthy.

I was put under deep sedation for forty-eight hours, and when I came out of it I was sure I had died and arrived, by some cosmic mistake, in paradise.

THERE was so much light, I could only bear it for the shortest while. Always, when I opened my eyes there was a pretty nurse in the room. She told me her name was Claudia. Whenever the light began to fade I'd become fretful, scared that it would go out altogether. But it never did. Always another nurse came in and turned on the lamps, and even when I slept there was always a small light burning. The night nurse was not as pretty as Claudia, but she was gentle and patient. Sometimes I couldn't stop talking. At others I was morose and silent, unable to change the fixed and horrible trend of my thoughts.

Every day the doctor examined me and chatted for a while about my illness, a psychic disfunction which would cure itself, he told me, with patience, a little sedation and the simple therapy of human communication. When I asked where I was, he said simply that I was in his clinic. I told him I had difficulty remembering, and that I couldn't concentrate even on a page of print. This, he explained, was the natural response of an organism taxed beyond endurance. It simply refused to function until it was rested and ready. When I asked whether I was still under arrest, he smiled and told me that I was free.

Gradually I began to take hold of the realities around me, but distant realities were still vague. I thought about Lili and Manzini and Steffi, but I could neither grasp them as present nor regret them as absent. Leporello, his wife, the Director, were so vague as to be almost irrelevant. I knew only that in some fashion I had survived them.

When they allowed me out of bed for the first time, I was astonished to find how weak I was. The short walk to the window left me dizzy and trembling. Even the view outside proved a shock. I saw it first in a single dimension. Then, quite suddenly, it fell into perspective. There was a terrace, set with cane chairs and bright umbrellas. Beyond was a lawn, flower gardens, and then a wall of cypresses, dark against a limpid sky. But it told me nothing. There were no people, no landmarks. After a few moments I was glad to go back to bed.

When I woke, the night-light was burning and Bruno Manzini was standing at the foot of my bed. He came and took my hands between his own and held them a long time in a wordless greeting. Suddenly I was weeping. Manzini wiped the tears from my cheeks with his handkerchief. Then he perched on the bed and talked me back to composure.

"It's been a rough road, my Dante. But you've survived it. In a week or so I'm taking you to Pedognana. You'd like that?"

"I would. I feel so lost. What's the matter with me?"

"You've had your season in hell. It takes time to recover."

"I suppose so. Where is this place?"

"Near Como. It's a small psychiatric clinic. I finance it. . . . Oh, don't worry, you're quite sane; but you wouldn't have been if they'd held you much longer."

"How did I get here?"

"I brought you. It took me ten days and a lot of bribery to find you. Then I had to get a judicial order for your release, which was harder. You're on provisional liberty, of course. Charges still lie against you."

"I can't imagine why Leporello let me go."

"He was convinced you were broken beyond repair. And the movement would have lost a large check from me. He may still get you into court. Fortunately, we now have medical evidence of your treatment, and I don't think he wants that revealed just yet."

"Everything's in pieces. I—I can't put them together."

"You put it all together before this happened. We have in our hands your notes on the microfilms, the tapes and photographs from the safe-deposit in the bank. We can break Leporello now—and the Director after him."

"Do you know what happened to Roditi?"

"Yes. They put him through the treatment, too. He'll be no danger to Leporello now and no use to anyone else."

"I'm afraid I'm not going to be much use to you, either."

"Listen to me, my Dante. You are a lucky man, too lucky to have pity for yourself. You cannot surrender now. You will not, because if you do, you hand the victory to Leporello, and all you have suffered will be useless."

"I'm so tired. . . ."

"Try a little hating, my friend. It's the best stimulant in the world. Relax now. I'll see you again in a few days."

I was glad to see him go. I wanted to feel sorry for myself. I deserved a little pity, and this old man had none.

The next day I sat for an hour on the terrace. The day after, I made my first circuit of the garden with my nurse. Then I was walking in the garden every morning, ambling like a monk in meditation, soaking up the sun. I was beginning to be a man once more. I could read for perhaps an hour at a time. Newspapers were brought to me, but these I did not open. The news was a responsibility which I was not yet ready to shoulder.

Then Manzini came again. He brought champagne and caviar and we made a picnic on the terrace, but I was wary of him. I did not want him to disturb my precarious comfort. He did not disturb it. He shattered it. "There is something you must know, my Dante. Lili Anders is in prison in Rome."

"No . . . it can't be true."

"It is. The Director called me yesterday to announce the good news. He asked me to pass it on to you."

"But why? How?"

"It seems you called her back, by telegram."

"How could I? I've been out of action for nearly four weeks."

"That's the way the Director tells it. You telegraphed that she was free to return, that you would meet her in Bolzano, where you were arranging to get married. She produced the telegram from her handbag when the frontier police looked her up in the black book and questioned her."

"It was a trap!"

"Of course. But she walked into it."

"We've got to get her out."

"How, my Dante? You collected the evidence against her and

broke the Woodpecker's network. You can hardly refute your own testimony, can you?"

"But the Director promised to let her go."

"He did. She came back. He's got her on illegal entry."

"What a stinking mess. I've got to get out of here, Bruno."

"If that's what you want, so be it."

We were halfway across the lawn when a thought stopped me in my tracks. I caught his arm and challenged him brutally. "Did you arrange this, Bruno?"

There was not a tremor in him. He stood straight and firm, staring me down. "Do you think me capable of it?"

"Yes, I do."

"Good. Then you have learned something."

"Did you do it?"

"I might have—if I had thought it useful. In fact, I did not. I think you fixed it yourself by your own talk, sometime in those fifteen days of disfunction. I know that you told things about me, because I've had to lie about them since—and we nearly missed the safe-deposit box. Leporello did get a judicial order to open it the day after we'd extracted the contents."

"Dear God! Oh, Bruno, I'm sorry!"

"Don't be sorry. Think about those who made a traitor out of you against your will."

"I'll kill the bastards!"

"Which is what they'll expect you to try—and if they take you a second time, there will be no escape. No, Dante, this time we'll do it my way. You're not setting foot outside the gate a minute before the doctor says you're ready."

The doctor was dubious. Under stress the disfunctions would again become acute. My memory would play tricks, concentration would lapse, I'd be subject to fits of depression and anxiety. He would let me go only if I understood the risks and would not force myself. It was easy to say I could handle it.

But with guilt for Lili's betrayal nagging at me, I lapsed into deep despondence the moment we drove out the clinic gates. Manzini let me brood for a while, and then he faced me with a blunt question. "How serious are you about this woman of yours?"

"I've asked her to marry me."

"When?"

"I wrote her just before I left Pedognana last time. I gave you the letter to mail through Chiasso."

"I thought you were supposed to be her uncle Pavel."

"I wasn't when I wrote the letter."

"Wasn't that rather foolish?"

"On the face of it, yes."

"So you don't know whether she wants to marry you or not?"

"No. Why?"

"I merely wondered. There's something else more important. I think we know the date of the *colpo di stato.*"

"When?"

"October thirty-first is being whispered among the initiates. And it checks with dates in the microfilms."

"That's five months ahead."

"Never count on time, Dante. It runs away too quickly. Leporello is a splendid organizer, and he's already intimidated or eliminated several important witnesses. As he thought he'd eliminated you. No, we have to move before summer."

"What do you want me to do?"

"For the moment, what the doctor ordered—rest. However, there is one thing you can do without prejudice to your health."

"What's that?"

"Entertain your friends. I assume you *have* friends of your own rank in the corps. Write a few letters. Make some phone calls. You've been ill. You'd like to see them sometime at Pedognana. We have plenty of guest rooms. There is riding and shooting. . . . They'll come."

"What are you looking for now, Bruno?"

"A praetorian guard. Ten men would be enough, so long as they were resolute and understood what was at stake. On your own showing, there's quite a bit of disaffection from Leporello and his policies."

"If you're asking me to stage a revolt of the armed forces, forget it. I'm not very bright at the moment, but that's madness."

"Who said anything about revolt? On the contrary, we need ten good men proud of the traditions of the corps, jealous of its honor and its oath; old-fashioned patriots who don't like seeing their fellow citizens kicked in the teeth and justice denied by perjured witness."

He would say no more then, and I was too tired to press him.

At cocktails that evening I discovered there was another guest at the villa: the Principessa Pia Faubiani. I was in no mood to lavish on this prima donna of Roman fashion the attention she very obviously demanded, but for Bruno's sake the least I could do was exert myself to be agreeable. I was amply rewarded. She was a witty and intelligent woman, with enough malice to survive in the rough world she exploited, and more than enough affection and good humor to spend on her friends. She was wearing the salamander pin from Fosco's exhibition, and when I commented on it she announced cheerfully, "It's a parting gift. This is my first and last season with Bruno. He's deserting me."

Manzini chuckled. "I've never deserted a woman in my life, and you know it. I'm just retiring from the field with honor. You're too young and I'm too old, my love, and I hate to be second best at anything. When do you open your show in Bologna, Pia?"

"Next Wednesday."

"And in Milan and Turin?"

"Each one ten days after the other."

"After that you're free. To do one last thing for me?"

"Not exactly free, darling. I have to go back to Rome, but . . ."

"I want you to hostess a party for me here for a couple of days. I've been promising to introduce Dante to people ever since he came to Milan. He's had a rough time, and I think he needs some diversion."

"Please, Bruno!" I said. "A party's the last thing I need."

"It may be the last one you'll get, Dante, if you go to trial. You'll do it for me, won't you, Pia?"

"You know I will."

"And if you see this fellow moping around like a barnyard owl, take him out, introduce him to your girls, seduce him yourself if you like, but bounce him out of his miseries, understand?"

"Your servant, Cavaliere."

"I wish you were, my love. Still, it's been fun, hasn't it?"

She laid a hand on his. "It's been fun, *caro*. I'm sorry about—"

"Enough, please! I'm tougher than they think. I've had a good life. And I'll tell you something—I've been in love, twice. That's more than enough for any man."

"I know about Raquela, darling. But who was the other one?"

"My wife."

We both stared. He gave us an odd, embarrassed little smile. "I've been thinking a lot about her lately, wondering if we'll meet again, and if we do will we recognize each other. I married her in Paris in 1934. She was nineteen. I was thirty-four. I had traveled all over the world and I thought she was the most beautiful creature in it. She fell in love with Pedognana at first sight. Ask some of the old ones, and you'll find how they still remember her. She was born to the land, and this place flowered under her hand in those two strange years.

"We were ludicrously happy. My affairs prospered, and Marie Claire became pregnant. For a man like me, who had never known a family life, this was like the announcement of the Second Coming. I was bubbling with wild plans for my son—because, of course, it had to be a son.

"In her fourth month Marie Claire fell sick and died within a week, of cerebrospinal meningitis. She's buried in the chapel. You'd have seen the inscription, Dante, if you'd bent that stubborn neck to pray. Marie Claire, beloved wife of Bruno . . . long ago and far away. Let's have coffee in the study. It's cozier there."

But when the coffee was brought he announced abruptly that he was going to bed. Pia made a move to go with him, but he pushed her gently back into her chair and bent to kiss her on the forehead. His tone was very tender. "Stay here, my love. I'm very tired. We'll talk tomorrow. Good night, my Dante."

When he had gone Pia Faubiani kicked off her shoes, curled herself in the armchair and gave a deep sigh of contentment. "I'm glad it's ended this way. I would hate to have hurt that man. He is—God bless him—very special."

"I know what you mean."

"He loves you, Dante."

"I know. He's told me."

"How do you feel about him?"

"I admire him. I fight him often. Sometimes I wish I could be like him. I never quite understand him. How sick is he?"

"He's not sick, really. His heart is tired. He could go quickly. I think he's more afraid of lingering too long. His big regret is having no son. Wasn't that a sad little story?"

"Very. It's the shortest story I've ever heard him tell. What are you going to do now?"

"Me? The same, with someone else's money. Give me a little sun and I can grow anywhere. Tell me about yourself."

"What is there to tell? I am an intelligence man who thought he could break the system. Instead the system broke me."

"You don't believe that."

"I do. Look at my hands. I can't hold a glass steady. Do you know why? I'm scared to go to bed and switch off the light. I know it will pass, but I'm still scared."

"I'll make you a promise, Dante. You'll sleep well tonight."

And I did. Without nightmares.

Across the breakfast table Bruno blessed us with a grin and a Venetian proverb: Bed is a medicine. Once again he was right.

I FOUND I could not write letters, so I made telephone calls all over the country to men who had once been friends. There were those who were delighted to gossip but were too busy to come, and others who said they'd come but found it hard to set a date. Only six of them expressed a care for an old friend and a concern about what they heard had been done to me. These would come, on various days of leave, to have a meal and chat with me. I wondered, with growing disillusion, why there were so few. As we sat in the study examining papers and photographs and tapes, Manzini gave me his answer.

"Cattle smell the wind, Dante. They turn their tails to it and wait for it to pass. Chaff blows away in the gusts and only the good grain settles. Be grateful, however small the harvest. I talked to Frantisek at the Vatican today. If you want, he will visit Lili, and if she wants to marry you, we can arrange for you to visit her and become betrothed in the prison. The regulations provide for that, but be sure you know what you are doing. You cannot live a lifetime on guilt and pity. And we may not get her out. Face it—for her, too—that there is nothing so destructive as a disappointed hope. So think carefully before you lay new burdens on the girl."

I knew I must. I knew also that I could not determine myself to a lifetime of lonely fidelity. I was not proud to admit that. I tried to put this fact out of my mind and concentrate on the work in hand—the collation of all the material at our disposal to see if it added up to a case which would unseat Leporello and the Director.

There were problems. My notes on the microfilms from Ponza were third-hand material, collated from memory. Even the originals had represented Pantaleone's plans for a military coup, which would not be held to be legal evidence against Leporello. All we had against him, in fact, were the photographs and tapes of his sexual activities in Roditi's apartment in Milan. With these we could make a scandal, but the scandal could be suppressed in Italy because the law forbids the publication of obscene material. If we published it outside the country, we would be open to accusations of forgery and political chicanery. But this was a risk we might be forced to take.

Whether we could make a legal case out of this material was also problematic. Photographs can be forged very easily, and Roditi was not available as a witness to their authenticity. Then the defense could claim that the tapes had been edited and thus also constituted a forgery.

We decided to concentrate our case on the photographs. I settled down to study them with a magnifying glass. There was no doubt that we had Leporello. I was concerned to see if I could identify any of his partners. The problem was that we had only contact prints of thirty-five-millimeter size and each had to be examined minutely. Finally I was lucky. In one frame I was sure I had Giuseppe Balbo. In another was a face which was very familiar to me. I groped vainly for the name, but my memory, jolted and jarred by my experience, failed me.

Manzini nevertheless was jubilant. "Balbo is all we need. A known criminal, probably a murderer, whom we can identify from a thumbprint and your testimony, and who was killed by Leporello's men in Leporello's zone of command. Yes, that would do it! The other one will come back to you. Now, listen! This stuff is too explosive to let out of our hands. We'll have to bring all the printing and enlarging equipment we need into the villa. Can you do the job?"

"No, only the basics. This needs an expert. One we can trust."

"I'll call my people in Zurich. Your party may be a victory celebration after all, my Dante.

It was still an hour to lunchtime. I paced up and down the terrace trying to reason a way out for Lili. Wherever I looked, there was none. Escape was impossible. Acquittal was unthinkable. There was enough material to convict her twenty times over. The thing she feared most was a present reality: the small room, the lights, the questions that came from nowhere.

Manzini came out to join me, rubbing his hands with satisfaction. The equipment was being packed in Milan. His expert would fly in from Zurich tomorrow. When the news failed to cheer me he snapped at me. "Matucci, stop it! Your Lili is no child. She will survive if she wishes. So long as she survives, there is hope. You do her no service with self-torment. Now, have you put a name to that face?"

"Not yet."

"Keep trying. I have set the party for four weeks from now. It will be a gala affair. This old place needs some life put into it. So do I, for that matter—and you."

"Truly, Bruno, I don't see—"

"You don't see the nose on your own face! That's your problem. You think you can go back to the service? Never! Even if they wash you in the blood of the lamb. You have to start again. Where?

As a street sweeper? Of course not. You want to begin as far up the ladder as you can. For that you need friends and recommendations. Hence we shall give the party, one that everyone will want to attend and will remember. I've left a book in your bedroom; you might find it instructive."

The book was the *Ricordi politici* of Francesco Guicciardini, and I found the gentleman entertaining company. Like me, he was Tuscan born, a Florentine, who by two Medici popes was named to high governing posts. He was utterly without mercy, but he knew how to govern and he loved women of all kinds and ages and conditions. The only man who could handle him was Cosimo de' Medici, who climbed to power on his shoulders and then kicked him into retirement. But Guicciardini was a natural survivor. He retired gracefully, grew vines, wrote books and died peacefully. The *Ricordi* were his secret notes, a kind of diary of opinion and experience, which were published centuries after his demise. Manzini had marked and annotated several passages.

> To be open and frank is a noble and generous thing, but often harmful. . . . It is often indispensable to dissemble, because men are evil by nature. (So smile, my Dante. Show them you are a man who has no care in the world, because you have aces in your sleeve!)
>
> I do not blame those who, on fire with love of country, confront dangers to establish liberty . . . though I think that what they do is very risky. Few revolutions succeed and, even if they do, you find very often they didn't win what you hoped. (Which is why I draw back from public disorder and seek rather to seduce the ungodly in secret.)
>
> Do not take people too seriously when they prate the advantages of freedom. If they could find a good job in a tyrannical state, they would rush to take it. (I would go further. If they could be tyrants themselves, they would climb over a mountain of skulls to arrive.)
>
> The past illuminates the future; the world has always been the same. The same things come back with different names under dif-

ferent colors. (You and I, my Dante, are trying to change the course of history. But let's not expect too much. The river is still the same.)

Nobody knows his subjects as little as their ruler. (This is what we are betting on, you and I. They think they have bought me. They know they have frightened you. They do not understand we have not yet begun to fight back.)

It was at that point that I laid down the book. I still could not turn out my light, but lay a long time staring at the ceiling.

Next day a variety of things began to happen at Pedognana. The artisans of the estate converted an attic into a photographic studio, and the expert from Zurich, sworn to secrecy, set to work installing the equipment which had come from Milan. Early in the evening, Corrado Buoncompagni, the editor of Manzini's newspaper, arrived with Milo de Salis, the noted film director. Dinner that night, with those two, turned into a council of war, at which Manzini exposed for the first time the scope of his design. Now at last I saw him plain and was amazed at the subtlety and the audacity of his genius. He was quiet, dispassionate, and yet he held us as no orator could have.

"I ask no oaths of you, my friends. From this moment we are all conspirators, all at risk. We shall have to use other people. We shall give them only the information they need to carry out their tasks. For the rest, we shall lie, conceal, confuse and obfuscate, so that the true issue is clear only to us.

"I will define that issue. We are attempting to discredit and remove from power men who wish to impose by force, or threat of force, a government by dictation. We believe that this form of government is unacceptable to the vast majority of the people. We know, however, that with all the modern mechanisms of control it can be imposed—and could be held in power for a very long time. Therefore, we must abort the *colpo di stato* which we know is planned.

"Now, Corrado, commencing with Thursday's edition you will

reverse the editorial policy of the paper. We are no longer Centrists but swinging to the Right. I want editorials that my Fascist friends will read. I want a big feature on Major General Leporello. The staff won't like it. It's your job to keep them happy. I don't want to lose either staff or circulation, but I want it known that I am prepared to support the Right—under conditions. I want them to invite me to lunch. Then I can invite them here instead.

"Milo, your job is more difficult, because of time and technical problems. Matucci has a mass of documents and notes, of which the most important are military maps and campaign plans. In addition we have a collection of obscene photographs and tapes. You have access to other material from film files and newsreels. You have three weeks in which to write, film and edit a ten-minute film based on all that material. The film will say that Major General Leporello is a deviate with his own troops, a murderer and a conspirator against the state. Matucci will edit the film with you. He will also appear as commentator and final accuser. As an actor, he needs much direction. I trust you will succeed where I have failed.

"Matucci, you will work with Milo. You will also recruit the praetorian guard we spoke of—senior officers who will agree to attend an official function and act with you if an expected crisis should arise. This is the riskiest point, because if they fail us at the crucial moment, we may all be brought low and the ungodly may survive stronger than ever.

"Now let me describe that crucial moment. I have just completed plans for one of the biggest ventures of my career, a chain of tourist hotels and marina developments around the southern coastline. Because it will bring tourists and tourist industries into the depressed South, this enterprise is of major interest to the government. A consortium of banks has now agreed to finance the whole project. I propose to announce that fact at a gathering in this house a little over three weeks from now. No press will be invited, but Corrado will attend as my personal guest and as pipeline to the media. If we fail here to abort the *colpo di stato*, we shall, for our own protection, publish all the material we have.

"The guest list includes senior ministers and functionaries—

among them Major General Leporello and his wife and the Director of SID. I believe that our new editorial tone will encourage them to attend.

"I am still not fully decided what will happen on that night. One thing, though, is clear. If we win, no one will thank us. If we lose . . . Eh! We'd better take the next plane to Rio!"

The next day I identified the second man in the Leporello photographs. It was Captain Girolamo Carpi—aide to the dead Pantaleone. This was a stunning surprise. It established a direct link between Leporello and Pantaleone. It also revealed a yawning hiatus in my own information on Carpi, since there was no hint of any deviate practices in his army dossier. I had hired him to work for SID, and I had arranged his safe exile to Sardinia. Now I had to arrange his return. This was not going to be easy. I was no longer in a position either to get at army files or to make requests to army authorities.

I took the dilemma to Bruno. He frowned. "This could be our most important witness. We must get him here, question him, break him, get him on the film. How do we do that, without showing our cards to the army?"

"If we could get him posted to Bologna . . . You must have friends in the army high enough to swing a transfer."

"I have. The problem is how far I can trust any of them at a time like this. How did you come to use Carpi in the first place?"

"Let me see now. He had been aide to your brother for about six months when the Director suggested we enlist him as a domestic spy. He gave me Carpi's dossier, which showed that he was living way beyond his means. My proposition was that if he worked for SID, we would pay his debts and give him a monthly stipend as well. He leaped at it."

"The Director gave you his dossier. You hadn't sent for it yourself? What does that suggest?"

"That it could have been doctored before I saw it."

"Exactly. We need your Captain Carpi. Somehow I will get him. With him here, we may well prove murder."

"Murder—for what motive?"

"Profit—on every level. Pantaleone dies. Leporello replaces him as military leader. Since Leporello has organized the murder, the Director moves in as chief of state, just to keep the record pure. Don't you see? And Carpi, Dante—think of Carpi as an intimate of Leporello, as an emissary of the Director, as a man with free access to Pantaleone's apartment—and as the man who killed my half brother."

"And think of myself as the man who employed him. That's very pretty!"

"Precisely. You told me the Director was preparing a black book on you. If we indict Carpi, you could be in trouble, too."

"Bruno, let's face it now. You can surround me with angelic choirs; I'm still up to my neck in the filth. I'm the man who started all this. I'm the man who must finish it. That's the way I'm constructing the film with Milo. If things go wrong, you must walk away from me."

He lifted his white head and gave me a small enigmatic smile. "Dante, son of my heart, never underscore the obvious. If we lose, I can't afford you. If we win, we shall both be very busy men. Too busy for dramatic gestures."

THE next three weeks were a period of mounting panic, suppressed only by the calm generalship of Manzini. The ballroom was invaded by painters, decorators and electricians. A barn was transformed into a studio and cutting room for Milo. The guest list was filling up. The press campaign had been well received by the Right. Leporello and the Director had consented to come.

My friends from the corps came, one by one, to visit me, and I probed them like a confessor before I dared hint at our project. All of them were troubled by the situation of the republic. They were divided on the remedies. In the end there were only four in whom I felt confidence enough to make my proposition.

"You will be invited as guests to an official ceremony here at the villa. You will wear formal mess uniform. I guarantee you each a pretty girl to escort. Now, here's the reason. The place is going to be full of important people, ministers, functionaries, that sort of thing. There'll be the usual security men, but we don't want them in the dining room. That's why I want you there, looking like happy guests. We've been told something may happen on that night. I can't tell you what. I want you to trust me and come for friendship's sake, and maybe for the sake of all the things we've talked about. You are committed to nothing beyond attendance. Now, can you accept that or not? If you can, will you accept one other condition? That this is a state secret, and you'll have to keep it a secret."

They accepted, and I believed them. They were friends of the heart, close as family, which is the one thing on which you can depend in this troubled land of mine. When I told Manzini I had only four instead of the ten he'd wanted, he nodded. "Ten officers in full uniform would be impressive, yes. But I'd rather have only these four than risk a single waverer!"

I asked him about Carpi. He shook his head. "Nothing yet. Tomorrow I am flying to Rome to see a friend in the Ministry of Defense. There is risk involved and some very devious staff work, but I hope we shall get him here in time."

He was disappointed. On the day of the great event Captain Carpi had still not arrived.

AT THE final council of war at three o'clock that afternoon it was decided that I should not appear at the function until its closing moments. My presence could prove an embarrassment to Leporello and the Director and introduce a dangerous note of uneasiness into a gathering whose success depended upon a careful contrivance of atmosphere.

After the meeting Manzini walked us around on a final tour of inspection. In the foyer the guests would be received by four of Pia's girls and led to the first reception room, there to be presented to Manzini and Pia and circulate for cocktails around an illuminated projection of his tourist hotel and marina development—models of the installations on a huge relief map of the boot of Italy.

After cocktails guests would proceed to the ballroom, which had been converted into a dining room for the occasion. The place was ablaze with flowers, and the lighting was contrived to flatter the least beautiful of women. The seating was unusual: a series of small rectangular tables seating only three persons a side, so that the guests faced one another in a small closed community. At one end of each table was a silver bucket containing six gold-wrapped party favors; at the other, a small television set connected by closed circuit to a central control in an adjoining room. The host's table at the far end of the room was arranged as a horseshoe, with its own television receiver.

For each guest there was a program card, illuminated by Carlo Metaponte and set, with impudent irony, in small silver holders in the shape of a salamander. The program was simple: a toast to the President and to the republic, an opening address by the Minister of Tourism, a reply by Bruno Manzini and the showing of a short television film on the new development, produced and directed by Milo de Salis. Manzini pointed out other refinements, too: three television scanners, two focused on the tables where Leporello and the Director were to be seated, a third covering the room, so that all the proceedings could be monitored and recorded on tape. Leporello and the Director were to be at opposite sides of the room, out of each other's line of vision. One of my praetorians was seated at each of their tables, with another at the table next in line. What Manzini had spent in terms of money was staggering; in terms of imagination and ingenuity, unbelievable. When the tour was over he took me back to his study, poured brandy for both of us and made a last toast to the venture.

"I will not say good luck, my Dante. What has brought us to this point is believing and working and daring. What happens at the end, of course, is in the hands of God . . . and though you may not believe it, He has to have an interest in tonight's affair. Perhaps that should be my toast: I pray that He may hold you safe, my Dante, and bring you to a quiet harbor."

I said amen to that, and it was the closest I had come to praying for a long time. We drank and set down our glasses. Then Manzini sprang his last surprise.

"Dante, my friend, have you thought about tomorrow?"

"Tomorrow?"

"Yes. It will come, you know—unless we die in our sleep."

"So?"

"So if our strategy succeeds, you will have the Director and Leporello under arrest. How will you proceed from there?"

"By the book. Depositions by the arresting officer and the accused. Documents sent to the magistrate. Examination, indictment, submission of pleas by the defense, public trial."

"Which will, of course, make an international scandal?"

"Inevitably."

"With profound political consequences for which neither the government nor the people are yet prepared."

"True."

"Read me the consequences as you see them."

"We shall have aborted a Fascist coup. We'll have damaged public faith in the senior bureaucracy. We'll have given new strength to the Left. On the other hand, we shall have affirmed that the state is capable of purging and regulating itself to the benefit of the people."

"And the final outcome?"

"Potentially healthy. That's my best estimate."

"Which leaves us still at risk—grave risk. And the first risk is yours. You will make the arrest, prefer the charges, file the indictment. Is the case complete?"

"Against Leporello, yes. Against the Director, no. A good lawyer could win it for him."

"And then you would go to the wall. Are you ready for that?"

"I hope so."

"You could avoid it."

"How?"

"Accidents happen—fortunate accidents."

"I know. 'The prisoner was shot while attempting to escape.' 'The suspect suffered a cardiac seizure while under normal interrogation.' No, Bruno! Not for me. Not for you. Not for the President himself."

"Not for the people, either? Your people, my Dante."

"The people belong to themselves, not me. I am the only man who belongs to me. You taught me that lesson, Bruno."

He gave me a long, quizzical look, then grinned and went to his desk. From a drawer he brought out a small velvet box. "It's a gift," he said simply. "I hope you like it."

I opened the box and found, slotted in the velvet bed, a gold signet ring. The symbol engraved on the seal was a crowned salamander. My emotions were still unsteady, and I was deeply moved.

"The ring is a symbol, my Dante, not a talisman. The only magical thing about it is the love that goes with the giving. Remember that, when I leave you, as I shall, as I must. . . ."

IT WAS only twenty minutes to six, and I had a long wait ahead of me. The guests would not arrive until eight thirty. They would not sit down to dinner until nine thirty, when I would go down to the control room to watch the monitor. The moment Manzini finished his speech, I was to go into the ballroom, take up my post inside and lock the door. If Leporello or the Director should try to leave, I could then detain them. In the meantime I must rest. I set my alarm and lapsed into a deep sleep.

I woke refreshed and strangely calm. I shaved carefully, bathed and put on my new uniform. When I looked at myself in the mirror I saw a man I hardly recognized: a serving officer of a corps whose oath still had a ring of royalty about it, whose tradition of service, however besmirched by individuals, still carried a blazon of honor. I felt some pride and a small hesitant affection for the man inside my skin. Enough! It was time to go.

As I walked into the empty foyer the majordomo opened the front door and let in Captain Carpi. For a moment he did not recognize me, and when he did he was nonplussed. He told me that he had been sent from Sardinia with urgent dispatches to be delivered personally into the hands of Major General Leporello. His plane had been delayed at Cagliari, and he had been forced to hire a car to bring him out to Pedognana. I told him the general was at dinner, but that I would take him in as soon as the function was over. I took him into the control room, fed him champagne and canapés, and drew Milo aside to warn him not to make any indiscreet comment. Then we settled down to watch the show, while I tried frantically to figure how I should make use of this very untimely arrival. By the time Manzini stood up to announce the presidential toast, I had made my decision.

The Minister of Tourism made an elegant and witty speech, aiming to impress the important people present—his colleague, the Minister of the Interior, among them. He praised the boldness of Manzini's vision, complimented the bankers on their confidence in the economy and the country's stability, assured all the participants of the benevolence of the government. He ended in a flourish of metaphor and sat down to polite applause.

Then Bruno Manzini began his own speech.

"I thank the minister for his confidence in our enterprise, which is itself an act of faith in the future of this beloved country of ours. This act of faith is the more sincere, because my colleagues and I have committed huge sums of money to Italian development at a time when, despite the optimism of my good friend the minister, the country is deeply divided. We are one people, under one flag, but we are also many peoples with many different histories. We have too many parties and too little consensus to achieve easily a government for the people and by the people. Too much wealth is concentrated in too few hands, my own among them. However, to attempt to reconcile these differences, as some seek to, by violent and sinister means is a dangerous folly that could negate all we have achieved since the war, all that we hope to build."

They applauded him then. This was a proposition they could all accept. Manzini hushed them with a smile and gesture.

"In the silver buckets at the end of each table you will find a number of packages. If the gentlemen will pass them around the tables, please? Don't open them yet. They will make no sense until you have seen the film, which is not, I must tell you, the one promised on your program. The press does not know of its existence. The public will never see it—only you, my friends and compatriots. Some of you, especially the ladies, may be discomfited. I beg you to be patient until the film justifies itself. Now, if you will turn your chairs a little, you should all have a good view of your television screens."

This was the cue. In the movement that followed, two of my praetorians stood up and leaned against the wall—a single pace would bring them to Leporello and Baldassare. Other men did the same, so there was an air of casual reshuffling. I hurried Carpi out of the control room, and we reached the dining room just as the lights went down. I locked the door, put the key in my pocket and focused on the nearest screen.

Milo de Salis had settled on a film method that was simple and devastating. It consisted of a series of direct and unqualified statements, in image and commentary.

"This is a photograph of General Massimo Pantaleone, who died in Rome this year, on Carnival night.

"This is the death certificate which states that he died of natural causes. In fact, he died of an injection of air into his femoral artery. He was murdered."

There was a gasp of surprise, a flurry of whispers, then silence, as the commentary began again.

"This is a photograph of the later autopsy report, signed by three very reputable physicians.

"This is a photograph of an office building in the Via Sicilia, where the general's papers were stored after his death. The papers were stolen and two men were murdered—the lawyer, Sergio Bandinelli, and Giampiero Calvi of the SID.

"This is the identity card of the man who murdered them, Giuseppe Balbo, a criminal who used a number of aliases.

"Among the general's papers were these military maps, which have since been altered in detail but not in substance. They show how, on the thirty-first of October of this year, a military junta plans to overthrow the legitimate government of the republic of Italy and establish a government by dictation.

"The maps and plans you have just seen are now in the possession of this man, Major General Leporello, who is here tonight."

Once again there was a stir as all heads were turned to identify

Leporello. They could not see him in the dim light, so once again the image and the commentary commanded their attention.

"This is a recent photograph of General Leporello's aide, Captain Matteo Roditi, who is now under psychiatric care. He was tortured into insanity to prevent his giving testimony in court.

"This is another photograph of Giuseppe Balbo, murderer, who was shot down while resisting arrest by General Leporello's men.

"This is the Club Alcibiade, a resort of deviates, where Captain Roditi met often with Giuseppe Balbo, who was, strange to say, an enlisted member of the carabinieri, under General Leporello's own command.

"This woman is the wife of Major General Leporello.

"This is a love letter, one of thirty, which she wrote to Captain Roditi, her husband's aide and true father of her children. Their love affair was condoned by the general, for good reason."

Instantly Leporello was on his feet, his tall frame monstrous in the half-dark. He shouted, "This is an outrage against an innocent woman. I demand–" He demanded nothing. My praetorian was at his side with a pistol rammed into his ribs.

Manzini's voice rang like a trumpet blast from the rostrum. "Sit down, General! Ladies and gentlemen, I beg that you control yourselves. We are not here to insult a woman but to prevent an imminent bloodshed."

There was a gasp of horror which I could feel physically. They waited until Leporello subsided into his chair, then submitted in silence to the last brutal revelations.

"These next photographs will distress you, but I beg you to look at them carefully. This one shows Major General Leporello engaged in a sexual act with Giuseppe Balbo, murderer.

"This one shows him in another act with the man identified as the personal aide, and probable murderer, of the late General Pantaleone. His name is Captain Girolamo Carpi.

"This man, Major General Leporello, was chosen to lead the *colpo di stato*. He himself, however, would never have assumed power. There was another man behind him.

"This man–Prince Filippo Baldassare, director of the Service of

Defense Information—plotted the death of Pantaleone, hired Carpi to kill him and then arranged for Leporello to replace him."

Again the audience turned around in the darkness, looking for Baldassare. I was one of the few who could see him. The Director sat calm and unmoved, sipping brandy from a crystal goblet as the film went on.

"Who am I? I am Colonel Dante Matucci of the same service. I collected this information. I, too, was imprisoned and tortured to prevent my revealing it. I take full responsibility for the substance and presentation of this film. I depose it as true, and I shall offer to the appropriate authorities documents in support."

The screens went dark. The lights went up, and a hundred and fifty people sat there, dumb and ashamed to look at each other. I moved forward into the silent room with Carpi, like a sleepwalker, at my side. I had one moment of blind panic. Then I found the words.

"The officers present will place the general and Prince Baldassare under arrest."

I did pray then—Dear Christ, make them move, please! They moved. They placed their hands on the shoulders of the two men. The act was final and complete.

I heard myself say, "Ladies and gentlemen, I have here with me, under arrest, Captain Girolamo Carpi, who will testify in the proper place."

Then, from his own table, Bruno Manzini took command. "My countrymen! You have been shocked and shamed tonight. I will not apologize. I tell you only that it is a small price to pay to prevent the bloodshed of a civil uprising and the oppression of a new tyranny. Now, may I ask you to retire to the salon, where coffee and liqueurs will be served."

They got up slowly and moved away like automatons, each carrying the supper gift, which was a dossier of the damned, with a card from the Salamander. Elena Leporello passed me without a glance of recognition. Finally there was no one left but the praetorians and the accused and Manzini and the Minister of the Interior and myself.

Manzini and the minister stepped from the high table and walked slowly toward me. They faced me, bleak and expressionless. The minister said, "Thank you, Colonel. You will do what has to be done with those gentlemen. I shall wait here. You will report to me before you leave."

Bruno Manzini did exactly as he had promised. He walked away.

It was an eerie moment. Three prisoners with their jailers, silent among the debris of a rich man's feast. We were like actors, frozen on an empty stage, waiting for the Director to move us. Then I understood that I was the Director and that, without me, the play would neither continue nor conclude. I must speak. I heard the words as if they issued from the mouth of another man.

"Prince Baldassare, General Leporello, will you please remain seated. You other gentlemen, will you please conduct Captain Capri to the control room and wait there till I call you."

The praetorians led Carpi, mute and unprotesting, from the room. When the door closed behind them I was, at last, alone with my enemies. I felt no triumph, only a strange sense of loss and a vague humiliation. Both men sat bolt upright, their faces averted from me. I went to Leporello first. I straddled a chair in front of him and found myself staring into a death mask.

"General, it is your privilege to be held under arrest in barracks, under custody of service officers, and you may elect to be tried under military law. If you waive this privilege, you become immediately subject to civil process. Which do you choose?"

He did not answer. He sat like a stone man, his lips locked, eyes blank as pebbles. His muscles were rigid; there was no twitch of recognition. Then I heard Prince Baldassare, cool and ironic.

"Classic fugue, Matucci. Total withdrawal. You'll get nothing out of him tonight—if ever. To cover yourself, I'd call a doctor."

I swung around to see him, calm and smiling, sipping a glass of brandy and puffing a cigar. He raised the glass in a toast. "My compliments, Matucci. Trial by television! I wonder why I never thought of that. It's very effective." He poured a goblet of wine and pushed it across the table toward me. "Sit down! Relax. I'm a cooperative witness. You can afford to be pleasant to me. You must be very satisfied. What's the next move?"

"You know the legal code as well as I do, sir."

"And I know the trade better, Matucci. You made your case against Leporello—though I doubt he'll ever stand to answer it. The man was always a psychotic. Tonight you pushed him over the edge. A good lawyer will plead him unfit, and the state will, in its own interest, concur. Against me, what have you got? Carpi will be frightened or eliminated before you get a line of decent testimony out of him. Still, it's your case, and you must make it, win or lose. Unless, of course . . ."

"What?"

"Unless you are open to a little lesson in statecraft. You were always weak in that discipline, as I told you."

"If you're proposing a deal, the answer's no."

"My dear Matucci! Do you think I would be so naïve as to propose a deal to a man both righteous and triumphant? On the contrary, I invite you to a mature consideration of realities. Statecraft has nothing to do with justice, relative or absolute. It is the art and craft of controlling large masses of people, of holding them in precarious equilibrium. All means are open to the statesman and he must be prepared to use them all—from the headman's axe to the circus holiday. Clemency for him is not a virtue but a strategy. You, Matucci, are still a servant of the state. You are not yet a statesman. Tonight you have the opportunity to become one." He broke off, sipped his brandy and smiled at me through eddies of cigar smoke. Then he began on a new tack.

"At this moment you are in a position of great strength. You have forestalled a military coup. In the minister you have an important patron, who is waiting for you to give him the right advice. What would you want if you were in his shoes? A discreet and well-managed triumph or a platter full of bleeding heads? One head is useful. You can display it for a warning to the populace. More than one is carnage. Which head would you select? In my view—which I admit could be prejudiced—the one with the fewest brains. You've got it, over there. Mine is worth much more to you and the minister if you leave it on my shoulders. I am discredited, so I can't do any harm unless you bring me to trial—when, my dear Matucci, I promise scandals that will be shouted from Moscow to the Golden Gate. On the other hand, if clemency were offered, I should respond to it gratefully. I would remove myself from the scene and leave a rich legacy of information to my successor. Do I make myself clear?"

I was ashamed for him then. For a moment he had been eloquent. Now he was merely plausible. I told him bluntly, "I have no authority to offer clemency."

"My dear fellow, I know that. Further, it would be dangerous for you to treat with me at all. You should and you must treat only with the minister."

"What are you asking of me then?"

"I want to speak to the minister privately, now."

"He may not want to speak to you."

"He will. And afterward he will ask to see you."

"And?"

"All I ask is that you give him honest professional answers."

"Can you be sure I'll do that?"

"No. I hope you will. I would not blame you if you pressed your advantage to the limit. However, I've read you the lesson; make what you like of it."

"Give me a hand with Leporello. We'll get him to a bedroom, and I'll call a doctor. Then I'll talk to the minister."

THE interview between Prince Baldassare and the minister lasted more than three hours. I was not present. I was closeted with Professor Malpensa, of the army's Psychiatric Unit in Bologna, who had been brought by helicopter to Pedognana. With him was Dr. Lambrusco, Manzini's personal physician. I had asked them to examine Leporello and render a joint diagnosis. They expressed it in writing: "A catatonic or pseudocatatonic state, induced by guilt and shock. It is our joint recommendation that the patient be institutionalized for clinical observation. It is our opinion that the patient is at present incapable of rational communication, and that to submit him to interrogation or confinement would be pointless and dangerous. Prognosis, doubtful."

I accepted the document and signed the general into the hands of Professor Malpensa. Then I went to Manzini. I found him alone in the drawing room, gray about the gills, but cheerful. "Well, Matucci, we did it!"

"Yes. It's very quiet now."

"What did you expect? Garlands and a triumph?"

"Blessed is he who expects nothing, because he is sure to get it. I think I'd like a brandy."

"Help yourself." He gestured in the direction of the study. "Our friend Baldassare is trying to strike a bargain with the minister. Would it surprise you to know that I have recommended it?"

"In what terms, Bruno?"

"I have represented that without his cooperation we could never have staged this evening's drama."

"That's not true."

"I know it. You know it. The minister knows it. But it happens to be a fiction that fits the moment. Objections?"

"I don't approve. I can see why it's expedient."

"You're learning, my Dante."

"The hard way. Could you reach your editor now?"

"Of course. Why?"

"I'd like him to file a report to the wire services."

"What do you have in mind?"

"I can't tell you until I've spoken with the minister."

He gave me a swift appraising glance. "At last I can approve of you, Dante. For a long time I wondered how much of you was man and how much a confection of circumstance. Forgive me! How does one know whether a nut is sound until one cracks the shell? You are a man full of contradictions. You are coward and hero, wise and foolish, soft as putty and hard as iron. I do not know how you will end, but I have not wasted myself on you. I'll call my editor."

He had been out of the room perhaps three minutes when the minister came in and, seeing that I was alone, announced brusquely that he had questions to ask me.

"At your service, sir."

"The charges you made tonight. Are they true?"

"They are."

"Can you sustain them in court?"

"I can sustain those against General Leporello."

"Could you guarantee a conviction?"

"Guarantee, no."

"But you would be willing to proceed?"

"As an officer of public security, yes."

"You have qualified that statement. Why?"

I handed him the medical report on Leporello, and waited while he read it. He handed it back to me. "I repeat, Colonel, why did you qualify your last statement?"

"Because, sir, I am commissioned to advise as an officer of public security. I have not been asked for a political opinion."

"I now ask you to offer, without prejudice, a political opinion. We have, thanks to your efforts, averted a national crisis. How should we act to avoid a national scandal?"

"We have two important men under arrest, sir. One is incompetent. The case against the other is incomplete; and even if we could complete it, we should risk his making revelations prejudicial to public security. We should risk also divisive enmities both in the republic and between the republic and her allies. I would advise, with deference and respect, that Prince Baldassare be permitted to retire from public life and remove himself within twelve hours from the republic."

"Could that be done without raising a public outcry?"

"There would be hostile comment, also political embarrassment. I would count that a lesser evil than a celebrated trial."

"What are your personal feelings about Prince Baldassare?"

"I admire his talent and have learned much from him. I disapprove of his politics and personal ambitions. I have very private reasons for wishing to see him brought down."

"What are those reasons?"

"He has imprisoned a woman, once a foreign agent, whom I love. He has damaged my career. He conspired to submit me to psychological torture, from which I am only recently recovered."

"But you would still recommend his release?"

"As a political expedient, yes."

"Would you arrange it and supervise it?"

"You mean, sir, will I accept personal responsibility? Thus absolving the ministry and the government, and placing myself in jeopardy?"

"You express it very accurately, Colonel. Would you like time to consider? Or a gift to sweeten the risk?"

"There is no time, sir. And I'm not for sale—not anymore. I'll do it for my own reasons. I'll get him across the border tonight."

"Thank you, Colonel. I should like you to report to me as soon as possible in Rome."

"May I remind you that I am still subject to charges laid by General Leporello?"

"The charges will be withdrawn. You are now restored to active duty. Answerable to me. By the time you return to Rome I trust to be able to confirm your appointment as Director."

He meant it as an accolade—manna in the hungry desert of a bureaucrat's career. Instead it tasted like Dead Sea fruit, dust and ashes on the tongue. For a moment I had felt like a patriot; then, with this reward, he had made me a whore again. Still, I had no choice but to play the game or toss the cards back on the table. I bowed. "Thank you, sir. You do me a great honor."

"Thank you, Colonel. Good night."

It was strange sitting in the Director's chair. For a man so elegant he kept a very dingy office. The only symbols of power were the gray filing cabinets and the scrambler telephone and the intercom switchboard, which would bring twenty people running to attend me.

Old Steffi sat on the other side of the desk and cackled. "So, Matucci! How does it feel? Does your backside fit the seat of the mighty? And what now, what policy? Left, Right or Center?"

"Middle of the road, Steffi. *Tolleranza.* I think we all need to breathe a little."

"Until somebody tosses a bomb or the police fire on rioters, and the boys up top get panicky and scream for action. I wonder how tolerant you'll be then! Well, here's hoping!"

"Come on, Steffi, give me time!"

"I can give you time. But will they? And what about yourself?"

"Please, old friend!"

"So, my nose is twisted out of joint. I'm sorry. What do you want me to do?"

"The commandant at the prison is expecting you. You present the minister's letter and mine. Lili is released to you. You deliver her to her apartment. I'll be there when you arrive."

He stared at me as if I were some curious animal. "Why don't you fetch her yourself? What have you got in your veins, Matucci, ice water?"

I was angry then, desperately angry, and I poured out on him months of pent-up fury.

"I'll tell you what kind of a man I am, Steffi. I bleed like everyone else. And I'm sick and tired of all the smug bastards like you who think they can sum me up in a line. You want to know why I'm not going to the prison? I'll tell you! Because the first time Lili would see me I'd be in company with the commandant and a notary and a turnkey with a pistol at his belt. I'd look exactly the way they do, and I don't want her to see me like that, because that's not the kind of man I am—at least not to her. I'll want to take her in my arms and kiss her and comfort her, and I wouldn't be able to do that while a gallery makes a dirty joke of it and every little jack-in-office smiles behind his hand. I won't submit her to that. I asked you to go because I thought you were my friend. Now get the hell out of here! I'll find someone else."

He sat there, downcast, his lips working. Finally he faced me, and there was compassion in his look, and a new kind of respect. He said quietly, "I'm an old fool with a bird's brain. I'll be glad to go for you, little brother."

"Thank you."

"You're scared, aren't you?"

"Yes, Steffi, I'm scared."

ITALIANA

"Softly, softly, eh! Take it very easy!"

I filled Lili's apartment with baskets of flowers. I had champagne cooling in a bucket, and canapés on a silver tray and a whole refrigerator full of food. I had documents ready to put up the marriage banns on Capitol Hill. I had even an emerald betrothal ring, especially designed by Bulgari.

The ring at the door was like camel bells in the desert. When I opened it Lili was standing alone and very still. I swept her into my arms and was astonished at how light she was. I kissed and hugged her and wondered where all the passion had gone. I sat her in the armchair and served her like a princess. And then I looked at her. She was almost transparent, shrunk to skin and bone. Her clothes hung on her like scarecrow garments. Her mouth was pinched, her hands fluttered. Those eloquent eyes were glazed and dull as pebbles. She ate and drank mechanically, and when I laid my hands on her brow and her cheeks, she submitted but did not respond.

I knelt beside her and begged. "Tell me, Lili, what happened? What did they do to you?"

"Sometimes they questioned me. Mostly they left me alone."

"Lili, you know I didn't send the telegram."

She stared at me blankly. "What telegram?"

"I was told you came back because of a telegram from me."

"There was no telegram."

"Then why did you come back?"

"I got your letter. I used to read it every night before I went to bed. One night it wasn't there. I thought I had mislaid it. The next day I was out walking. My friend from Lugano, the engineer, stopped and offered me a lift. I got in his car. Someone put a pad over my face. The next thing I remember, two men I didn't know were driving me to Rome. That's all. Except they told me you were in prison, too."

"Oh, darling, darling. I'm so sorry."

"It doesn't matter."

"Listen, sweetheart. I'm going to get you well, and we're going to be married. After that, no problems. You're under the personal protection of the director of the SID forever and ever. How does that sound?"

"Most beautiful, Dante. But I don't want it."

As I stared at her, not understanding, I saw the first flush of life in her cheeks, the first dawning of emotion in her eyes. She told me, very gently, "Dante, I know you love me. Your letter was the most touching compliment I have ever read in my life, but I'm going to give it back to you. I couldn't bear to keep it. I don't want to destroy it."

"But you said the letter was gone."

"They gave it back to me in prison. They do strange things, cruel and kind; you never know which will be next. I love you, too, Dante—I suppose I always will—but not to live with forever and ever."

"Lili, please—"

"No, listen to me, Dante! I don't understand you Italians anymore. You are so warm and kind; then, suddenly, you are devious and so cruel, it makes my blood run cold. You have no loyalties, Dante—only to the family and to today. Outside the family, after today, everything is doubt and calculation. Oh, Dante, I hate to hurt you, but I have to say it. You're the people who always survive, no matter what happens to you. That's wonderful, a hopeful thing. But it is also very terrible, because you will trample each other down to get the last drop of water in the world. Even you, my Dante! I can't face that. I want to live secure, with a little book that tells me what to do. I want to be sure that if I keep the rules, the rules will keep me safe—safer than promises, safer even than loving. In Switzerland I can do that. Not here. I cannot risk you anymore."

What could I say? It was all true. The ring on my finger symbolized it: the fabulous beast that survived the hottest fire. And yet it wasn't true. Not the way she said it. The book of rules wasn't the answer. Not for us, the sun people. How could we believe in permanence who walked to the office over the bones of dead emperors? We couldn't trust tomorrow; we could only make do with today. I knelt there a long time, my face buried in her hands, whose pores still exuded the stale smell of prison. I loved her, and I could find no words to comfort her or myself.

Then I heard her say, "Will you help me pack, please, Dante, and see if you can get me a flight to Zurich. I'd like to leave as soon as I can."

It was then I discovered how important it was to be the Director. I was able to command a first-class seat on an overbooked aircraft. I was able to park the car in a prohibited zone at Fiumicino. I was offered free drinks in the distinguished visitors' lounge. I was able to walk Lili all the way onto the aircraft and settle her in the seat and commend her to the good offices of the chief steward. All that, because of a small piece of card in a black leather folder, stamped with the arms of the republic.

I drove back to Rome and telephoned Pia Faubiani. She wasn't at home; she had gone to Venice to open her show there. I called an agency and commissioned them to find me a larger apartment in a more fashionable district. I needed a better *figura,* a better image, now that I should be dealing with high men and large affairs. I dined at my old place in Trastevere, but found it suddenly cramped and provincial. Even the musician seemed to have lost his touch. I went home early and tried to read a little of my old poet namesake before I went to bed. I was too sleepy to concentrate on his ponderous imagery—and besides I didn't believe a word of him. No, that's not true. There were three lines I had to believe:

> *And she said to me: "There is no greater grief*
> *Than to remember happy times, in misery;*
> *And your teacher knows it, too."*

Morris West

The Salamander is the fifth novel by the immensely popular Morris West to appear in Reader's Digest Condensed Books. In a recent letter Mr. West described himself as a "novelist of the moral dilemma," and discussed his work. In *The Devil's Advocate* (Condensed Books, Volume 4, 1960) he dealt with the dilemma of a churchman who lived a life ritually perfect but totally lacking in charity. In *The Shoes of the Fisherman* (Condensed Books, Volume 3, 1963) "the dilemma was that of a man who claimed to exercise power in the name of God" and who retained his faith "even though its preservation involved the destruction of a man." In *The Salamander* the hero must also reconcile and come to terms with conflicting allegiances.

Morris West was born in Melbourne, Australia, in 1916. He was educated at schools of the Christian Brothers order, which he joined as a postulant when he was fourteen and left twelve years later without taking final vows. During World War II he served in Army Intelligence and, after writing for radio and television for several years, realized that he needed the freedom to write what *he* wanted to write. He has done that ever since.

Mr. West has lived and worked in Italy for the best part of ten years; now, with his wife, Joy, and their four children, he lives in Sardinia.

LIFE PHOTO BY L. BURROWS

A Thousand Summers

Upon those who love,
Ungenerous time bestows

A Thousand Summers

A CONDENSATION OF THE BOOK BY

Garson Kanin

ILLUSTRATED BY BARBARA FOX

When it's all over—when you add up your life—what does it come to? For Freeman Osborn, looking back, there was only one answer. Sheila. Because of her he had had a life. They could not marry—both were already married when they met—and they could see each other only now and then. All the same, Sheila had been his world. Luckier than most, thought Freeman. I have something to remember.

Garson Kanin's new love story is as unforgettable as Freeman's crowding memories.

ONE

IN THOSE days, if you got something in your eye, you headed for the nearest drugstore. There the druggist would remove it. In some instances he would then wash the eye, or apply an ointment, or sell you something, or nothing, or charge a fee (usually a quarter), or not.

Freeman smelled her before he ever saw her. The scent was uncommon, and so powerful that it cut through the antiseptic odor of his drugstore, a small resort-town establishment in Edgartown, on the island of Martha's Vineyard, Massachusetts.

He was in the back room when he heard the musical bell that signaled the entrance of a customer. A moment later he became aware of that scent. Normally he would have called out to the customer to wait until he had finished compounding the prescription on his table. ("And *never*—do you hear me, son?—*never* let *anything* interfere with completing a prescription. You'll come back to it and pick it up fine ninety-nine times, and then the hundredth, you'll err and somebody'll die because of you.") He had adhered to this as he had to all of his father's superior advice, but this time he committed an exception. That scent! He knew it belonged to a stranger, which made him curious. Further, it seemed a night aroma and incongruous at this early hour. He had opened the store no more than fifteen minutes earlier. He put aside his mortar and pestle, rinsed his hands, dried them—why was his heart pounding?—and walked out into the shop.

A one-eyed woman stood at the counter. His being responded with the awe invariably inspired by pure beauty. A tremor, goose-flesh. "Good morning," he said, his voice sounding odd.

"I'm afraid I've got something in my eye." Her hand—long, delicate, lovely—came down from her face. She had two eyes, after all. "Can you get it out?"

Freeman studied her, looking for a flaw, until she repeated, "*Can* you?"

"I can try," he said, and added, "Good morneing."

"Good morning," she echoed, and laughed a perfect laugh. "You *are* Mr. Osborn, then? The pharmacist?"

He thought it best not to speak again, since his voice had gone so loony. Instead, nodding, he beckoned her into the back room and then beyond that into his small office. As he moved he checked himself in the mirror. Thank God, this was one of his handsome days. He was often told how attractive he was, but could not see it—except on certain days when he held his tall figure erect, groomed himself carefully, and lifted himself out of his habitual melancholy. On these occasions, he noted, his eyes turned from gray to blue.

He closed the door and pointed to a straight chair beside the shelves that held a collection of Japanese *kokeshi* dolls. He wondered if she would ask about them. The dolls were often conversation pieces. He twisted a gooseneck lamp into position, switched on the light to test its throw, and went to his cabinet. There he prepared a swab, using absorbent cotton and a toothpick, got out a fresh hand towel, and brought them to the desk beside her. He moved to the washbasin and began to scrub his hands in the manner of a surgeon. He blushed as he realized he was showing off.

"This is most kind of you," she said.

"Not at all." (Voice still wavy, damn it!)

"It happened over an hour ago. I've just been waiting for you to open."

"You should've knocked."

"Oh?"

"Here. On the rear door. I'm always here by seven. Gives me a couple of hours for this and that before I open the store."

"Well," she said. "Next time."

"Oh, no. Let's hope there won't be a next time. Nasty things, cinders."

He came close to her. She lifted her face to him. He began to tremble, and wondered if he were going to be able to perform the simple operation. He took her head gently in his hands and moved it into position. He picked up the swab.

"Now, let's see," he said. "Can you feel it?"

"Yes. When I blink."

"Left, right? High or low?"

She blinked, winced, and said, "I can't tell. Sorry."

"No matter."

He slipped a headband, which held a magnifier, over his head. He placed two fingers carefully above and below her eye. He moved his head closer to hers. "Ah!" he exclaimed. "There it is. Now. Please hold still. Still as you can."

Freeman brushed the swab lightly over the cornea of her eye. A cry escaped her, and she pulled away.

"Did I hurt you?" he asked.

"Yes, you did," she said with no little exasperation. "And it's still *there!*"

They exchanged a look to which she contributed irritation, and he, dismay. She began to rise. He put his hand on her shoulder.

"Not again," she said. "It really is *too* painful."

"I know. That's a badly insulted eye."

He dropped the swab, snatched off the magnifier, threw it aside, stepped closer to her, took her head in his hands.

"What are you going to do?" she asked.

He did not reply. Instead, acting with resolution and force, he lowered his head to hers. One hand moved to hold open her eye, the other steadied her head. Now he brought his mouth above her eye and, all at once, brushed his tongue over it. She gasped. His tongue moved again, cleansing her eye. Again. Again.

He released her and stepped away, flushed.

She, conversely, had turned pale and appeared to be speechless. When finally she found her voice she said, "It's out! I think." She blinked several times, stood up, and said, "Yes! It is. Oh, I *do* thank you." She impulsively put her hand on his arm. "I'm grateful to you—beyond expression. What a relief!"

"Thank Sergeant Hufstader," he said.

"Who?"

"The old army regular who taught me that technique. He'd learned it in Mexico—from an Aztec water boy—during the Spanish-American War. A dusty war, apparently."

He led her to the basin and prepared an eyecup.

"What's that?" she asked.

"Boric acid solution. You'd better bathe it morning, afternoon, and evening. For the next four days."

"Like this?" She put the eyecup to her eye and let her head fall back.

He became aware of her finely sculptured profile, the flowing lines of her long neck, and her closer-to-red-than-brown auburn hair. He looked at the outline of her gloriously molded breasts. And that skin. The scent.

"That's fine," he said. He handed her a towel. She dried her face and handed it back.

"What do I owe you?" she asked.

He looked at her for a long time before he answered, "A quarter."

They moved slowly, together, from the office into the back room and from there into the still-deserted drugstore. He took his place behind the cash register. She gave him a dollar. And he gave her the change.

"Thank you again," she said. "I think I'd rather have a *baby* than something in my eye."

"Have you ever had a baby?"

"No," she said.

"I thought not. Or you wouldn't say that."

"I suppose *you have* had a baby."

"My wife has. And it's more trouble than a cinder, I assure you. And takes longer."

"And costs more than a quarter," she said.

"Yes."

They laughed together. She made ready to leave. He could not bear the idea. "May I offer you some refreshment? Our soda fountain is rarin' to go."

"I *could* do with a sip of water," she said.

He went behind the fountain, she moved to it. He suppressed a cry of exultation as she lifted herself gracefully onto one of the tall bent-iron fountain chairs.

"You sure you wouldn't rather have a ginger ale? Checkerberry soda?"

"No, thank you."

"Homemade root beer?"

"Whose home?"

"Mine. I made it myself."

"In that case," she said, "I *will* have some."

He prepared to serve it as he said, "I thought if I was going to have a fountain, I ought to have at least one *spécialité de la maison*." He put the glass before her. "*Voilà! Madame est servie!*"

"You speak French."

"My wife is French," he explained. "I might say *extremely* French."

"How nice."

"Is it?"

"Isn't it?"

"My wife is very nice when she's in France, but here–"

"Mr. Osborn! I think you're forgetting I'm a perfect stranger."

"Perfect, yes," he heard himself say. "Stranger, no."

She finished her root beer swiftly, slipped from the chair, and reached into her purse. He shook his head and waved his palm from side to side. She started out. At the door she turned back to him, smiled, and said, "Morning, afternoon, and evening. For four days."

Those were her words, but they seemed to convey another meaning. He was not sure what it was.

He watched her go through the door and up the street, until he could no longer see her. He washed the glass she had used, fingering it sensuously. The scent of her was still about. He replaced the glass on its shelf.

He started for the back room to resume his work, but stopped and clutched the counter as he felt himself go weak. Two thoughts had struck him with force at the same moment: He loved her. He did not know her name. Suppose she never . . .

REMEMBERING all this, the old man began to cry.

His porch mate, who had been rocking in the chair beside him, rose discreetly and shuffled to the other side of the long porch. This is the established protocol at the Falmouth Sunset House on Cape Cod, Massachusetts. The privacy of misery is respected, and it has long been understood, by guests and attendants alike, that there is nothing to be done. They know that old people weep at many things: a sense of being bereft; anger at the body's unwillingness to respond to an order; loneliness; disappointment in the undone, or lost opportunities; the irritation of muddled memory; above all, at the inevitability of what lies so close ahead, or at the immutable permanence of what has gone before. Here it has been learned that the old cannot be comforted. They cry themselves out, as they did when they were infants and cried for more innocent reasons. But in the elderly the needed energy is in short supply, and as a rule the spell soon ends.

The old man blew his nose, glanced over at his recent companion, and nodded reassuringly. He put away his handkerchief and looked out at the sea. It was blue gray today. The last of his tears blurred the friendly sight and assisted the recovery of memory in the way that darkness bridges the journey to sleep. Fighting disorientation, he placed himself in time. He was seventy-nine, or as he preferred to put it, "in my eightieth year." He saw his signature before him: Freeman T. Osborn. Unlike most signatures it was clean and clear and perfectly legible; a copybook example of Palmer-method penmanship. His father, permissive about most aspects of child rearing, had bullied him about this single detail.

"If you're going to be a pharmacist—and you are—then you'd better set down a hand that can be read by all. The damned M.D.s can scribble—and most of them do—but don't *you.* You're setting down vital records—and *vital* means life or death. What's more, people who write clear, think clear. Those sloppy scrawlers are drawing you a picture of the macaw's nest inside their heads!" Freeman smiled as he played back the sound of the familiar voice, vibrant and fresh, although his father had been dead for nearly fifty years.

Pharmacy. Had he ever considered anything else? Probably not. It was almost as though he had been born a pharmacist, in the way that a prince is born a prince. He reviewed the succession of signs over the entry of the corner store where he had worked most of his life:

THE EDGARTOWN PHARMACY
SETH M. OSBORN, PROP.

THE EDGARTOWN PHARMACY
SETH OSBORN AND SON, PROPS.

EDGARTOWN DRUGSTORE
F. T. OSBORN, PHARMACIST

OSBORN'S
DRUGS—SUNDRIES—SODAS

EDGARTOWN DISCOUNT DRUG
(FORMERLY OSBORN'S)

He discarded the last two and moved back in time to the Edgartown Drugstore days on the island that he could see from here, on clear days, just across the sound. This was the part of his memory world in which he felt more at ease and more alive. He picked up the thread of his remembrance, reflecting that it was now the core of his existence. Well, hell. At least he had something to remember. Not everyone did. Sheila. He smiled, recalling that on that first day he had failed to learn her name. Sheila. What a meeting! And what a waiting for the second. He remembered that four endless days had passed before she . . .

TWO

FREEMAN had reviewed the extraordinary adventure many times during the next four days and nights. His wife was away on one of her trips to France, and he was living the solitary life to which he had become, in succession, accustomed, resigned, attached. Until now. Now he was stirred with longing for more than his days and nights held. Who was this intoxicating woman?

On the fifth day, at seven fifteen a.m., there was a sharp knock on his back door. He opened it. She stood there, surpassing even his idealized memory. She wore white, and a single yellow rose in her bodice. "May I come in?" she asked.

"Of course."

She went at once to the straight chair and sat.

"Which eye is it this time?" he asked.

"Neither. Both."

He locked the door and went to her. They kissed. It seemed to them a perfectly natural expression. It was as though they had kissed many times before.

"Thank you," she said. "Although that is not entirely what I came for. I wanted to ask you about that remarkable collection of *kokeshi* dolls."

He sat down near her. "You know about *kokeshi* dolls?"

"Yes. Why does that surprise you?"

"Because in the five years I've been collecting them, you're the first person to know what they *are*."

"We did a tour of duty in Japan—three years. I have some *kokeshi* of my own. Not as fine as yours, I'm afraid."

"Choose one. Please. I want you to have it."

She looked over at the dolls and said, "I'm meant to say no, of course, but I believe I'll say yes. Or, since it's this part of the country—don't mind if I do!"

She went to the collection, studied it carefully, and finally selected a small, exquisitely wrought, and subtly painted doll. "This one," she said.

"Bravo."

"Why?"

"It's the best one. The most valuable."

"I know."

She came to him, said, "Thank you," bent down, and kissed him. She resumed her chair and asked, "Have you ever been to Japan?"

"Not yet," he said. "It's one of my dreams."

"Be prepared for another world. The Japanese not only think in different categories, but they feel in them. Death, for instance. To them, death is not the *end* of life, but a *part* of life."

"Never mind life and death," he said. "Tell me about those mixed communal baths."

"The water is very hot."

"Did you do it?"

"Of course. But not without a certain amount of unease, I confess. You know the saying, 'When in Kyoto . . .' "

In the next half hour he learned that her name had been Sheila Hanrahan, that she was now Mrs. Thomas Van Anda, wife of a man high up in the Foreign Service, that they were here for the summer, that she was in need of companionship.

Later, Freeman prepared coffee and they sat—he with his back to the desk, she in a nearby armchair. "May I compliment you on your coffee?" she asked. "It's outstanding."

"Thank you. You must remember that I'm a chemist of sorts. I prepare coffee the same as I do a prescription. Also, I'm a superb cook."

"Are you?"

"Yes. My wife's away a good deal, and I find it best to do for myself. I'm partial to Japanese food. Island ladies grow pale at the sight of anyone eating *sashimi.* I've pointed out that it's only *raw* fish—while they cheerfully slurp oysters and clams—*live* fish. But it makes no impression."

"We get so set in our ways, don't we?"

"What's worse is that we get set in our *parents'* ways. It's taken me years to shake off some of my father's. More coffee?"

"Please."

He laughed lightly as he poured a second cup for her and said, "I'm the sole owner of this emporium here. My father insisted I buy him out. You'll never guess why."

"Tell me."

He handed her the cup and kissed her.

"Thank you," she said. "And thank you."

"The soda fountain. He put it off from year to year. Finally, as his partner, I had to tell him we couldn't buck the trend any longer. And he said, 'Well, then. It's me or the gadget, son. I'm a pharmacist, damn it all, not a confectioner—and I won't be both! It's up to you.' Well, painful as it was, I had to choose the gadget, and I bought him out. He drove a hard bargain, and I suspect I paid too much. Still, I respected his Yankee trading. And him. He died only two years ago. Before that he'd come in almost every day for guess what? An ice-cream soda! Is *your* father alive?"

"Yes. Wyoming. Cattle."

"Brothers? Sisters?"

"Two brothers, both older—with my father. One sister, younger. She lives in Rome, and we're out of touch. We quarreled over my mother's legacy and never made it up. I was right, incidentally, and she was wrong."

"Of course."

"I'm afraid I don't cook at all," she said, frowning. "I've never had to learn. Do you think less of me?"

"Yes, but no matter. I'll do the cooking."

There was a long pause before she whispered, "You will?"

"I'll do everything," he said. "When our time comes."

They shared a long silence.

"I'm a superlative photographer," she said.

"Good. You can take pictures of me cooking."

They laughed.

"Wait!" she said. "I just remembered. There *is* something I can do in the way of food. It's not cooking, precisely, but it *is something*. It's called an *ensoku*."

"Of course," he said. "A picnic."

"How do you know that?"

"My love, you'll learn, in time, that I know much more about Japan and the Japanese than you do. Even though I've never been there. Maybe *because* I've never been there. I've read the books and memorized the maps and studied the history and absorbed the art—and, of course, my *kokeshi*. I've learned a lot from them."

"When shall we have our first *ensoku*?"

"Whenever you say."

She frowned in thought. "Let me see, on the first—that's in two weeks—my husband goes to Washington for a five-day conference. One of those days?"

"All of them," he said. "The way I see it, our whole *life* together is going to be a picnic. Speaking of your husband—where does he think you are now?"

"My husband sleeps till noon. He reads—he writes—late into the night. It's his way. He grew up in a city. He's a night person. But I grew up on a ranch. *Our* days began with the light and ended with the dark."

"There's a lot to be said for the dark."

"Oh, I'm sure of it. I thought we were talking about why we are as we are."

"I don't care *why* you are," said Freeman. "I'm just grateful to God that you *are*."

"I'll have to phone New York for some of the things. I can get the fish here, I suppose. Poole's?"

"I'll get it," he said.

"No, no. Please. I *want* to. I can't tell you how important it is to me."

He stood up quickly and said, "Squibnocket Pond."

"I beg your pardon?"

"It all comes clear," he said. "Don't tell me there's no design in the way things happen. Or no guiding intelligence. There is—*must* be."

"Of course."

"Listen to this," he said, moving closer to her. "Six—no, seven years ago—a few months after I came home from France and the army—I bought these nineteen acres on Squibnocket Pond—that's way up-island, near Gay Head. No sense to it. I read an ad in the *Gazette*, drove over, and said yes on the spot. An impulse, and so unexplainable that I didn't even try to explain it to my wife—my *new* wife, she was, at that time."

"Nineteen acres."

"Most of it is wooded, but the pond is grand. And there's access to the sea. But what I loved about it was that it put me in mind of photographs and prints I'd seen of Japan. The light, I imagine, and, for some reason, the foliage. Hundreds of little trees underfoot that might be bonsai. Some of the plants *may* be Japanese, for all I know."

"But how *could* they be?"

"Don't you know about our island? We're the *world*. We're pretty cosmopolitan—though we seem to be country bumpkins leading bucolic lives."

"Not at all."

"Our fathers and grandfathers used the island as a base. For the most part they were out at sea—whaling and trading and, of course, bringing back souvenirs. Have you seen our pagoda tree on South Water Street?"

"I've seen many trees, but—"

"Come on," he said. "I'll show you." They left the office and walked a block and a half up the still-deserted street. As they approached the tree he took her arm and stopped her.

"There it is."

"Yes," she said. "I've seen it, but—"

"A pagoda tree." He led her closer until she could read the wooden plaque.

GIANT PAGODA TREE
(A Chinese Huai Tree Sophora Japonica)
Brought from China in a flower
pot in 1837, by Captain Thomas Milton
to grace his new home then being built.
This is believed to be the largest of
its kind on this continent.

"Think of it!" she exclaimed, and grasped his arm as though to root herself, for the moment, in the present.

As they walked back to the store he went on. "And Beetlebung Corner. Have you seen it?"

"I'm afraid not."

"We'll stop there when we go to Squibnocket. It's right on the way. A whole clump of beetlebung trees—brought to the island, I suppose, the way the pagoda was."

"And that's why you think the ones on your land may be—"

"Oh, I don't know," he said. "It may be imagination. Still. It means something to me."

"Are you all right?" she asked. "You've gone pale."

"Yes. I *feel* pale."

They returned to his office. He went to the back room and returned with a small bottle of aromatic spirits. He removed the top and sniffed it.

"I've what my mother used to call the vapors. I'd feel ridiculous if I fainted at your feet."

"Please don't," she said.

"It's just that I'm—what shall I say?—*overwhelmed* by the supernaturalness of it all. There's no explanation for it. No. That's not what I mean. There *is* an explanation for it, and that's what makes it overwhelming." He sniffed the bottle again.

"I'm not sure I follow," she said, frowning.

He reached over and gently removed the frown from her forehead with his thumb. "Look. Seven years ago, on an impulse, I bought a piece of land. A Japanese spot. I had no particular use for it. I haven't been there more than half a dozen times in all these years. And then a certain infinitesimal cinder blows into a particular eye—and the design is complete. I bought the land for us, Sheila. I've been holding it—waiting. Some part of me knew—without knowing—that you were on the way."

She reached out and touched him. He kissed her hand. . . .

ON THE porch in Falmouth the season had changed. Late autumn contained intimations of a harsh winter to come. The old Freeman sat, wearing an overcoat, hat, and gloves. The attendants had long ago given up trying to control him. He was one of those stubborn, independent, own-way creatures.

He was alone on the porch, which suited him perfectly. The consecutiveness of mind he had cultivated thrived on solitude, suffered when interrupted or distracted.

Lucky, he thought. Lucky she came in when she did. A few years earlier (years and days were interchangeable now) and it might have been his father who would have dealt with the cinder. Thank you, God.

Yes.

His father had retired in 1920. Freeman had returned from the war, which he had greatly enjoyed, having been stationed in Paris for virtually his full term of service as master sergeant-pharmacist at the base headquarters hospital. He had met and married Colette, the daughter of a distinguished French obstetrician, Paul-Louis de Vallande.

He had brought her home to Edgartown, which she loathed on sight and to which she never adjusted. She fell ill constantly, became a perennial invalid occupied with her maladies, and lived only for her frequent returns to France. A month each year, at first. Later, a season each year. When, in 1939, World War II interfered, she took to traveling to Canada, Mexico, South America. After the war ended she went to France and stayed for a year to make up for lost time. For the rest of her married life she spent half of each year at home and the other half abroad, to her a fair, even generous arrangement. She died in 1959, at the age of sixty-three, when the small plane carrying her from Paris to the Côte d'Azur crashed in a storm a few miles south of Avignon.

She had successfully staved off motherhood for several years, but in 1925 she found, to her horror, that she was pregnant. She did not inform Freeman, but left at once for France to consult her father about aborting the unwanted birth. Dr. de Vallande's reaction astonished her—she knew him no better than she knew her husband—and she found herself forced to bear her child under his constant supervision.

Freeman went to Paris to be present at the birth of their daughter, Jacqueline. He had fought hard to have the child born in America, but lost.

Poor Jacqueline. She was to endure a childhood compounded of neglect and systematic rejection from a mother who resented her existence. Her father, attempting to compensate, smothered her with too many things, an overabundance of attention, and succeeded in spoiling her. By the time she was sixteen she was a nervous admixture of self-doubt and arrogance, shyness and aggressiveness, joy and misery.

Odd, thought Freeman, that it had all turned out so well. There she was now, in Denver, working with her eminent husband and so involved that she emerged from their laboratory only for summers in Chilmark, on the Vineyard, or a Christmas trip to see her father.

Freeman remembered her visit this past Christmas. She had been deeply troubled by his move to the Falmouth Sunset House. It seemed to her a living death. He agreed, secretly, but insisted that it was the most practical arrangement. She informed him that she would not come again. Next year he would come to see her and Max and the boys in Denver. They would have a proper Christmas, not one of these damned plastic nonsenses.

He smiled. He could hardly wait until next Christmas to see if it would come about. He would make a bet with himself. How much? He began to laugh.

He stopped as he realized that he was being observed from either side. A man who cries and laughs in the course of five minutes must surely be regarded as peculiar. What had he been crying about? It took him a straining time to bring it back to mind. His year in prison? No, that was part of *yesterday's* remembering. The photograph this morning in the *Vineyard Gazette*? The Japanese house. Squibnocket Pond. The visit. Those people. Had it happened, or was memory determined to torture him? Sheila. That second meeting, so full of promise . . .

THREE

Sheila did not appear the next day, although he had been certain that she would. But on the day following that she came again, this time through the front entrance in midafternoon, accompanied by a tall, portly, clearly important man, who wore an old blazer with a Yale pocket patch. "Mr. Osborn," she said, "this is my husband, Thomas Van Anda."

"How do you do?" Freeman was relieved that they were not standing close enough to shake hands.

"Mr. Osborn, Thomas, is the gentleman who helped me with my eye."

"Yes," said her husband absently, looking about the shop. That "Thomas" struck Freeman's ear. Why not "Tom"? Why not "dear"?

Sheila took a shopping list from her bag and handed it to Freeman. Purple ink on pale yellow paper. The handwriting small, perfectly placed on the page, delicate. When would he find the first flaw in this creature?

He began to fill the order, at the same time observing her husband. A bottle of aspirin tablets. Van Anda's hair was white. His slightly puffed face was the kind Freeman associated with drinking men. Five safety-razor blades. From time to time he exhaled in a way that betrayed weariness and the heavy weight of responsibility. A tin of tooth powder. Freeman was good at guessing ages and placed Van Anda in the forty-to-forty-five range. A box of cough drops. He knew, as well as he knew anything, that Sheila was thirty to his thirty-four. That scent of hers was making him giddy again.

"Will that be all?" Freeman asked when he completed the order. "Thomas? Anything?"

"Nothing. Come along." Van Anda floated out of the store, the bell reverberated. Freeman wondered why it had had another sound on the day it had preceded her first appearance.

"This is going to be heavy," he said. "Let me send it."

"No, no," she said. "We can manage. Thomas will carry it."

"Will he?"

"Of course."

He handed her the package. "Tomorrow?" he asked softly.

"Tomorrow," she replied.

At seven a.m., when they met at the store, they could not speak of themselves, nor of their plans. The news of Charles A. Lindbergh's successful solo flight to Paris had come through. Ronnie Pease, a schoolboy who lived two doors from Freeman, had built a crystal radio set and this morning had heard the news announced over WGY, Schenectady, as well as KDKA, Pittsburgh. He ran to Freeman's and told him at breakfast. When Freeman repeated it to Sheila all other subjects seemed dwarfed by the momentous achievement.

What would it mean in terms of the future? Would passengers be carried across the seas by airplanes in their lifetime? Would *you* go? Would *you?* It was an exciting day.

The next morning they returned to themselves and to one another. Freeman, with persistent questioning, elicited the story of her life.

The ranch. The agony and loneliness of boarding school in Denver, Colorado. The year of chaperoned travel with her aunt Rhoda. The decision to go to Wellesley and why. The sudden awakening of social consciousness as a result of a campus lecture about settlement houses by Jane Addams of Hull House, Chicago. Her summer there. Her wartime job in Washington. Her meeting with Thomas Van Anda. His proposal. Her trip back to Wyoming to think it over. Her acceptance. Japan, France, Denmark, Venezuela. Washington. Here.

Freeman thanked her for sharing the details of her life. He needed them desperately to establish his own place in it. On the following day the tables were turned and Freeman told her about himself. What interested her most was the subject of his aspiration. What was his aim? A second pharmacy? A chain of them?

"No," he said. "I've no ambitions in the business line. I'm afraid I'm not much good at it. Does that trouble you?"

"What are you good at?"

"Bluefishing, chemistry, and loving you."

"Chemistry. What do you do about it?"

"What I'd like to do," he said, "is to put together just one damned thing that'd be useful. I don't aim as high as a cure for the common cold. But suppose I could find something that would keep insects off people. Or an antidote for ptomaine. Or a harmless pain reliever. That's what I want to do—relieve pain or discomfort in some way."

"Yes," she said, studying him and finding a new dimension of his personality.

"There's so damn much pain in the world. We get smart at so many things. Most often—the wrong things. We fly across the ocean, but we can't stop the croup."

"Of course we can," she said. "Just give us time."

"Time," he echoed.

TEN days later Van Anda left for Washington. Car to Vineyard Haven, ferry to Woods Hole, train to New York, change trains, to Washington.

Sheila accompanied him to the ferry. When it had sailed she dismissed the car. Freeman told Mrs. Petschek, his part-time helper, that he was going to the jobber's on the Cape for supplies, and gave her lockup instructions.

Mrs. Petschek was a registered pharmacist who had been with Caswell-Massey in New York City for twenty-two years. She had come to the island seven years earlier to spend her vacation. Instead she arranged to keep her room at Captain Cauldwell's Guest House on an annual basis and did not return to New York. In fact, since her arrival she had not left the island. "Why should I?" she said. "Where's it better than here?"

Her deal with Freeman was casual and suited them both. She came in to assist or take over whenever Freeman needed her.

He put the wicker picnic basket that Sheila had delivered at seven that morning into the back of his Nash and drove, at the appointed hour, to the small bridge on Howard Avenue in Vineyard Haven. Sheila was strolling across it slowly. He pulled up beside her and stopped.

"Good morning," he said. "Can I give you a lift?"

"Undoubtedly," she replied, and got in beside him.

He took a circuitous route because he wanted to show his love some parts of the island she might not have seen. Up the North Road to Tea Lane and left, down toward the sea. Through the hills of Chilmark, on toward Gay Head, and another left turn into a wood. Turns and twists and finally a locked gate. Freeman left the car, unlocked the gate, drove through, relocked the gate, and continued.

"We're home," he said.

"It's beautiful," she said. "But it's not Japan."

"Wait."

An old stone wall and, beyond it, a rock garden. Then a wild copse and, a few yards on, a small glade.

They left the car. She walked away from him to explore. He watched her as she looked about, bent down, straightened, touched a tree, and returned to him.

"Yes," she said. "It is. Thank you. They're not bonsai. But close enough."

He took her hand and led her on a tour of his domain. It took the better part of an hour. They traveled the path to the pond, and he showed her the easy access to the open sea. On the way back he promised her a surprise. "You've seen our sea. Our pond. Now here—is our pool."

Suddenly, in a thicket, there it was. So splendidly arranged it might have been man-made, except that man would have been more modest and made it not quite so large. It was enclosed by bushes and shrubs, and had a mossy bank. The water, gushing up from springs, was crystal clear.

"We can swim in it," he said, "if you like."

"Really?" She kicked off her shoes. She bent down and brought her dress up over her head. The slip came off, and the chemise. Freeman closed his eyes, then opened them. Now she was in the pool, swimming about as though it had been built around her. Floating on her back, undulating gently through the still waters, blending with enveloping nature.

Freeman found himself in the water beside her, although he could not remember undressing. They swam together and reveled in the sense of feeling welcomed by nature—welcomed back.

They came out of the pool hand in hand and stood at its edge, looking at their shimmering images in the disturbed water. As the water quieted they were mirrored clearly.

"Yes," she said. "A most satisfactory sight."

"I agree," he said.

"Would you hand me that bath towel, love?" she asked.

He moved quickly in the direction of her pointing finger before he caught the joke. He laughed and said, "You should have thought of that before you got all wet."

"Yes."

"*Now* what are you going to do?"

"I've no idea. Wait until I'm dry, I suppose."

"I know a good place to wait," he said.

"Good."

He led her through an opening in the hedge behind them to a grassy knoll. Branches above formed a transparent ceiling.

"Here it is," he said.

"Yes," she said. "Here it is."

And they were together, astonishingly to them both, not as tentative, apprehensive first-time partners, but as a practiced, confident, exchanging pair.

"Never before have I known perfection," she whispered, looking at him and the sky.

"Nor I," he said. "Only you."

They lay in wonder for a suspended time before rising to dress.

The *ensoku,* new to him, was a surprising delight. Cups of hot soup (*misoshiru*) from a thermos bottle; then out of a symmetric series of black and red lacquered boxes came *sushi, sashimi,* pickled vegetables, and lotus root. Sauces and ginger and tofu. Sake and, later, tea.

He ate too much.

The day had taken on a shape and color of its own.

She lay back on the picnic blanket and said, "I am very happy."

His arm moved quite naturally under her head. Her head found its place in an indentation of his shoulder. Two halves had joined to become one. They slept. The birds and small animals, which had been somewhat noisy—their privacy having been invaded—grew quiet, as if respecting lovers' rights.

She awoke first and, for a minute, thought herself in Japan. She did not regret her error when she realized where she actually was and with whom. She turned to him and kissed him awake. He trembled, opened his eyes, and looked at her until she became real.

They repacked the picnic basket and put it into the car. They changed, pulling on bathing suits. They walked to the edge of the pond. From there, by rowboat, they made their way to the open sea. An hour of sea bathing followed in the throbbing, living waters of South Beach.

They rested on the sand and talked of pleasant things: childhood memories of summer, teachers, travel.

It was late afternoon when they returned to the car. After they had dressed he brought forth his surprise: an ice bucket that held a shaker of martinis. They sat on the running board and sipped.

"I'm *so* glad you're a pharmacist," she said. "We wouldn't have this grand medicine if you weren't."

Their talk turned now to more practical matters.

"Where shall we put the house?" he asked. "I've often thought that hillock there."

"Yes, love, that would seem the obvious place—forgive me—but there are other considerations. The direction of the prevailing winds and the sunrise-sunset positioning. Sea views—"

He laughed. "You're in charge. I can see I'm no match for you on this."

"What's more," she continued, warming to the subject, "the choice of an architect is vital. If it's going to be a Japanese house—"

"It is."

"Then we need a Japanese designer."

"And builder, too, don't you think?"

"Possibly," she said. "But if we find the right man and if he's willing to supervise, Yankee craftsmen are remarkably versatile."

Sheila paused, then went on. "A *small* house, don't you think?"

"Yes," he agreed.

"It isn't going to be planned as a full-time residence, is it? Or is it?" she asked.

"Whatever you say."

"Well, I may change my mind, but right now I see it as a hideaway for special days."

"Like today."

"The sort of place we can take care of by ourselves. No need for anyone else around."

"And above all, no guest room. But it's going to take a long time, you know. Some of the materials—parchments for the shoji, for instance—may have to be sent from Japan."

"What does it matter *how* long it takes?" she asked. "So long as we know it's going to *be*?"

"Right."

"I'll begin at once. A library. The nearest good one is in Boston, I suppose. I'll go there. Tomorrow."

"Tomorrow?" he said incredulously.

"Oh," she said, coming out of her reverie. "I *am* sorry. Carried away."

"We're going to have tomorrow here," he said. "I can't tell you how important it is. I've got to prove to myself that I'm awake and not asleep. This is all—well, hard for me to believe."

"Believe it, my love," she said. "Believe."

The second day at the pond was much like the first, except that it began earlier and ended later. The picnic, prepared by Freeman, was strictly New England: deviled eggs, cold lobster mayonnaise, cucumber-and-tomato salad, cold chicken, coleslaw, fresh strawberries, and homemade banana ice cream. He had cranked the freezer himself that morning.

They ate and swam and slept and loved and walked and planned. A site for the Japanese house was enthusiastically agreed upon. Sheila had brought a few of her cameras and used up a dozen rolls of film.

Afterward, over whiskey sours made from his store of medicinal bourbon, he said, "I think you *should* go to Boston tomorrow. And I'll go with you."

She frowned. "Is that wise? This is a *very* small town, love. We're—all of us—conspicuous."

"I'm in and out all the time," he said nervously. "Anyway. I don't care."

She looked off into the distance, as though looking into time to come. "You'll *have* to care. We both will, if we're to survive. We must be discreet."

"Fine," he said. "We'll be discreet in Boston."

She took a suite at the newly opened Ritz-Carlton Hotel, overlooking the Public Garden.

He was assigned to a room on the floor above.

They spent two days in Boston: mornings at the public library's architectural section, copying plans and details of Japanese houses. A meeting with the Japanese consul general for information as to imports and available materials in the United States. Lunch the first day at Durgin-Park's in Faneuil Hall market and the second day at Locke-Ober's. Afternoons at the museums, looking for Japanese effects. They had their first dinner at the new Ritz; their second was a seafood feast at the Union Oyster House. At the Plymouth Theatre they reveled in the celebrated Winthrop Ames production of *The Pirates of Penzance*. The second night they were fascinated by an innovation: the Vitaphone (films with *sound!*); the feature film was John Barrymore in *Don Juan*. They walked to Chinatown, had supper, and went back to the Ritz.

By noon the next day, after a late breakfast of codfish cakes, they were on the road, heading for the island. They went directly to the pond. There, sketches and notes in hand, their plans moved closer to realization. "I think the house is well on its way," Freeman said. "But what about us?"

"Oh, yes," she said. "I wish we could be arranged with blueprints and specifications, too. The others involved. We have to consider them. Must."

"I don't anticipate much trouble at my end. We've been living out a mistake. She'll be relieved, I'm sure."

"But Thomas, you see, is in public life, and that means—"

"Have you ever called him Tom?"

"No. Why?"

"Nothing. I just wondered."

"I can't do anything to hurt his career. He's been utterly kind and generous always. He's a fine man—could be, perhaps, a great one. He's devoted to public service—he really does want the greatest good for the greatest number. He doesn't want power for himself—it frightens him, actually—but only to use for what he thinks right and good."

He regarded her carefully. "I think you love him."

"Yes, I do, in a way. With that part of love that's respect and admiration—reverence, even. But we are not *in* love. I see now that we never were."

"Why now?"

"Because of you and me."

"Yes."

"I'm selfish, of course. But I couldn't do anything that could damage him in any way." She smiled. "But then, *that's* selfish, too—because I wouldn't want to live with a burden of guilt."

"What are we going to do, then?"

"I don't know. For now, for today and tomorrow, nothing. Wait and see."

"That's not much of a life, is it?"

"Depends what you see after the wait," she said.

They returned to Edgartown in the darkness. He drove slowly, his left hand on the wheel, his right holding her hand tightly, desperately.

She did not turn up the following morning, which surprised him. He spent the better part of the day composing a letter to his wife. After many drafts it read:

June 6, 1927

My dear Colette,

I hope this letter will not be as painful for you to read as it is for me to write, but as adults we should have learned the necessity of facing facts and dealing with them honestly.

Our marriage is a failure, as witness how little we share it. Maybe *failure* is the wrong word. Our marriage is simply useless, giving neither of us comfort or joy. I have been asking myself many questions about us for the past few years. I have no doubt that you have questions as well.

You never liked it here on the island. But I love this place. It is where my life is and my work and, I suppose, my future. At thirty-four I can hardly be expected to begin again elsewhere.

On the other side of the coin, there is your problem of displacement. You seem to have solved it by your trips. Are you aware that they have become longer and longer? And that they may be having a harmful effect on Jacqueline?

This brings us to our daughter, the one beautiful thing we have created together—and the one who must be considered above all. We are responsible to her and for her. I am perfectly prepared to assume the task of her upbringing, since it is no secret (between us) that I was the one who wanted her.

Further, since you are only thirty-one and extremely attractive and charming, I have no doubt that a more suitable marriage partner will be forthcoming. It might be best, therefore, from your point of view, to be unencumbered.

Needless to say, I am grieved about all this. It has lain between us, unspoken, for so long. I wish I had found a way to say it earlier. I have a strong suspicion that you have probably been undergoing a similar struggle.

My dear Colette, I am so sorry to have failed you. I beg your forgiveness. I bear no ill feeling, no bitterness—only a deep sense of disappointment.

Please let me hear from you as soon as possible.

Kiss Jacqueline and tell her I am sending her a picture letter.

In all sincerity,

Freeman

Toward the end of the day, Sheila came into the shop. She browsed until the customers left, then sat at the soda fountain and ordered an orangeade.

As Freeman prepared it she said, "A change in plans. We're leaving for Washington day after tomorrow."

He stood still for a few seconds before continuing his work. "I see," he said.

"We hope to be back—perhaps more than once—before the end of summer."

"Tomorrow?" he asked.

"Impossible."

He served the orangeade. She drank it. He watched her. She paid and left.

Early in the morning on the day of her departure she came to the back door of the store, knocked, and entered the office. They embraced. "I haven't much time," she said.

They sat down to talk. "I've written a letter." He showed her a copy. She read it, nodded, and handed it back.

"Have *you* done anything?" he asked.

"Yes. Quarreled."

"What about?"

"Nothing—like most quarrels. Arrangements. He sensed that I don't want to leave and it irritated him. It led to words and, of course, we each said far more than we meant to."

"We're *never* going to quarrel. I'll see to it."

"Poor man," she said, looking out the window. "He's under a great strain. A new appointment is being discussed. A great promotion. Enormous responsibility. He honestly doesn't believe he's up to it. He's said so to President Coolidge, but the President, being a New Englander, thinks people can do anything they put their minds to."

"He may be right," said Freeman.

"So Thomas is torn between his own misgivings—he's truly modest—and his wish to serve."

"The appointment. Is it something that would take you away somewhere?"

She touched him and said, "I can't tell you. Not yet. I'll know in a few weeks perhaps."

"And meanwhile—Washington?"

"Yes," she said.

"May I write to you there? A post-office box?"

She thought it over. "No. Better not in Washington."

"The telephone? I have a private line here." He jotted down the number and gave it to her.

"Of course, I'll try. If only to keep you informed." She glanced at the clock, which had begun to hammer away the time with ear-splitting loudness. "I must go," she said.

"Well," he said, and took her shoulders. "These days. They've been the best I've ever known. I have no words to—" His eyes filled with tears. "I love you," he said. "Now. Always. Whatever."

"We share love," she said.

He kissed her with gentleness, but with deep feeling.

She was gone. He went to work.

FOUR

COLETTE's reply to his letter was her reappearance three and a half weeks later.

That afternoon Sheila had telephoned to say that Thomas Van Anda had accepted the appointment. He was now a roving ambassador to United States embassies throughout the world, reporting on each to the President and the Secretary of State. It would take two years, perhaps longer, with possible periodic returns to the States.

Freeman had spent the rest of the day attempting to come to grips with the shattering reality of the situation. He had walked to the lighthouse at Starbuck Neck. He had talked to a dog. He had talked to himself.

He had closed the store at nine thirty p.m. and walked a long route home. As he approached his house on Cooke Street he saw that lights were on. He went into the living room to find his wife sitting there, still in her traveling clothes, including hat and gloves.

"Colette!" he exclaimed. As he bent to kiss her she turned her head away. He stepped back, saw that her eyes were blazing.

"Where's Jacqueline?" he asked.

"Home," replied Colette. "In Marnes-la-Coquette."

Freeman's attempt to control his anger made his heart pound. "You left the child *behind?* Alone?"

"She is not alone," said Colette tightly. "It is better for her there—not here with a father who wishes to break his home."

"I hoped," he said quietly, "that after all these years—"

"You shall not have a divorce. Never! I have come now only to leave you once for all. But divorce? You will see me dead, or I will see you dead. I am no foolish American wife without spirit. You wish to exchange me for something better—as you do your automobiles. I am no machine, you hear? She will not have you—*who* she is!"

"Don't be ridiculous, Colette. Of course there's no one else."

"Liar!" she screamed. "I am not fooled! There has been much talk in this dirty little village. You believe I am with no one here, but I have friends."

"Friends!" he said bitterly, and wondered if indeed some word might have come to her. "Colette, I swear to you—"

"*Cochon!*" she screamed, and rushed from the room. Sobs overtook her halfway up the stairs. She sank down and wept.

Freeman moved to her. She struck out at him with her handbag, pulled herself to her feet, and made her way upstairs. A door slammed. The wall brackets trembled.

But Colette did not leave, after all. The storm passed. Life fell into its old pattern of resignation. Jacqueline was brought home by Colette's widowed sister, who stayed through the summer.

Freeman spent more and more time in his office at the back of the store. For almost a year he worked on a cold cure. It came to nothing. He returned to his efforts to develop an insect repellent. The work provided a needed distraction.

Some evenings, after the store had been closed, he pursued the dream of the Japanese house. He corresponded with Japanese architects in the United States as well as in Japan. He kept three filing drawers: INTERIOR, EXTERIOR, GARDENS.

This, research experiments, his daughter, and his love became, as years passed, the four corners of his existence.

With Jacqueline he fished and sailed and talked. Like most of the island children, she was an expert sailor, moving steadily from dinghy, to catboat, to sloop, to yawl. She raced, often won; swam and dived. She grew to be beautiful and became increasingly eager to get away from the unspoken tension of her home.

Sheila and Freeman met only twice in the first two years following her departure.

Once, during a weekend when she and her husband came to visit island friends, eight months after Thomas had undertaken his new assignment.

She and Freeman went to the pond in separate cars as dusk fell one evening.

It was as though they had been separated for no more than a day or two. They were together.

He told her of Colette's continuing inflexible position.

"It doesn't matter," said Sheila. "Our time will come."

Freeman reached over and took her hand.

He had brought along some new plans for the house. They were discussed as though realization were imminent.

Sheila and Freeman parted, more secure in their love than ever—more determined to be patient and discreet.

Another year was to pass before their next encounter. New York, this time. Three days at the St. Regis, never leaving her suite.

Herbert Clark Hoover had become President. Thomas Van Anda joined his government at a high level. Van Anda's considerable assets were placed in a holding trusteeship to avoid conflict of interest. Within the year the historic stock-market collapse occurred. Technicalities made it impossible for Thomas Van Anda to deal with his securities. He was sold out and informed over the telephone, one October morning, that he was bankrupt.

Sheila took the news stoically, but within a month Thomas suffered the first of a series of heart attacks that were to incapacitate him for a decade.

They returned to New York. Sheila went to work as a salesclerk at R. H. Macy & Co. She had not been able to turn her skill in photography into a means of livelihood. Later she found more lucrative employment in various publishing houses and by 1939 had become east coast story editor for Universal Pictures.

She and Thomas, a semi-invalid, lived quietly in a cheerful, small apartment on Riverside Drive. On his good days he tried to continue with a book on the Foreign Service he had been writing for many years.

It was during this time that Freeman found himself living three lives. There was the workaday one, involving the duties and responsibilities of his daily existence: letters from Jacqueline, at boarding school; conferences with his wife (they no longer conversed, only conferred); political anxieties and economic clouds.

Then there was the more vivid ongoing life he lived in imagination. This one involved the future, which he shared with Sheila. They traveled and worked together. They went each year for an indefinite stay in Japan. This aspect of his life was made partly of memory, mainly of plans.

The third of his lives was the one he had in reality with Sheila, during which his blood flowed more swiftly through his veins, and affirmation filled the surrounding air. However limited, cruelly spaced—these periods represented fulfillment. He longed for the time when the latter two would become one. There was no question in his mind that it would come.

Sheila and Freeman met infrequently, but always with joy. They were often forced to settle for odd times and curious places, but nothing mattered so long as they could be together. Their life developed, as do all lovers' lives, areas of interest, a language, private jokes, and shared subjects. She brought more music into his life, especially Mozart, Mahler, and Brahms. And Bach.

He reintroduced her to nature, on which, by and large, she had turned her back since leaving the ranch of her girlhood. Animals and weather and flowers soon returned to charm and inspire her again. Their life together was rich, richer.

They shared worries, illnesses and recoveries, ecstasies. The passionate interest in Japan was a bond from the start, and as the years passed, it became a consuming one.

"Did I ever tell you about General Nagaoka?" she asked one night. "The man with the mustache two feet long?"

"Did you say *two feet?*"

"One foot from here to here," she demonstrated. "The other, here to here. It was truly resplendent. He headed the Japanese air force, I believe, and it was quite the thing to be photographed with him—in the way one is with the Leaning Tower in Pisa. And we were—Thomas and I. I have the photograph still. Well. Listen to this. A letter from my friend Iwasa Ito—now I *have* told you about *him.*"

"The innkeeper."

"Son of," she said. "Here's his letter. 'Most Honored of Friends'—Oh, I can skip some of this—and then, here. 'You shall be interested to hear of the death of our old General Gaishi Nagaoka because of kidney. An ancient of seventy-five and doubtless you are remembered of his outstanding growth of mustache—precisely one-third of his own full height. Before his immolation, at his instruction, came his eldest son, cut off mustaches. Same were wrapped in finest white burial silk, placed upon cushion of satin in casket of its own, and buried with honor. Not cremation as was man to whom belonged these celestial mustaches. . . .' And then it goes on. Isn't that a splendid account?"

Freeman was regarding her.

"You look eleven years old," he said. "I could get arrested."

IN LATER YEARS they relaxed discretion and began to exchange letters. Hers were sent to the store, his to her office. When the letters were no more than friendly, Sheila and Freeman learned to read feeling into simple announcements.

He once wrote:

Jacqueline is in love. She has not said so, but I see her smiling secretly to herself; she cries at Brahms; she is reading Edna St. Vincent Millay.

First love. Is there anything sweeter? Yes. In France, when they say "*Si jeunesse savait* . . ." the rest is implied, meaning, "If youth but knew; if age but could!" But then, as you know, I am not greatly in sympathy with the philosophy of the French!

On another occasion, in a letter of hers:

Thomas's bad days are beginning to outnumber his good days. He is extremely patient (I am not!) and courageous and more understanding. We had planned a weekend in Old Lyme with friends recently. At the last moment he informed me that he was simply not up to it. I'm afraid I behaved less than gracefully. When he begged me to go out somewhere by myself, I did. I called several friends (some of them long distance), but could find no one. What do you think I did? You'll never guess! I went to three movies. Yes. Three! In one day. *The Grapes of Wrath* (well made and moving, but no match for the stupendous book); *Pinocchio* (turned me into a child—a terrified child); *The Westerner* (you may consider Mr. Cooper a hated rival!). All this and phoning Thomas in between, of course. Imagine it. A day and part of an evening spent watching other people's dreams! What am I coming to?

Freeman to Sheila:

Still another birthday. This one distinguished by the fact that it went unnoticed by all—wife, daughter, you. I thank you for forgetting, but I resent them. They owe me—well, at least a Woolworth card.

What an odd factor is time! Here I am—getting on, as they say—yet younger than I have been since the days when I was one of the football heroes at the Edgartown High School.

You have done this, my love. You have given me youth. Shall we call it your birthday gift to me? Yes. Thank you.

I feel young, I am healthy and reasonably happy, and—oh—how impatient!

Sheila to Freeman:

Dearest, I make lists. Questions I want to ask you. Things I want to tell you. Places we must visit together. Activities. The agenda grows longer. Will we have time for it all? I get scared sometimes. Am I hoping for more than is possible? No. Life—our sort of life—is limitless, isn't it? Tell me that it is. You have so enriched me in so many ways. I see and hear and touch and smell and taste so much more vividly since you. Since us. Yet I only half enjoy these newfound sensitivities. I need you near to share them. How often I think, "He would like this." "He would laugh." "I wonder what he—" I wonder. I wonder. Please know that you are with me always. I thank you for removing loneliness from my life. You have given me so many lovely memories. You provide so much to hope for. I do not send you my love, because you already have it. Keep it safe, my darling, as I do yours, warming me always.

WHEN in 1941 Pearl Harbor was bombed and war declared, Thomas Van Anda put his illness aside, flew to Washington, and volunteered his services to the Secretary of State. He was offered a post in London, where diplomats with organizational experience were needed. He accepted with a single provision: that his wife be given employment in the same area. Granted.

Sheila and Freeman had a day together before she flew to London via Air Transport Command. He told her that he had called the navy recruiting office in Boston and had been told that there might be something despite his age—forty-eight. Qualified pharmacists were at a premium. In all likelihood he would be sent to the Pacific to fight his second war.

Their own problems seemed infinitesimal when the world was

on the verge of destruction. Their farewell was purposeful and austere.

In 1943, through a series of curious coincidences and one classification error, Freeman found himself on his way to London. The naval officer who had been assigned to head the pharmaceutical unit of Operation Overlord had proved to be not a pharmacist, but a farmer. Freeman, a chief petty officer in training for Pacific duty, was swiftly located, commissioned commander, and flown to England.

He telephoned Sheila from London Airport. She was working in the publications division of the OWI and living in a flat just off Piccadilly. She was not in her office, but a secretary, responding to the urgency in Freeman's voice, gave him Sheila's home number.

Thomas Van Anda answered, and Freeman found himself unable to speak.

At length: "Hello. This is Freeman Osborn."

"Osborn?"

"The drugstore. In Edgartown?"

"Osborn! What are *you* doing here?"

"I'm in the navy, I think," said Freeman, trembling. "It's all happened so suddenly, I haven't adjusted to it yet. I'm a commander. They needed someone to run a pharmacy. Theirs is bigger than mine, but I'll manage, I guess."

"Congratulations."

"And how are you? Both."

"Hectic," said Van Anda. "Along with the rest. You must come in for a drink one day."

"Thank you. Whenever you say."

"Drop Mrs. Van Anda a note and tell her where you are."

"Certainly."

"She's out shopping somewhere. Fortnum and Mason's, probably." He laughed. "She's never out of the place. Good of you to call. Good-by."

Freeman found a taxi; threw his gear (duffel bag, Val-A-Pak, footlocker, and flight bag) into the front; got into the back, and said, "Fortnum and Mason's, please." They drove off. At the shop he negotiated a waiting price, and the cabby arranged to pick him up at the rear entrance.

Freeman went in and searched for his love. After half an hour of fruitless exploration, and noting that a floorwalker was beginning to regard him suspiciously, he made a purchase of tea biscuits, went once more through the store, left, and found his taxi.

His billet was a two-room flat in Knightsbridge, a short walk to the naval supply depot, where he was to make his headquarters. He unpacked and went to the naval officers' mess for dinner. The food was plentiful and surprisingly good. He walked, finding his way to Piccadilly Circus, Leicester Square, Trafalgar Square.

Night fell quickly, and he was confronted with the phenomenon of the blackout for the first time. Despite his recent training and briefing, he was unprepared for the aspect of a city truly in total darkness: traffic crawling, people bumping into one another. It took him just under three hours to find his way home.

The night that followed alternated between deep sleep and intense wakefulness filled with visions of what might be expected in the months to come. The whims of war had brought them to the same place, but how could they manage a life?

In the morning he reported to his station and was swept, without delay, into the complex world of D Day preparation. He forgot to lunch, and it was not until the afternoon tea break that he found himself free to call Sheila.

She was not in, a secretary informed him.

"Can you tell me where I might reach her? It's rather urgent. I'm a friend of hers. Commander Osborn."

"Yes, I know. As a matter of fact I've been trying to track you down all day, but your navy hasn't been helpful, I *must* say."

He gave her his addresses and phone numbers, then said, "You're sure there's no place I can reach her now?"

"Actually she's gone to the doctor's, and I don't think she's—"

"Is she ill?"

"I'm sure I don't know, sir."

He hung up and worried.

At five o'clock he went to Fortnum & Mason again. He could think of nothing else to do, having rejected the thought of calling her office again, as well as the idea of trying her at home. He wandered aimlessly about the shop, only half searching. At the back, as he stood looking at a shelf of tinned goods from Portugal, an unmistakable scent hit his nostrils with the force of a punch in the nose. He whirled about.

There, on a high stool at the service counter, he saw a familiar back and the bun of hair so dear to him. Sheila. Sheila. He moved toward her at once, but hesitated as he saw that she was in conversation with a handsome man. He approached the couple. "Excuse me."

"Freeman!" she cried, and put out her hand, smiling radiantly. She introduced the men to each other. "Freeman!" Sheila repeated. "Of all people! I'd ask you to join us, but we're deep in business. I'm trying all my wiles on this man to make him do something for me, but so far they're not working."

"They're working," he said. "And pretty soon *I'll* be working. Harder than I like."

Sheila regarded Freeman, her face flushed. "Aren't you supposed to be in the Pacific?"

"Diverted," said Freeman.

"I'm *so* glad. Thomas mumbled something about a call from you, but he's so vague these days, I couldn't be certain. I asked the office to check, and they reported you as nonexistent."

A pause. Freeman knew that he must leave, yet he waited.

"Look here," Sheila said suddenly. "I'm meeting Thomas in about half an hour. Please come. He'd be *so* delighted to see you. *Please!*" It struck him that she was communicating on another level. "We're meeting at the Cavendish." She pointed. "Out that door and across the street. Half an hour. In the bar."

"All right. Pleased to have met you, sir." They shook hands. Sheila turned away.

Freeman went to the Cavendish bar and ordered a Scotch and water.

"Out, I'm afraid," said the waitress.

"What *do* you have?"

"Dubonnet, pink gin, vermouth, and–"

"That'll do. Pink gin."

He wondered what it was, and was beginning to find out when Sheila arrived. "Same for me, please." Then loudly, looking about, "Thomas not here yet? That man is *never* on time."

Freeman spoke softly. "Is he coming?"

"No. Of course not," she said quietly. "He'll be in conferences tonight."

Her drink was served. They raised their glasses to each other. "Cheers," he said. "Isn't that what we say over here?"

"Cheers," she said.

"Why the doctor?"

"What?"

"Why did you have to see the doctor?" he insisted.

Sheila blinked. "I'll kill that girl."

"My fault. I forced her into telling me. I was desperate to find you. Now," he insisted. "Why the doctor?"

"I'm overweight. You must see it."

"Yes, I do."

"You're supposed to say, 'But it's *so* becoming.' "

"But it's *so* becoming," he said.

"If I'd known about you turning up, I wouldn't have let it happen. I'm sorry."

"It doesn't matter at all!" He signaled the waitress. "Would you like another?"

"No, thank you. I just went on a strict diet."

"One more for me," he said to the waitress. He took a deep breath, relaxed with his second pink gin, and looked about. "What a nice place."

"I'm *so* glad you like it," she said over the rim of her glass, "because you live here." She handed him a key. "In four-oh-five. It's one room–what they call a bed-sitter." She turned cockney and added, "Evah so noice!"

"Have I been in it long?"

"Only since this morning. A lad from my office brought your bags over and checked you in. The hall porter will need your passport for an hour or so."

Freeman shook his head slowly and contemplated her with wonder. "Sheila, Sheila," he said.

A few minutes later he said good-by to her at the door, saw the porter, and went up to 405. There he found the most pleasant of rooms: old, but beautifully appointed. There were flowers, a basket of fruit, a tray of drinks, American magazines, and a copy of the *Vineyard Gazette.* This last item confirmed who had arranged the room.

The bags—not his—had been unpacked. Uniforms hung in the closet, shirts and socks, pajamas and underwear, had been put away, toilet articles arranged.

A knock on the door. He opened it. Sheila came in. He closed the door and locked it as she went to the windows and closed the shutters. They moved toward each other and touched.

"Welcome home, my darling," she said.

"Thank you," he whispered. "For everything. For my life."

There were no further words for a long, loving time.

Later they sat, she in a man's dressing gown, he in his raincoat, each eating a piece of fruit. "What is cholesterol?" she asked.

"Why do you want to know?"

"Because I've got it," she said.

"*Everyone's* got it, you goose."

"Then why's the doctor so frowny about it?"

"Maybe you have too much. Then it's a problem."

"Serious?"

"Not very. A question of diet, that's all."

He caressed her. "I don't feel any cholesterol," he said.

"What is it?"

He explained in full physiological detail. Sheila listened with interest.

"What it comes down to, then," she said finally, "is that I eat too much of what's wrong. Yes. I always do when I'm discontented. Unsatisfied."

"We all do. It's the quick and easy answer. However, you look *quite* good to me."

So began their war years, the best of their life together. Freeman moved from his billet, and the Cavendish remained his home until four months after V-E Day.

The months to D Day were charged with excitement. They both felt increasingly useful in their work, and the sense of being part of a plan of high purpose was invigorating.

They began by respecting and admiring many British individuals, and ended by loving them en masse. The spirit, the will, the devotion, and, above all, the humor of the people enchanted them.

The first time Thomas Van Anda had to return to Washington he phoned Freeman. "Look here, old man. I'm off for a week or two, and I wonder if you'd do me a *great* service."

"Of course. Whatever I can."

"It's only to keep an eye on Mrs. Van Anda. We have very few personal friends over here. Could you possibly give her a ring each day and see she's all right? Perhaps take her to dinner once or twice and, of course, she loves the theater here. You might escort her if you can spare an evening. I'll want to reimburse you, of course."

"Oh, no."

"Now, now. I insist. Oh, and if any problem should come up you can use the State Department telex. And if you can't reach me, my secretary is Mrs. Roos. R-o-o-s."

"Is that here or there?"

"Both places. She's coming to Washington with me, of course."

"Right."

"I appreciate this, old man. She will, too. Mrs. Van Anda."

Sheila swore that she had not engineered the plan directly or indirectly. They went out nightly. The Sadler's Wells Ballet. The Old Vic. Freeman could not shake his feeling of unease. In all the years, he had never felt the slightest guilt. The liaison was completely honorable, in his view. But now, to be shepherding Mrs. Van Anda about at the request of *Mr.* Van Anda was embarrassing. "I wish he hadn't called me," Freeman said to her.

She took his arm. They were walking on the Hyde Park path, on their way to dinner. "Love," she said. "Please don't. People who live our sort of life have to make many compromises. It's a question of whether it's worth it or not."

"It's worth anything," he said.

THOMAS Van Anda returned from Washington, and as June 6, D Day, approached, the meetings between Sheila and Freeman became less frequent.

The monumental D Day arrow was being pulled back, back on its bowstring.

The planners began working nights, Sundays, and holidays. The fateful Tuesday morning came. The landings began.

Freeman's duties took him back and forth across the Channel almost daily. For a time he could think of nothing but the next trip.

They were together in the Cavendish, however, when V-1 rockets made their first deadly appearance a week after the invasion of the Continent. There had been no air-raid warning, only a sudden succession of fierce explosions. Half an hour later antiaircraft fire began, and the alert sounded.

Sheila and Freeman went to the window to watch the sky. They left the hotel. In the street the mysterious bombardment was being discussed by small groups everywhere. Overhead, from time to time, flaming crosses could be seen. Twenty or thirty seconds after the flame went out, an explosion would occur. Antiaircraft fire became more intense. The air-raid wardens were ordering people off the streets.

Sheila phoned her husband at his office. "Are you all right?" she asked.

"So far. You?"

"Yes, but I'm afraid I can't get home."

"Where are you?"

"Leicester Square," she said, and described an earlier incident. "I was at the movies, but I left when they began flashing the alert on the screen."

"All right," said Van Anda. "Find a comfortable spot and sit tight until the all clear."

"What's going on?"

"I'm not sure. It does seem, though, that Hitler's long-touted secret weapon has finally turned up."

"Yes. Well. Take care, dear."

She and Freeman returned to the Cavendish and went to bed, fully dressed. They clung together as the raid continued.

"Wouldn't it be awful," she said, "if this were it?"

"Don't think such things," he said. "Shall I tell you what's really going to happen? We're going to win the war in about ten months. Then, as soon as things have calmed down in the Pacific, we're going to Japan together. I haven't decided whether we're going to fly or go by sea from San Francisco."

She waited for a deafening burst of antiaircraft fire to subside before she spoke. "Why not fly one way and boat the other?"

"Perfect," he said. "We'll fly there, and come back by boat."

An explosion shook the room.

"On second thought," she said, "we'll go by sea both ways. We'll make love and eat *sashimi* and study Japanese all the way there."

"And the same coming back."

"No. Coming back, we'll be planning the house."

"Of course," he said. "Stupid of me."

This was to be their last night together for eleven months.

As the invasion thundered on, personal communication became increasingly difficult, especially after Sheila went on detached service to the OSS, and security regarding the movement of intelligence personnel became critical. He heard accidentally that she had been transferred to the Continent. It was not until three weeks after V-E Day, on May 7, 1945, that Freeman learned Sheila was now in Paris and that her husband had gone to the Pacific two days after the German surrender.

He managed a trip to Paris. The Hôtel Scribe was the headquarters for the press as well as the intelligence services and he went there at once. Sheila Van Anda was, indeed, registered, but she was not in. He walked about the busy hotel and the surrounding streets until well after midnight. He went back to the Scribe, inquired again. She had not returned.

He went to his own billet and slept, clothed, for a few hours. Then he walked to the Scribe, waited until the dining room opened at seven a.m., and went in. As he was finishing his breakfast he looked across the room and saw two portly, uniformed women sharing a table. He could not make out if they were American or British. They laughed. One of the laughs was stunningly familiar. He got up and rushed across the room. Sheila jumped up as he approached. They embraced. She felt strange in his arms, bulky to the touch.

"You rat!" she said. "Sneaking up on a girl like that."

"I wasn't sure it was—I mean, I've never *seen* you in uniform before."

"Isn't it dashing?" she asked. "Made by Omar the Tentmaker."

She introduced him to her companion, a young Frenchwoman attached to SHAEF. After an aimless chat Freeman said, "Finish your breakfast. Sorry to have barged in."

"And finish yours," said Sheila.

He realized that he was holding his napkin in his hand.

"Call me up sometime, won't you? Soon," she added meaningfully.

Half an hour later he phoned her room.

"Seven-oh-seven," she said. "Hurry, love."

They talked all day, loved all night. They ate and bathed and drank at random. They were catching up.

She was hazardously overweight now, as a result of months of terror and loneliness and the recent temptations of Parisian food. He assured her that he found her Renoir-like ampleness attractive, which was true. When, however, he learned that she had not had a recent cholesterol count, he took her privately to a confidential clinic on the top floor of the Hôtel Meurice, run for the convenience of ranking officers. The result of the test was not encouraging. A diet and a system of exercise were prescribed. Freeman had every intention of supervising her treatment with care, but was precipitously ordered to the Pacific. Okinawa.

FIVE

When the war in the Pacific ended, Freeman could not resist promoting, for himself, a trip to Japan. He wandered about on invented missions for twenty days, traveling by boat, train, army transport, and on foot. Osaka (the puppet theater). Kyoto (the temples). Nagoya (the Shinto shrine). Yokohama (the devastation). Sasebo (the naval base).

Despite the gaping war wounds, the numb hostility of many, and the postdefeat chaos, Freeman found Japan all he had dreamed and more. Moreover he had the unmistakable impression of Sheila at his side throughout the journey.

When he went back home to Martha's Vineyard, life went on from where it had left off four years earlier. Colette waited long enough to attend Jacqueline's graduation from Radcliffe, and left for France immediately afterward.

Freeman and Sheila met as often as they could: on the island, in New York, in Washington. Sheila and her husband had come to an amicable understanding with regard to their future. Their marriage had clearly run its course. The details of their divorce had only to be worked out.

Freeman and Sheila, whenever they met, talked of this and of the new subject that had come into their lives: Freeman's project. In Japan he had encountered an English-speaking chemist who had told him of his unsuccessful attempts to compound an effective insect repellent, much needed in the Sasebo area.

Freeman, long interested in the subject, had gone back to work on the problem. The drugstore was now being effectively run by Mrs. Petschek and Martin Stein, a young Boston pharmacist. Thus Freeman was able to devote long periods of time in the Chilmark barn he had converted into a laboratory. He came close to the solution on several occasions, but each time there was a flaw: irritating to sensitive skins, too medicinal in odor.

One windy autumn day he left his work to meet Sheila at the St. Regis in New York. He knocked softly on the door to 1103-1105. It opened. He walked into the sitting room of the suite. It was filled with the flowers he had sent. He heard the door behind him close, the bolt thrown.

He turned to find her moving toward him. They were lost in their kiss. His hands moved over her body. It was as though he needed reassurance that she was there, real. Long pent-up hope was expressed, desire fulfilled.

They smiled at each other, as they often did. He took a bottle of wine from the cooler and uncorked it. It was Pouilly Fumé, a memory of their Paris time. They touched glasses.

"I love you," he said.

And she said, "I love you."

They made themselves comfortable, close to each other, on the large sofa.

"I've got a little bad news," he said. "The formula's still no good. Now it smells bad."

"But you said you thought the chlorophyll would—"

"I thought wrong. Three months on the wrong track!"

They sipped in depressed silence. "You know what I'd do right now if I still smoked?" she asked.

"What?"

"I'd have a cigarette."

"I wish you hadn't said that," he said, pressing her to him. "Because it's been on my mind. I sell them, of course, in the store. And I wish I didn't. More and more we're learning the worst. Bob Nevin told me the other day that he went to a medical convention, and about three thousand doctors were in the hall, about half of them smoking, when this fellow from the Sloan-Kettering here in New York read his paper on the latest findings. He showed slides and recited statistics. Bob says it took almost an hour, and by the time he was finished not a single doctor in the place was smoking. Of course, I suppose they all started again. But why do I *sell* the damned things and make money on them?"

"My love," she said, "you're a good man—the best I know—but you can't remake the race."

"I'm not as good a man as I could be. I could put up a sign THIS STORE DOES NOT SELL CIGARETTES—and tell why."

"They'd go somewhere else for them," she said.

"Bad argument."

"Do it, then."

"I may at that," he said. "Would you approve?"

"I'd be proud of you," she said.

They sat together for a time, in thought.

"Imagine it," he said, and began to caress her. "Had it not been for a single particle—lodged in your eye—I might have lived and died and never known love. This is love. To care more for someone than for self. To live *with* someone, *in* someone else. To feel that the other half of yourself has been joined to you. I revere you. Here am I, a middle-aged man, catapulted back into youth. I'm old and young and in love. New feelings, never-before sensations."

"You are my love," she said.

Two months passed before he was able to implement his no-cigarette-sales principle. The jobber who supplied him with tobacco products handled other goods as well and, fearful that Freeman's move might encourage others, refused to sell Freeman what he wanted selectively. Freeman's attempts to make other arrangements for his needs failed. A complicated, rooted franchise system was in force.

There were further talks with Sheila. At length the sign appeared in his store:

THIS STORE, PROFESSIONALLY CONCERNED
WITH THE HEALTH AND WELL-BEING OF THE
COMMUNITY IT SERVES, DOES NOT SELL
CIGARETTES, CIGARS, PIPE TOBACCO,
TOBACCO IN ANY FORM, NOR ANY OTHER
POISONS EXCEPT BY PRESCRIPTION.

F. T. OSBORN

Edgartown buzzed. The Boston *Globe* ran a front-page story. It was picked up by the Associated Press, which circulated the story widely, in a version that made Freeman seem like a Yankee eccentric. But as long as Freeman owned the store no tobacco was sold there.

Meanwhile he continued to work, unsuccessfully, with various forms of chlorophyll to make his insect repellent odorless. Then one morning, leafing through a long-dead whaling captain's journal he had bought at a rummage sale, he came upon a passage on ambergris and its uses. Could ambergris be the answer? A week later he acquired a sampling of the stuff and began a new series of experiments.

He tested the new substance on himself again and again. He sought out swampland and marshes. He walked through particularly infested parts of the state forest. His substance worked!

He engaged a group of twelve high-school students to assist him. Three boys and three girls became a control group; the remaining six used his spray. The results were dramatically affirmative.

His next step involved a trip to New York to consult with patent attorneys. When they told him it was safe to proceed he went to Cincinnati. There he met with the head of the pharmaceutical firm he most trusted. Acceptance was immediate. A simple letter of agreement was drafted and signed; the full documents would take months. Freeman's new partner-friend took him to the airport. As they parted, the man asked, "Well, sir, how does it feel to be a millionaire?"

"It feels fine," he replied.

Flying back to New York to meet Sheila, he thought he had at last, in his fifties, done something useful. Sheila would take pride. Nothing mattered to him more.

His creative thoughts turned to the Japanese house they would build on Squibnocket Pond. His new affluence made it possible to think in new categories. Why not buy *all* the wood and stone and parchment in Japan? Bring Japanese craftsmen over to erect the house, and gardeners to do the landscaping? The only way. It would cost—who cares what it would cost? He looked forward excitedly to discussing it with Sheila.

The day was marred. She failed to arrive for their meeting at the St. Regis. A special-delivery letter came instead on the following day. It was typed, and bore as a return address: Cavendish, P. O. Box 1144, Washington, D.C.

This had been their code for some time. The letter:

Love,

We must go home for a few days. Home! For some reason still unknown to me my presence is not only desired, but imperative. Forgive me. How did it all go in Cincinnati? Are you as thrilled and pleased and proud and delighted as I am? Wait for me in New York if you can. I shall do better than my best. Meanwhile be happy. As you deserve to be. Here is my heart.

He read it several times, tore it into small bits, and flushed it down the toilet, a safety precaution of long standing.

He phoned his daughter, now a graduate drama student at the University of Texas. "Jackson?" (This was his name for her, now that she had outgrown Jackie.)

"Dad! Where are you?"

"New York. In the splendor of the St. Regis. I've got a parcel of grand news, and no one to share it with."

"What is it?"

"I'll give you this much. Your old dad's had a marvelous stroke of good fortune. And there's a good chance that you'll be a rich young lady. Even now I'm prepared to offer you a sample."

"What're you talking about, Cap?"

He trembled. She had not used this name since their regatta days, when he was Captain and she– "Well, listen, Mate," he said. "I want you to tell me three things you want–not wishes, *things*. I can't grant wishes, but I can come up with things."

"Are you serious, Cap?"

"Try me."

"How about a new car?" she asked.

"What kind?"

"A Studebaker Champion."

"What color?"

"Red."

"What else?" he asked.

"Dad!"

"What else?"

"I'd give anything for a bigger apartment."

"I'm doing the giving today. But not a bigger apartment. I want you to buy a house."

"*What?*" she shouted.

"A small house. You're a house girl, Mate. You were born and raised in a house, and you'll always be happier in a house."

She was crying now. "Cap," she said, "you're a very wise man."

"Don't look for a bargain—you'll find, later, that there's no such thing, really. Look for a house you want to live in. You can always sell it when you're done with it. What else? That's only two," he reminded her. "Studebaker, red. House, small."

"Well, we could use some money. There's this terrific script—with one of those surefire parts in it—but nobody'll put it on—even for a tryout. I believe in it, though."

"Who's *we?*"

"Me and Brad. The boy I'm going with. He wants to marry me. I'm not ready for marriage, but he's at me all the time."

"Of course. He's after your money!"

They laughed together.

"Look here," he said. "What time is it out there?"

"Ten fifteen a.m."

"All right. I want you to buy your things right now. This offer is only good until six p.m."

"Cap. I think you've gone crazy. The car, yes—but not the house. I can't possibly—"

"Sorry, miss. By six p.m. or it's all off."

He hung up. A few minutes later the phone rang. He knew it was Jacqueline. He sat smiling at the phone, but did not answer it.

He lingered in New York for three days. He bought tickets for the Old Vic season, hoping that Sheila would turn up to go with him. When she did not, he went to the theater alone, turned in his extra ticket, and later observed with interest, each time, the buyer at his side.

The first night it was an intense, haggard young man, who did not remove his coat and sat clutching a pile of magazines throughout the performance of *Henry IV*, Part 2. The next night provided a sweet-faced, beautifully dressed, elderly lady. She applauded *Uncle Vanya* vociferously at the end and shouted, "Bravo!" but said not a word to Freeman.

On the third night, *Oedipus Rex* was to be played on a double bill with Sheridan's comedy *The Critic*. The lights had already gone down when a small figure slipped into the seat beside him. Freeman saw that it was an exceedingly attractive young woman. She fished in her handbag, found eyeglasses, put them on, and leaned forward. She gave her full attention to the performance and did not change her position by so much as an inch.

At the end the stunned audience sat in silence before exploding into its ovation.

Freeman made a move toward the aisle, but could not pass as the girl was still sitting forward, holding on to the back of the seat in front of her.

"May I?" he asked.

"What? Oh. Sorry." She rose and stepped back.

"Aren't you going out?"

"No." She smiled. "I can't believe I got this seat, and I'm scared someone may get it away from me if I leave it, even if I am dying for a cigarette after that. Like you."

"I don't smoke," said Freeman. "I've got an idea. You go ahead. I'll guard your seat. With my life."

She leaped from her seat and ran up the aisle, returning just as the lights were dimming. "Thanks," she said.

The Sheridan farce that followed was spirited. Freeman and the girl looked at each other several times, sharing the fun. The evening ended in a joyous burst of appreciation from the audience and players alike. The girl continued to look toward the stage, although the curtain had fallen. "Well," she said gravely, "I would say that this has been the greatest single evening I've ever spent in the theater."

They moved up the aisle together.

"Are you the one who turned the ticket in?" she inquired.

"Yes."

"Then I certainly want to thank you. What happened?"

"My wife," he answered, "was delayed. Out of town."

"Well, I'm sorry for her and glad for me."

"Would you care for a dish of ice cream?" asked Freeman.

She laughed. "Certainly not. Try champagne. That's the only appropriate thing after a super event like the one tonight."

After a pause Freeman asked, "Would you care for a glass of champagne?"

"Yes," she replied brightly. "Yes, I believe I would. How'd you guess?"

They walked toward the Plaza in silence.

"Are you troubled about something?" he asked, halfway.

"Yes," she said. "I'm not sure I should be doing this."

"Doing what?"

"Letting myself be picked up by strange men."

"Oh. Do you think I'm strange?" he asked.

"I meant—stranger."

"That's even worse," he said.

The tension broken, they moved into the Plaza contentedly. Freeman asked for the wine list and ordered champagne.

She said, "I was only kidding. Honestly."

"Well, anyway, my name is Freeman Osborn," he said. "I'm a pharmacist. I live in Edgartown, Massachusetts. I'm fifty-six years old, and the top of my life was three days ago."

"I'm Diana Boyle." They shook hands across the table. "I'm an actress." The champagne arrived and was served. After half a glass she went on. "Two parts in three years. A small one in a hit and a big one in a flop. In between, modeling, radio, TV, commercials. I come from Rochester, New York. And I'm twenty-five. And I live at the Three Arts Club on Eighty-fifth Street, and the bottom of my life is right now."

"Why?"

"Listen. I feel quite dizzy all of a sudden. Maybe it's the champagne—and I haven't eaten all day. Should I get some air?" She looked, more than anything, frightened.

"No," he said. "Food." He signaled the captain. "What's ready?"

"Roast beef, chicken aspic?"

"Roast beef. Right away, would you? The young lady doesn't feel well."

She sat, resting her head on her fingertips, listening wanly as Freeman talked about the plays they had just seen, about the Old Vic in London during the war. The food arrived. "Eat it slowly," he advised.

It worked. She felt better, drank more champagne. He ordered ice cream for them both. "See?" he said. "A dish of ice cream after all. Why didn't you eat all day? Not economy?"

He noticed that his question had made her blush.

"Was it?"

She nodded once.

"But that damned ticket tonight. You paid six dollars for a theater ticket and didn't *eat?* You're out of your mind."

She looked at him and said quietly, "No, I'm not, Mr. Osborn."

"Anything more?" he asked.

"No, thank you. I'm fine."

"Check, please," he called. Then to her, "*Now* some air." As they left the hotel on the Central Park side he asked, "How long since you took a carriage ride through the park?"

"Never," she said.

"Shall we?"

"Why not?"

In an ancient carriage they moved slowly through the surprising, verdant park. Freeman spoke. "The bottom of your life, you said. Why?"

She hesitated. "I'm thinking of some advice my mother once gave me: 'Never tell a man your troubles.' "

Freeman laughed. "Your mother was giving you the right steer there. But, after all, I'm not a man in the sense that she meant. So go ahead."

"Well," she began. "It's not very original. Man trouble. One stubborn no-good man I'm so madly in love with I can *taste* it! Even talking about him—and I've got wet palms, my mouth's dry. I don't know if you can hear my heart going, but *I* can."

Taxis and cars overtook their carriage, sped past, giving the impression that it was traveling more slowly than it was. The pace seemed to break the headlong velocity of the city about them. They rode in silence for a time, each comforted by the presence of the other. At Seventy-second Street she spoke again. "This is my fourth time in love," she said, "but it's my first time. Does that make sense?"

"Certainly. Where is he?"

"In Maine," she replied miserably. "He's a potter."

"Is that supposed to impress me?"

"What do you mean?"

"I've never heard of them," said Freeman.

"Who? Oh! I don't mean he's a *Potter*. His name is Rosen—Jerry Rosen. He's a *potter*. He makes pots and bowls and urns."

"Oh," said Freeman. "I see."

"Actually he's probably the greatest living potter in the world today."

"Then what's the trouble?"

"This. I'm here and he's there. What I'm trying to do, I have to do here. New York is the only place. What he does, he could do anywhere. But he won't. He says he's not ready. He works for another potter for room and board, and that's it. So how're we ever going to put together the seven thousand he needs to go on his own? Equipment and a kiln and a wheel. Also a place—and time. He figures a year and a half to be self-supporting."

"He sounds like a practical chap."

"That's his trouble. He's *too* practical. So we made this plan. Work and save. Thirty-five hundred each, and as soon as we've got it he comes down, we set up, and even get married, if it's not too expensive." She sighed. "That was over a year ago. So guess where we are? He's got forty-five dollars from two pieces he sold, and I'm sixteen hundred in debt. And on top of that it's after one, and I've got to be in by two—that's the rule—after that the door's locked, and you need a letter from the Secretary of Defense to get in."

They abandoned the carriage abruptly. Freeman hailed a taxi and told the driver to hurry. They reached Eighty-fifth Street and Broadway by one thirty. "A nightcap," said Freeman.

In a booth at the Bretton Hall Hotel bar, Diana ordered beer, which surprised him. He asked for J&B on the rocks and said, "Excuse me."

She was halfway through her beer when he returned. He handed her an envelope.

"What's this?"

"It's a loan. I consider it a good investment. Now it's up to you and Mr. Rosen not to let me down."

As he spoke she opened the envelope and looked at the check inside. It was drawn on the Edgartown National Bank and made out to her in the amount of seven thousand dollars. She gasped, and handed it back, saying, "What *is* this?"

"Take it," he insisted.

"Jerry'll think—who *knows* what—"

Freeman stood up and looked down at her angrily. "If Jerry believes anything other than what you tell him, you've no business marrying him anyway. Now shut up and let's go, or you'll be locked out."

They walked swiftly through the lobby, down Eighty-fifth Street to the Three Arts Club. "Look at me," she said huskily on the way. "I'm staggering. On one beer."

At the door he took her hand and kissed it gracefully.

He walked away. At the corner he turned. She waved to him from the doorway and went in. Buoyantly, Freeman walked all the way back to the St. Regis.

He never saw Diana Boyle again, nor was he ever to meet Jerry Rosen, but the seven thousand dollars was repaid within two years with carefully calculated interest. From time to time he recognized Diana on a television show, and once he saw her in a Broadway play. A year or so after the encounter, Freeman received an invitation to a private showing of Jerry Rosen's work at a Fifty-seventh Street gallery, thought of going, but decided, at the last minute, against it. . . .

ON THE porch of the Falmouth Sunset House, Freeman was again remembering. This time pain flooded through him, beginning in the pit of his stomach, it seemed, and reaching—octopuslike—in all directions. When it had permeated him completely, it turned into a sickening nausea. What he recalled was Sheila's pregnancy and their never-born child.

In all their years it was the one time he had seen her weep—and she did so bitterly, abandonedly. Yes, he had thought as he held her close to him, but providing small comfort. No wonder. She is weeping for all three of us.

Years had made the memory more vivid: its colors richer, its sounds vibrant. He now saw a kind of beauty in that contorted face, in the wracked body.

Could they have taken another road? Had there been a better way they had failed to see? The questions haunted him, but even now he was unable to think of a course of action other than that which they had followed.

She had gone to New York, ostensibly to merely consult a specialist. Actually he was a gynecological surgeon who operated a small, furtive clinic in Gramercy Park.

She was confined there for five days. Thomas phoned her each day from Washington precisely at noon. (Freeman could almost hear the soft, self-effacing voice of Mrs. Roos saying, "It's just coming on to twelve o'clock, Mr. Van Anda. Shall I get Mrs. Van Anda now?")

Freeman came to New York and visited her at the clinic every day. Somehow he managed to make his calls above suspicion. He went on errands, brought newspapers, magazines, books, and flowers, and spent hours each day at her side. When Sheila left the clinic she went to the St. Regis for a week with Freeman. Their time together was interrupted only at noon each day by the customary telephone call from Van Anda.

Freeman took care of Sheila expertly, in the manner of a superlative male nurse.

"Oh, thank you," she said one evening after he had carefully bathed her and given her a gentle massage using almond oil and rose water. "I feel deliciously spoiled. You really are a superb nurse." She closed her eyes. He lay down beside her and held her in his arms. In a few minutes she was asleep. He watched her as she slept, wondering what was going on inside that beloved head. At times she smiled gently; often there would be a frown; once, a troubled moan. When this occurred he moved her head with a caress and broke the dream. Presently she was smiling again.

He took five careful minutes to slide out of bed so as not to awaken her. He closed her bedroom door silently, called room service, and ordered dinner.

As he served her soup she asked, "How is it we never seem to quarrel, love? There must be times when you disagree with me. Is it that you don't say so?"

"Of course."

"Like when?"

He thought, served himself, and sat opposite her. "I can't remember," he said. "Shows you how important it was."

"Thomas and I quarrel a good deal. I think he enjoys it."

"Do *you?*"

"Not at all."

"Why do it, then?"

"I have to express myself or I'll explode. You've no idea how difficult it is—Washington life. We can't say what we think and feel in public. It all needs to be calculated and considered for possible effect. And we thrive on gossip and inside stuff. I suppose that's why men in government are always taking frustrations out on their wives. Some of the wives fight back, others simply bear it as a hazard of political life. In either case it makes for a tense atmosphere."

"We used to quarrel," he mused. "Colette and I. When we were first married. Once she threw a kettle at me. Another time she slapped me. I've often wondered why I didn't slap her back. I'm glad I didn't, though. It would only have led to more of the same, and first thing you know it's a habit. And I can think of *nothing* more boring than two people going through life cuffing each other around. But that was only in the early years, in the beginning. Later on we lost interest. Not in each other, you understand, but in our marriage."

"I'm afraid I *don't* understand."

"Well, she's interested in me—she must be—otherwise she wouldn't go on finding so many faults. She's interested in me the way a person is in a possession—a house or a horse. And *she* interests *me* as an unnatural phenomenon."

"Unnatural?"

"She doesn't change. Everything changes. Not only nature. Inanimate things, too. Paintings or music. They change because *we* change. I'm always hearing new things in old music—aren't you? Two weeks ago I read—maybe for the fifth or sixth time—*The Mysterious Stranger* by Mark Twain. I swear there were scenes in it that weren't there before. Change. But not Colette. She's fixed, frozen in amber. She thinks now what she thought twenty years ago. She hates our town—but no more or less than when she first encountered it. If she got to hate it enough, she'd leave it, I suppose. But it's just a sort of static distaste. And she lives with it."

They finished dessert. "All right, now," he said. "Onto the sofa and feet up."

"No. I like it here."

"Feet up," he said. "Or no coffee."

"There you are!" she said. "We're quarreling."

"At last," he said.

He made her comfortable on the sofa in the sitting room and covered her with a blanket. He gave her coffee and brought his own to have beside her in a drawn-up easy chair.

They drank their coffee and looked at each other, into each other. They lived together in silence for an hour, savoring their joy in each other.

She fell asleep. He leaned over, put his head on the arm of the sofa, and in a few minutes joined her in happy oblivion. . . .

Sheila and Freeman met for a midweek weekend at the Ritz in Boston. As he came through the door of her suite he knew that something was wrong. He did not ask what, nor did she tell him until sometime later.

At dusk, lights came on in the Public Garden and the Boston Common. Neon began to slice the sky, and the Charles River took on a new aspect. They did not put lights on in the suite, but sat or moved about in the restful dimness.

He knew that bad news was coming and wanted to stave it off as long as possible. He explained in minute detail all that had happened in Cincinnati. She thrilled to it.

"Are you hungry?" he asked.

"Not yet."

"All right, then," he said. "Tell me the worst."

She collected her thoughts and began. "Thomas is going to run for the Senate. He resisted it until they proved to him that there's no chance of his losing."

"What does it mean to us?"

"Another year or so," she answered. "He said it was up to me. If I didn't want to wait, he'd understand. But if we divorced now, he wouldn't run—couldn't, in fact."

"So it goes," he said. "Shall we have dinner here or go to Charles's?"

"Here, please."

They talked of many things in the course of the next two days. They discussed the differences in their life that might come about as a result of Freeman's deal. They considered going abroad to live for a time, but always their thoughts and their plans returned to Squibnocket Pond.

"That's where we began, really, and that's where we should end," she said.

"We're never going to end," he said. "We're going to live forever. The man who invented the insect repellent will now perfect a death repellent."

Talk of a trip to Japan occupied them for one whole afternoon. He got out a Japanese phrase book he had found at the Old Corner

Bookstore, looked up "I love you," and said, "*Anata o aishi masu.*"

"Thank you," she said. "What a curious phrase to put in a phrase book!"

"You never know when you'll need it," said Freeman.

"I need it right now," she said.

At dinner that evening Sheila became aware of Freeman's preoccupation. They had grown to be unfailingly sensitive to each other's moods.

"What is it, love?" she asked.

He shook his head briefly.

"Come on," she urged.

"Jacqueline," he said. "Trouble."

"Oh, dear. What?"

"I try not to burden you with problems—"

"I wish you would," she said.

"While she was at Radcliffe she met this Harvard fellow—a drama major, too—and went off to graduate school in Texas with him. I didn't mind *that*—if that was what she wanted. It was the *why* she went that bothered me. It was just to get away from her home and the damned abrasive atmosphere. I felt responsible. Well. Anyway, a few months ago they were married."

"I remember."

"And now it's over. So she distrusts marriage more than ever. She has dropped her involvement in the theater and is escaping into science. She's gone to work for UNESCO. Leaves for Africa in a week. I'm sick about it."

"My love," said Sheila. "Haven't you learned that we can't live other people's lives for them? She has to be allowed to make her own mistakes. And who knows? Maybe it'll turn out not to be a mistake at all. . . ."

How right Sheila had been! As always, instinctively wise and knowing and gentle.

From Africa, Jacqueline had been assigned to a month-long convention in Venice. There she met Dr. Max Tarloff, an American scientist concerned with the world's food supply. Venice did its work, and after a swift and explosive love affair she and Max were married.

Freeman recalled Jacqueline's account of how they bought a car and toured Italy. On the superb beach at Alassio they lay side by side, hand in hand.

"Next to one I know in America," said Max, "this must be the best beach anywhere."

"And what beach is that?" Jacqueline asked.

"South Beach. On Martha's Vineyard."

"But that's where I'm from!" she said.

"You are?"

She propped herself up on an elbow. "Of course. Edgartown."

"Well, I'll be damned. How come I never found you? I've spent every summer there for fifteen years—except three war ones. And four year-round ones."

"No! Where?"

"Chilmark. I own a house there."

"Oh, no wonder," she said, lying down again. "We don't speak to Chilmark. Too intellectual. How'd you get to the island anyway? Looking for me?"

"No," he said. "I was with the Marine Biological Laboratory at Woods Hole. I commuted on the ferry."

"I've crossed on that ferry a thousand times. Probably with you, several."

"Amazing, isn't it? There we were—the two of us—and we didn't meet until here."

"You hardly know *anything* about me, do you?" she asked.

"I know enough."

Freeman smiled as he recalled Jacqueline's account. . . .

SIX

THE year of Thomas Van Anda's campaign was a difficult one for Freeman and Sheila. She had not realized the extent to which it was necessary that she be involved. Not only victory, but decisive victory became the aim. The closer they moved toward election day, the more time she and her husband spent in his native Indiana.

Jacqueline and Max, now living in Denver, awaited the birth of their first child. As the scheduled time approached, Freeman flew to join them, and the minute he saw Max he knew that he was needed. Max, the cool and disciplined man of science, had gone to pieces.

"I've seen nervous fathers," Freeman told him. "I believe I was one myself, but you take the cake."

"Sorry. A million things can happen. I wish I were ignorant. I've got too much physiology in my head—that's the trouble."

Freeman sat with him, walked, drank, stayed awake—and on the morning of the birth actually held his trembling hand.

Freeman's grandson, eventually named Seth (a continuing family name), held him hypnotically for a month. Freeman was fascinated by the tiny creature struggling to become a human being. He reflected for hours on the gossamer thread of life that had culminated in the infant wriggling in the bassinet: Colette and her Gallic forebears; his own ancestors crossing the Atlantic, breaking with the Puritans, moving to the island. There conquering land and sea and seasons. Fishing, then whaling, and finally fishing again. Max's parents, meeting in steerage. His father from Poland. His mother from Lithuania. Both en route to the promise of freedom, and gold in the streets. New York. Marriage. His father beginning as a peddler, ending as a successful leather-goods merchant. His mother working in a shirtwaist factory until the day before his birth.

Now this lad. So much of the world in him. He would need it all—and more—in the unknowable years to come.

On his way east Freeman stopped in Indianapolis. From his motel he phoned Van Anda's campaign headquarters. "Mrs. Van Anda, please."

"May I ask who's calling?" a man's impatient voice inquired.

"Mr. Cavendish. I'm a personal friend."

"Hold on." Voices. Typewriters clacking. Freeman visualized the smoke-filled room typical of the American political scene.

"John?" Her voice, speaking the rest of his fictitious name, startled him. "What on earth brings you to Indianapolis?" she asked, acting.

"Love," he said.

"How nice," she said. "Can you stay long enough to see him?"

"Well, yes. If forever's long enough."

"Where are you?"

"At a motel nearby," he said, urging her. "I could pick you up. I've rented a car. And drive you right to my door. It's very private. I'm sure you want privacy these days."

"Yes. Still, it's difficult." Then she continued in a voice so low that he had trouble hearing her. "We're sort of celebrities here. If we weren't, a million dollars would've been wasted."

The telephone made a clicking noise. "Hello?" he said.

"Sorry," said a woman's voice. "Thought the line was free. Will you be long? Who's on?"

"Me, Mamie," said Sheila. "Mrs. Van Anda."

"Oh, I'm *sorry!*"

Click.

"Tricky," said Sheila. "As you see."

"I'll wait here," he said. "I won't move."

Thirty hours later she called him. He had not left his room. "It looks hopeless," she said.

"I'll wait. Nothing's hopeless."

"Thank you, love."

That night he attended a political rally at the speedway. He saw her on the brightly lighted platform, looking more radiant than ever before. He moved closer, then closer still. At one point photographs were being made with supporters. At length the Van Andas were alone.

"Kiss 'er, Senator," shouted a photographer. Thomas Van Anda obliged, after which his press representatives dispersed the cameramen. The speeches were about to begin.

Freeman made his way to a seat in the fourth row on the side. He kept his eyes on Sheila. In time she saw him, looked away, looked back, smiled, looked in the other direction, waved, and blew a kiss. Then she looked at him again as the first of the speeches began. Her face remained in repose, as did his. The din faded for them, and in the silence, across the space between them, they exchanged multitudes.

Freeman waited another day, then left Indianapolis. He felt curiously satisfied. He had seen his love.

Thomas Van Anda won the election easily. Sheila was occupied for two months in finding a summer house on the Vineyard, furnishing and staffing it. The arrangements were worked out, and she phoned Freeman to tell him the happy news.

"We're taking the Bliss house on North Water Street for six months," she said. "May through October. I'm going to headquarter there, and Thomas is going to come up from Washington for weekends—when he can. This has been a too tiring time. I'm exhausted. I need a rest."

"You've earned it, my love," he said.

"I think—no—I *know* our life is beginning, my darling."

Freeman flew to France to confer with Colette. After a few amenities he said, "What I propose is this: you're to receive half my royalties in perpetuity. I'm told that this half share may be worth as much as a hundred thousand dollars a year for ten or twenty years."

"So," she said. "We have become wealthy. And what you wish now is to buy me off, yes?"

"I wouldn't have put it so crudely, but—"

"Oh, yes. I am crude."

"I'm not asking for much, Colette. Only for an end to something that doesn't really exist."

"You wish to marry again?"

"Possibly," he said.

"Then my answer is no. And as we are man and wife, the half is to me no matter. I have spoken to many advocates."

"Very well." He handed her a document. "Show this to your advocates and then tell me what you want to do." He left abruptly.

Her lawyer explained that the paper outlined the setting up of an irrevocable trust fund into which Freeman's royalties would flow, after which they would be funneled by its trustees (the Edgartown National Bank) to such pharmaceutical research as they deemed worthy.

"But he can do this? He has the rights?"

"Yes."

"But half is mine, no?" she asked.

"No. It's not actually yours until you've got it. And he's giving *his* away, too."

"No," she said bitterly. "No, he is *not!*"

Her next meeting with Freeman, their last, was charged with passion. "You would do this, eh?" she shouted. "You would give away the millions only to spite me?"

"No, Colette. Just to save us—both of us—from drowning in bitterness."

Freeman returned to the island. A month later, through her lawyers, he learned that Colette was prepared to divorce him pursuant to the conditions Freeman had first proposed.

He called Sheila, and they jubilantly planned a celebration. Thomas made no objection to the suggestion that she wanted to take a trip through New England to see the wild flowers. In a large, comfortable camper they rented, Sheila and Freeman made their way north. The convenience of not having to trouble about hotel arrangements overwhelmed them.

"You're part of a lovely lie of mine," he said one evening as they cooked a bouillabaisse together, having collected the ingredients from roadside stands all day.

"How nice!" she said.

"I redid my will last Thursday. Should anything happen to me—say as a result of eating this scary-looking bouillabaisse—my half of the proceeds from the windfall goes to you."

"I hope you're joking," she said.

"Of course not. I want you to have it. You deserve it a lot more than she deserves *her* half."

"You're mad—sweetly mad. It must never happen—but if it did, how could I ever explain—"

"Please!" he interrupted. "Don't you think I've thought all that out? And the codicil—if I do say so myself—is a dilly. 'To my friend Sheila Hanrahan Van Anda,'" he said as if reading, "'I bequeath the interest in the proceeds of All-Off, now owned by me. All agreements between myself and the Sebring Corporation shall be transferred to her, her heirs or assignees in perpetuity and without restriction of any kind.'"

"It's not a dilly so far," said Sheila.

"Wait," he continued. "'A word of explanation as to the reason for this bequest may be seemly, in view of the fact that Mrs. Van Anda and I have enjoyed no more than a casual acquaintanceship. However, Mrs. Van Anda, in a visit to my store one day in May 1927, asked if such a product existed. When I replied in the negative she suggested that it would be well if it did. On subsequent occasions she urged me to attempt the development of such a product and became, as it were, an associate. It is to her that I owe not only the end of my search but the beginning.'"

"Yes," she said. "That *is* a dilly. Thank you, my darling. And now please see that it never comes to me."

"I'll do my best," he said. "I hope this thyme is going to work."

"Better if it were fresh," she said.

They returned to the island and spent the three final days of their adventure on Squibnocket Pond.

Before they parted she told him that she was leaving, with her husband, for Italy, Greece, and Yugoslavia to be gone for five weeks; an important senatorial junket. "I couldn't tell you before," she said. "It would have spoiled our time."

Freeman was jolted.

There was no way out, but this would be the last of the trips. A promise.

When she had gone he spent troubled nights for two weeks. Then, on an impulse, he took a sleeping bag and went out to the pond. It was better there.

In the store the following morning his first customer was Ollie Luce, the harbor master. Freeman smiled. Ollie and his antics, his gossip, and his fibs rarely failed to amuse Freeman.

"Mornin', Doc," said Ollie. "I need me a bottle of that there Geritol."

"Okay. Something you did or something you're going to do?"

"Both. I been up half the night helpin' Rosella close up the Bliss house for them Van Andas."

"What?" Freeman waited for the joke. Houses were never closed until the fall. Never.

"Yup. The big man hisself—the Senator—come up to do the supervising. With his secretary—she's not bad, by the way. If there's one thing I hate more'n a Senator, it's a *supervisor.*"

Freeman, in a panic, heard himself shout, "What the hell are you talking about, Ollie? You and your bloody jokes can be a real pain sometimes, you know it?"

"Hey, now there!" said Ollie, holding up an admonishing finger. "What's hit *you?* You got no call to chew me out, mister."

"I'm sorry, Ollie. Just tell me what you know, please."

"Not much. He flew in to close up, seein' as how his old lady just *cooled.*"

A sound escaped Freeman. Ollie took it to be a question. "I thought you'd heard. Yup. Joined the majority, she did, as they say. In Europe someplace. Or Greece. Hell of a time gettin' her remains back in the country, they say. Probably couldn't have done it if he hadn't've been a Senator."

He went on talking. Freeman was watching his lips, but now, oddly, no sound emanated. Freeman began to suspect that this was a dream. No, a nightmare. The color left the store. He saw it all—and Ollie—in a fuzzy black and white.

Now Ollie was touching him. "You all right, Doc? How about that Geritol?"

Freeman went through the motions of a transaction. He saw Ollie leave. He was alone. He began to cry, the sobs originating in the pit of his stomach. He tried to move into the back room, but stumbled. He held on to doors and counters, trying to regain equilibrium. His knees gave way, and he sank to the floor. There he remained, kneeling. What if someone were to come in? His brain sent signals that went unobeyed. Now he was two beings:

the first, physically out of control, retching, strangling on held-back tears; the second, a dismayed observer.

His observer self became aware that the sobs had come to an end. Now what? He stood up and made his way to the back room, to the office. He drank water until it made him nauseated. He started to prepare coffee, but the sight of the two cups on the shelf jarred him, and he stopped. He sat down.

He wondered, for a hope-filled minute, if it were not possibly all a mistake. That Ollie. He might easily have got it all wrong. All wrong. Was there someone to call? Wait. Henry Hough at the *Gazette* would know. "Henry? Freeman here. Say, I wanted to ask you about my ad. I've been thinking. Maybe I ought to run it on the front page after all."

"It's up to you, ol' fella. You got a cold?"

"No, must be this damned telephone."

"About the ad?" asked Henry.

"Oh, yes. Could I see a proof of the new setup?"

"Sure. Come on over anytime after tomorrow." His voice took on the sound of finality.

Freeman tensed. "What's new?" he asked as casually as he could, but heard his voice break. He turned it into a fake cough and added, "I may be coming down with a cold at that. Anything doing on the island?"

"No, not much. . . . Oh, I suppose you've heard about poor Senator Van Anda. . . ."

Freeman was on his feet. He *knew* it! Ollie had got it twisted. The *Senator*. "No," he managed quietly. "What *about* him?"

"Lost his wife," said Henry.

After an eternity Freeman heard, "Hello? . . . Freeman? . . . Hello!"

"What?" asked Freeman. "Cut off, I think. This country phone."

"I was telling you about Mrs. Van Anda dying."

"Yes, I heard you." A deep breath. "What happened?"

"Well, I don't have all the details yet. I'm going over there in a bit. Mrs. Roos, his secretary, is giving me a copy of the announcement. We want to run something special, of course. After all, a Senator's wife. It was a heart attack, I understand. On a boat going to Crete."

"Shame," said Freeman.

"She was an awfully nice woman. You knew her, didn't you?"

"Oh, yes. Awfully nice. Did you say Crete? Or Greece?" asked Freeman.

"Crete. But it's all about the same, isn't it? Well, then," said Henry. "We'll shift you to page one and see how you like it."

"Thanks, Henry."

It was over, then. There was no mistake. What was he to do now? Not in the days to come or weeks or months, but now. Today. This minute. What was the next step? Behave well, correctly. That was what he wanted, above all, to do. A telegram? Sent where? Flowers. The funeral service . . . where and when? Does one simply go, or do you wait to be asked? What if it is to be in Washington? Could he go then? No, of course not. How would it look? If here, all right. Could it be? Hadn't she once said– Did she mean it? We say all sorts of things out of the depth of feeling or from the height of passion. Hadn't he once said– he remembered it chillingly–that he would follow her without delay in death? Romantic talk. The very definition of sentimental. Copping out? he asked himself. Not at all. But that is for later. What of *now*?

The immediate now became a month–as time, for Freeman Osborn, stood still. He had never before lived in limbo. In the years to come he would spend hours trying to recall that lost month–or was it two?

He could recollect pieces, flashes–but only in disorder. His office at the back of the store. Shaving. Mrs. Tremaine, his long-time housekeeper. "Are you all right?" she asks.

"Why, yes, of course. Why?"

"Well, you haven't been home in four days. I got to worrying."

"I've been working."

"You mean you haven't been out at all?"

"No. I don't think so."

"But what about food?"

"Ice cream," he says. "Candy bars. Wafers. Cones, did I mention cones?"

"Mr. Osborn, it's not my place to say it. But I like you and always have. You ought to stop *drinking!*"

When she had gone he laughed. In all this time he had not had so much as a drop of alcohol. It was there, but it never crossed his mind.

In any event he went home that night. He was grateful to Mrs. Tremaine for having called his absence to his attention.

He is shaking hands with Senator Van Anda. Where? And was this before Mrs. Tremaine or after?

Shaking hands. Mrs. Roos, then the Senator. He is one of many in the room. North Water Street.

"Liked you very much, Osborn. *Very* much. Thank you for coming. Most kind. Oh! And London. Do you recall? You were most helpful to her there. She often said—"

The funeral. Washington. How did he get to Washington?

Driving to Boston. Rain. One bad skid, during which he smiled happily, hoping for the worst, the best.

Logan Airport. A huge plane. To where? Washington, D.C. The plane goes up and comes down. Trouble? No, it has arrived. A seemingly endless taxi ride to—where was it? He had forgotten to make a hotel reservation and so—with the taxi driver's surly assistance—drove from one hotel to another. Rain. Finally, at the Hay-Adams, he is told that the only space available is a large suite. He takes it, is shown up. Alone, he walks about from room to room. There are four. What's this? A grilled cabinet contains miniatures of every sort of alcoholic drink. Soda. Tonic. Bloody Mary mix. The cabinet is opened and provides a blessed numbing. Instructions to the operator to ring at eight a.m. and again at eight fifteen and eight thirty. To send up breakfast: double tomato juice, Worcestershire sauce, scrambled eggs, and sausages well-done and dry, rye toast, and double coffee with hot milk. A rented car at nine fifteen.

There is no morning in his memory, but the church is there indelibly, in all its musty splendor. There are few mourners. Most of those asked—officially—have sent surrogates. Freeman haunts the shadows at the rear, is regarded suspiciously by an usher, takes a seat in the last pew. The usher approaches and motions him to the front. "I have a bad throat," Freeman explains hoarsely. "May start coughing. And have to leave."

The usher nods understandingly. Freeman's eyes are on the flower-blanketed coffin. He has come to grips with the fact of Sheila's death, yet in his mind she has never been more alive.

They are swimming together. She is in the car at Heathrow Airport in England. They are visiting the Frick Collection in New York. They stand before painting after painting, shoulder to shoulder, their bodies in communication. Rain. Where? A taxi. They jump in and find that the back seat overlooks a deep puddle. They sit, feet up, and laugh. Music. They hold hands and listen in the Salle Pleyel. They are at the UN building, in the basement, looking for *kokeshi* dolls. Another time. Earlier? Later? A violent unceasing rainstorm. They read aloud, a children's book, alternating chapters. What book? A man of consecutive mind, he refuses to go on until he remembers. Cannot. Try. At last. *Stuart Little* by E. B. White. Her laughter. Their discussion of Adlai Stevenson's campaign strategy becomes a bitter quarrel, their first and only. They make up. And they are in one Japanese restaurant after another.

He listens to the music and the prayers and the ceremony, but hears none of it. He is thinking only of what lies inside that coffin. What, he wonders, have they dressed her in? He reconstructs her, anatomically, in his mind. He is gripping the back of the pew before him. He is drenched in perspiration.

He is on the ferry, making the long-familiar minivoyage from Woods Hole to Vineyard Haven. It is night. A sliver of the new moon. Wait, memory. Where is the in-between? Did he join the single file that passed beside the bier? Cannot remember. Try. No use. Did he check out of the Hay-Adams? The flight home? Gone. The ferry, however, is there and clear. The ride home, as well, is fixed in recall, since it marks the first time in his life he ever ran out of gas. He stands at the roadside near Bend in the Road, imitating the hitchhikers he has seen so often. Two girls. They are great. They take him to the Depot Service Station, wait for him, take him back to his car, help him to start it.

He is home, moving through the days and nights in reflex motion. He suddenly finds himself doing something. Or nothing. There is a fire one night. He rushes to his volunteer post. It is a difficult fire. All night. He finds himself fishing. It is the time of the Bluefish Derby. He wins something.

He sits in his office for one long night and contemplates methods of achieving an end to it all. It will be simply part of their life together. A promise. How? It is no more than a question of choice. He is surrounded, literally, by enough substances to put an end to a *thousand* lives. What is to be gained? Peace. An end to those awakenings, feeling fine, stretching—the stretch abruptly broken—being overwhelmed by the realization of things as they are. What is to be lost? Air, sensation, the morning and the evening. Largely meaningless, now that it is all unshared.

And what of their Japanese house on Squibnocket Pond? It would never be, now.

That was the night he decided to build it. As a monument, a memorial? Perhaps. Not to her alone, but to them both. Or was he simply postponing, out of cowardice, his own end? His head was throbbing. He swallowed two Empirin-codeines, went home and to bed.

He knew that he was living in a state of shock, and held on, determined to wait until he had regained his equilibrium before deciding definitely on anything. What began to concern him was that his periods of lucidity and full consciousness were diminishing. He had thought it would be the other way about.

Then came the bad day. Freeman was at his worktable, mixing a simple prescription, when he heard the bell. "Be right with you," he called out. He finished the mixture, put aside the mortar and pestle, washed his hands, dried them, and made his way into the store.

A tall, bronzed, handsome blond girl—of the new breed—stood there in a bikini, one hand over her left eye.

"Excuse me," she said. "I've got something *fierce* in my eye—"

"Please!" he said, staring at her. "*Please!*"

"What?" she said, confused. Her hand came away from her eye, and he saw that it was really in need of help.

He closed his eyes. "Go away," he said. "Please!"

The girl, frightened, started out swiftly. "Okay," she said placatingly. "*Okay.* I just asked, that's all." At the door she turned back to him and said, "You're weird, mister, you know it? I mean *weird.*" She was gone.

He made his way to the back room, where he opened a drawer, reached in, and picked up a handful of ammonia ampules before proceeding to the office beyond. He cracked two ampules, put them near his face, and took a deep breath. His head snapped back. He heard and felt a loud crick. He sank to his knees, stretched out on the floor, face down, and lay still for a long time.

He heard the bell, a voice, and after a time the bell again. Dimly it occurred to him that a customer had come and gone. He decided to rise, sent the appropriate messages, but his body would not respond. He thought himself paralyzed and was, in fact, suffering a temporary form of that disability.

The phone was ringing. He managed to make his way to his desk and answer it.

"Where were you?" asked Dr. Trask. "In the john?"

"No. Hello," said Freeman.

"Listen. Make up this prescription for colic, will you? I know you've done this only about ten thousand times, but I'm making a little change in it today—there was a piece in the *Journal.* It's for the MacAlliney's baby—had a bad night and the parents are in a state. They're babies themselves. It's getting to be like the Old South up here. Teen-age grooms and child brides. Anyway. Label it two-point-zero drops every two hours in warm milk as needed for colic."

"Two-point-zero drops every two," Freeman repeated, writing it down.

"Yes. The baby's only five weeks old. Here is the new version: Tincture of belladonna, elixir of paregoric, elixir of phenobarbitol, equal parts, twenty-point-zero cc's each. Dispense in a dropper bottle."

"Let me read it back," said Freeman, and did so.

"Right. Ted's on his way in from Chilmark now to pick it up."

Freeman looked up from his scribble and said automatically, "It'll be ready." He moved out into his back room. He began to work on the emergency order, concentrating, then feeling torpor overcoming him again. He stood still for over half an hour, breathing deeply. The bell startled him.

"Mr. Osborn?" a charged voice called. "It's Ted MacAlliney."

"Be right with you, Ted. I'm working on it."

He looked down at his work, realized he had stopped while in progress. He remembered now. The first two ingredients had gone in. He was about to continue, when he stopped. He was certain, still . . . His father's admonition surfaced: "There's a world of difference, son, between certainty and certitude." Play it safe. Begin again. He discarded the contents of his mortar and began again, slowly, carefully.

Meanwhile from the store: "Doc?"

"Right with you, Ted." Freeman was damp with nerves.

"He said it'd be *ready* by the time I got here," Ted shouted. "My kid's *sick!*"

"Working on it," said Freeman steadily.

Minutes later Ted appeared in the doorway just as Freeman was typing out the label on the clacking old typewriter. "Give it here," said Ted, picking up the bottle beside Freeman's elbow. "It don't need a sticker. I know what it is."

Freeman snatched the bottle out of Ted's hand. He held up a warning finger. "Mind your manners, Ted. I appreciate you're overwrought, but I've got a responsibility. Now move out of here while I finish."

Ted lost control and reached for Freeman. "I'm going to punch you right in the mouth!" he yelled.

Freeman retreated, then turned to finish typing the label. He wet it with a small sponge, affixed it to the bottle, and handed it to Ted, who ran out with it.

Freeman began to shake convulsively. It had been too much. All day. Home and some food. Had he had dinner? He could not remember. Lunch? When? He closed the store methodically and walked home. At last, in the privacy of his bedroom, Freeman fainted across the bed.

When he came to, it was dark. He put on some lights, drank water, and considered calling Dr. Trask. He walked about from room to room. Finally he fell asleep in a chair in the sitting room.

He was awakened hours later by a strong hand clutching his shoulder and shaking him brusquely. He looked up to find Dr. Trask standing over him.

"Don!" he said. "Am I glad to see you. I feel awful."

"Sit still," said the doctor, already taking his pulse.

"Did I call you? Or not? I don't remember. Give you an idea of the shape *I'm* in."

"No," said the doctor.

"How'd you know, then? I mean, you're *here*."

"Pulse okay. Let's go to the kitchen." They did so, Freeman leading the way.

"Do you have any oranges?" asked the doctor.

"I think so. Mrs. Tremaine keeps the place well stocked." Freeman found oranges and extracted the juice, using the electric appliance on the counter. They sat down at the kitchen table and talked of the need for rain and of kitchen improvements, while drinking their orange juice.

When they had finished, the doctor asked, "How do you feel?"

"All right," Freeman answered. "That hit the spot."

"Blood sugar," said the doctor, frowning. "Freeman. There's trouble. And we're part of it. The MacAlliney baby. It's dead. Four forty this morning. I got there at about three, but there was nothing I could do."

"Yes," said Freeman, "that is trouble. How's Ted taking it?"

"Well," said the doctor slowly, "for the moment, I've got him locked up in jail."

"I'm not following this, Don. What're you trying to tell me? What did he *do*?"

"He threatened to kill *you*. He was on his way here when I had him picked up. He's beside himself, of course, but that's not the point."

"What *is* the point?"

The doctor reluctantly put his hand into his pocket and brought forth a bottle of medicine. Freeman recognized it at once. He had typed the label badly. Crookedly.

"This is what killed it."

Freeman was on his feet. "Now, you wait one damn minute, Don. I'll stake my *life* on that compound. I'll admit I've not been myself for a time, but it's made me *extra* careful. I started that one, was interrupted, and—just to make certain sure—I threw it away and started again."

"No complaint with the medicine." The doctor handed him the bottle. "It's the label."

Freeman studied it. A spasm as he read: "20 drops every 2 hours in warm milk as needed for colic." He stared at the label. It went out of focus. When it came back it read, correctly: "2.0 drops every 2 hours in warm milk as needed for colic." A moment passed, then wishful illusion became shattering reality. "20 drops every 2 hours in warm milk as needed for colic."

"Oh, no!" he said.

"We're both to blame," said the doctor. "Mine is largely professional. The association, you know, frowns on telephone prescriptions. Unless absolutely necessary. And then only those containing harmless—well, *you* know. This is why. You can bet I've given *my* last on the phone."

"But for pity's sake, Don! I wrote down what you said, read it back, so how can *you* be faulted? It's me. All me."

"No, but as I was about to say, yours is legal—technically, that is. I've got Coby Saltonstall waiting. Out in the car. I wanted to tell you first."

"Why Coby?"

"He's your lawyer, isn't he?"

"Yes."

"Well, you'd better talk to him, then. I'm going to leave now."

Freeman turned away, looked out at the backyard, and said, "Whatever happens, I'll never, so long as I live, prepare a compound again. How could I ask anyone to trust me? Good God, I don't even trust myself." He turned back into the room, but the doctor had gone. Freeman started out to the front of the house and encountered his lawyer in the hallway.

"Come in, Coby."

Coburn was tall and thirty and every inch a Saltonstall. He wore his celebrated surname like a badge. His thousands of hours of intense reading had given him, in addition to myopia, a permanent frown. He frowned when he smiled or laughed. He was not smiling now. He had, in the past two hours, gone through the thick buff-with-red-back books, seeking the latest disposition of like cases. He had already telephoned one of his celebrated uncles in Boston for advice and was awaiting a reply. They sat down.

Freeman spoke. "How bad is it, Coby?"

"Depends. We'd better begin with A-B-C." He consulted a sheaf of notes. "Dr. Trask—he *did* call you at six thirty-five p.m.?"

"I didn't notice the time, but he called me, yes."

"You filled the prescription personally?"

"Yes."

"And the label?"

"I typed it. Not very well, I'm afraid, but I typed it."

"Now. For the crux. When Dr. Trask gave you the prescription, did you write it down?"

"Wrote it and repeated it, yes," said Freeman.

"Including the directions?"

"Including the directions."

"Now I have to ask you this. Important. How did you happen to get it twisted?"

"It was simply—"

"No, wait!" Coby said. "Was the light bad? Your eyes? A lapse? Was someone in the room talking to you? I'm not trying to put words into your mouth, Freeman—"

"Yes, you are," said Freeman, and managed a small smile. "You're doing your best for me, but it's a simple case, really. I made a mistake. We all make mistakes. Some of us are not supposed to. This one was a fatal mistake. It cost a life. I'm prepared to take the consequences, whatever they are. Tell me, Coby. What happens now?"

"Well, unless the MacAlliney boy cools off, he'll swear out a warrant. You'll be arrested for criminal negligence—the charge is involuntary manslaughter. Remanded. In a few months—tried."

"Can't we cut through all this?" asked Freeman. "I did something wrong, and there you have it. Why go through all these motions?"

"Because the law has to operate in its own way, Freeman. Besides, there may be extenuating circumstances."

"Not a one."

"You may not recognize them. You're not a lawyer."

They went into the kitchen and remained there for over two hours. They drank coffee while Coby, with practiced skill, elicited the moment-by-moment story. He filled pages of notes. By the end of Freeman's account his face held his curious frowning smile. "I knew it!" he said exultantly. "We've got a case."

He rose, and as he paced the kitchen it became a courtroom. "A respected old pharmacist gets an emergency prescription over the phone. He begins to prepare it. The customer for whom it's intended bursts in. A sick child has driven him into a frenzy of nerves. He charges into the workroom and belabors the old pharmacist. The pharmacist gets rattled. The man grabs up the bottle—unlabeled. The pharmacist, sticking to the letter of the law, will not permit it. The customer threatens to assault him. The pharmacist, deeply agitated, hurries to complete the order. In his confusion, caused mainly by the boorish and impetuous man, he admittedly makes an error. Such a thing has never happened before, not for—how many? Fifty thousand prescriptions? Get me the exact number. If it's impressive we'll use it. A tragedy, yes. But in many ways Mr. MacAlliney brought it on himself. A misfortune, of course. Human error. It must, in the circumstances, be forgiven. If this is criminal negligence, then I do not understand the English language. . . . How does that sound?"

"It sounds fine, Coby. There's just one thing the matter with it."

"What's that?"

"It's full of holes."

"Show me *one*."

"What time did Don phone me?"

"Six thirty-five."

"What time did Ted turn up?" asked Freeman.

"Seven ten."

"All right, then. Why wasn't it ready when he got there?"

"I don't know. Why wasn't it?"

"I don't know, either. I started, stood there—woolgathering. When the bell rang he was there, and I'd only begun. So I threw it away and started again."

"Do you often have lapses like that?" asked Coby.

"In the past month, yes."

"Do you have any idea—"

The doorbell. A few minutes later Coby and Freeman, joined by Sheriff Manter and his deputy, Henry Weir, were discussing the formalities of Freeman's arrest.

"You'll be back here in an hour," said the sheriff. "You could be held, but you won't be."

"What about Ted?"

"They got a head doctor over from the Cape to talk to him. And Judge Whiting saw him. Tough as hell he was on him, too. Told him: 'The doc made a bad mistake—you're making a worse one. You can't go around threatenin' people's lives. I'll keep you in here till you're old and gray if you don't behave yourself!' He's going to hang on to him awhile."

They proceeded to the courthouse. Freeman understood little of the language spoken.

In the end he was remanded into his own custody, after he had sworn not to leave the island without permission until a trial date had been set. He phoned Jacqueline and Max, explained the situation, and begged them not to worry. He would keep them informed. He again turned the management of the store over to Mrs. Petschek and Martin Stein.

He and Coby met daily and talked. Coby filled one notebook after another with details. He was building a case he believed could win, if not an acquittal, at least a suspended sentence. There was no question as to guilt or innocence, merely of mitigating circumstance, if any. Many things were in Freeman's favor: his longstanding good reputation in the community; his war service; his personal integrity. On the other side, Ted MacAlliney was still undergoing psychiatric treatment and was clearly a hysteric who might easily have upset anyone and caused error.

As the days and the meetings went on, however, one area revealed itself more and more as the weak spot: that thirty-five minutes between Trask's call and Ted's arrival. What *had* Freeman been doing? No matter how many times he was asked, his answer was a consistent "I don't know."

One morning Freeman suggested that they drive somewhere.

"Where?" asked Coby.

"Anywhere. And *do* something while we talk. All this sitting and jawing. My back's beginning to complain."

"All right, Freeman, but I'm not dressed for a boat or clamming."

"Come along," said Freeman abruptly, happily. "I'll take you somewhere."

They drove up-island through the morning mist along the Middle Road, stopping only once to buy fruit and ale. As they bore left at Chilmark, Coby lit his pipe and asked, "Where we going?"

"Gay Head. A place of mine."

When they made the turn to Squibnocket Pond, Coby said, "Holy smoke! I know this place. We camped out here when I was a scout."

The mist, which had been slowly rising, had stayed, caught, here in Freeman's wood. They walked about, Freeman outlining the boundaries of his property, and settled at length on the peak of the knoll. Coby was properly surprised when Freeman threw open a camouflaged hatch door, under which lay a metal trunk-sized box. He opened it with a key from his ring and brought out a picnic basket, tablecloth, napkins, plates, utensils, and a small wicker basket containing several bottles of liquor.

They drank bourbon and water, while Freeman lit the Sterno stove, heated a can of baked beans, and prepared sandwiches (tinned brown bread, deviled ham, peanut butter). The ale was kept cold in the spring until needed.

"This is great," said Coby.

"I love it here," Freeman said softly.

"Had it long?"

"Thirty-five years."

"Wow. You must have a neat capital-gains situation going."

"This land," Freeman said tightly, "is *not for sale*. Will *never* be for sale."

"What are you going to do with it? Anything?"

"Yes," replied Freeman. "Something."

In the long pause that followed, Coby opened his briefcase and studied his notes. Freeman, meanwhile, poured himself another bourbon (strong, Coby noted) and drank it in a long, slow, contented draught. He loosened his collar and lay back, his hands cradling his head. He studied the rolling mist as it journeyed through the treetops.

"Can we start?" Coby asked.

Freeman did not reply. He was in another time. Moments, sights, sounds, aromas, tastes were being summoned up from his memory. Sheila was here with him. She was, even in death, as much a part of this spot as the earth or growth or sky. She was in the mist. He saw her in the pool. He felt her moving, with nature, above him.

"Freeman!"

The sound of his name, spoken loudly and sharply, broke his reverie. He sat up and looked bemusedly at Coby. "Yes?"

"Sorry," said Coby. "Were you asleep?"

"No."

"And you didn't hear me? I called you pretty loudly."

"Why, yes. I answered, didn't I?"

"The fourth time. Freeman, listen. This could be extremely important. Has that always been a habit of yours? Going off like that? Into yourself?"

"No."

"But you did it just now," Coby insisted. "And after Trask called."

"Yes."

"Any other times?"

"I suppose so, yes."

"Can you recall specifically?"

"Coby, you're asking me to remember not remembering."

"So I am. But if you do it all the time, how can you say it isn't a habit?"

Freeman looked away. "It's only in the last five weeks and three days that I've had these—lapses."

Coby pounced. "Why five weeks and three days?"

Freeman stood up and walked away. He returned in about five minutes and said, "Get on to something else, Coby. There are certain matters I'm not going to talk about."

Coby stood up, too, and spoke harshly for the first time in their long alliance. "Listen, Freeman. I'm your lawyer. The fact that you tell me something doesn't mean we're going to use it—doesn't mean it'll go any further. You and I are in a privileged relationship. I can help you best if I know everything. Let *me* decide what to use and what not, will you? There'll be a lot of questions pretty soon. Once you've been sworn in, you've got to answer any question the judge allows."

"No, I don't," said Freeman.

"Really!" Coby shouted. "You are one stubborn old man. Look. If you go to a doctor, don't you tell him everything?"

"That's different," said Freeman. "You called me a stubborn old man, you know that? Actually it was the 'old' that hurt."

"I'm sorry. I apologize." Coby walked into the wood. He re-emerged to find Freeman having still another drink and beginning to show the effects of the liquor.

"Let's go on," said Freeman. "I'll try to be more helpful."

"All right," Coby said, and sat down. "Do you remember exactly what you were doing when Trask called?"

"Yes."

Coby waited. "Well, what?" he urged.

"The telephone brought me to."

"You were asleep?"

"No. I was in a state of shock."

"Where?"

"On the floor."

This was good, thought Coby. Had Freeman purposely omitted this important detail, or was it simply an oversight? "How long had you been on the floor?"

"Between ten and fifteen minutes, I should judge."

"Now, look. This *could* be a line of questioning they'll pursue, so be careful. . . . What *caused* the lapse?"

"I'm not going to tell you that," said Freeman. "There are parts of this, Coby, that're nobody's business. And that goes for *you*."

They exchanged a long, uncompromising look, the meaning of which was clear to both. Coby packed his briefcase carefully. Freeman poured himself another drink. Straight, this time. He knocked it back as Coby stood up.

"Sit down, Coby."

"It's no use. Get someone else."

"Sit down."

Coby sat and tried to relight his pipe, which had gone out. His trembling hand made the effort awkward.

"I'm going to tell you," said Freeman. "And when I do, you'll see why you can't use it. One day, a long time ago—1927—over twenty-five years ago, a quarter of a century, God help me—early in the morning—nine fifteen—my life—it was the thirteenth of May—my life began. . . ."

He told, then, of his first encounter with Sheila, and of the days that followed. He went on, his voice and his spirit gaining clarity and confidence. He grew more lucid as he continued, and by the time he was telling of their days and nights in wartime London his account was perfectly organized and eloquently conveyed. He told of their plans for a future, of the idea for the Japanese house.

He realized that he owed his discovery and his fortune to the fact that he had buried himself in work to blunt the pain caused by her frequent absences.

He grew cold and shivered as he considered, for the first time, that the physical condition which may have caused her death—the elevated cholesterol count—was brought about by *her* loneliness and despair.

He recounted, without bitterness or self-pity, the many frustrations and anxieties they had endured: their desire to spare others; the solution finally in sight; their last, merry conversation; hearing of her death from Ollie, crudely and cruelly; the hours that followed; the kaleidoscopic, unreal time; the funeral; the bikini-clad girl with the cinder in her eye. . . .

When Freeman had been silent for some time, Coby said, "Thank you."

Dusk had fallen and the wood was dark. They sat silently for an hour. The mist was gone. They put away the supplies and walked out of the wood to the car.

"So you see," said Freeman.

"Yes. If you could tell that, there's not a jury that would punish you other than technically. As it is—" Coby shrugged. "Right now, I'd settle for a guilty verdict and a suspended sentence. I think the revocation of your license will be automatic."

"Yes."

"And no matter what the outcome of the criminal charge, you'll still have to face a civil suit for damages by the MacAllineys."

"I'll give them whatever they want," said Freeman. "I don't see how anyone can put a price on a life. Who can tell what that child might have meant to the world?" Tears welled up in his eyes as he spoke.

Coby pretended not to notice. "What I've got to do now, Freeman—based on all this new information—is figure out our plea."

"Guilty," said Freeman.

"Not so fast. Guilty of what?"

"The charge."

"Not if the charge is involuntary manslaughter! Hell, no. We plead *not* guilty to that."

"But what's—"

"I don't want to talk any more now, please," said Coby. "Or tomorrow, for that matter. I need time to sort it all out. It's become another story."

They drove back to Edgartown without further conversation.

THREE days later Jacqueline, Max, and Seth arrived. Freeman met a new Jacqueline. He had known a clinging, fretful child; a moody adolescent; and from her boarding-school days to these, a cordial but arm's-length friend. All at once their relationship was changed. Upon her arrival she took charge of the house with strength and efficiency. She arranged with Mrs. Tremaine to come daily rather than three times a week, and engaged an up-island girl as a baby nurse. She rented a second car. She had the dry cleaner pick up a load of long-neglected clothes, and found a twice-a-week laundress in Oak Bluffs.

She did all this in order that she might be free to become familiar with her father's case. She appropriated all of Coby's free time; went to his office or had him come to dinner and spend the evening. On these occasions their talk usually went on until three a.m. This did not keep her from rising at her habitual seven o'clock. Freeman worried about it and warned her that she was unwise to rob herself of sleep.

"We'll sleep when it's over," she said, and went her way.

Freeman came to know Max, as well, during this time. Their relationship had been tentative, their meetings scattered: one busy weekend a few months following the marriage; a lunch in the Oak Room of the St. Regis, New York (during which time his mind was on Sheila, waiting in the suite upstairs); a first-anniversary reception in New York to make up for the European wedding. Then, other than the time he had gone out to Denver for the birth of the baby, there had been little contact.

Now here was a new old friend. In the days ahead, Freeman found Max not a son-in-law, but a son. Seth, too, was a comfort. Freeman watched him for hours at a time, thought he could see him growing. Often, as he wandered about the house in the middle of the night, he would look in on Seth. The sight of his grandson invariably made him smile.

Neither Jacqueline nor her husband made any attempt to dissuade Freeman from his planned course, but they made certain he was aware of the possible consequences.

During one of the long, incomprehensible wrangles in the courtroom, Freeman reflected that the tragedy had, in a sense, given him a daughter.

The trial itself turned out to be an endless nightmare, not only for Freeman, but for his friends, several of whom were on the jury. It had proved impossible to impanel a group that did not include friends of the defendant. Thus, by common consent, prospective jurors were not challenged on this point.

Freeman followed the proceeding attentively, but in time to come could remember only parts of it. He remembered that he had insisted on entering a plea of guilty, even though Coby assured him that the bill of particulars was so vague as to make this unnecessary. He could not recall, however, the actual plea or the reaction to it by Chuck (Judge Charles Eliot Whiting) or the members of the jury, although he was certain he had been watching them carefully at this point.

Both the MacAllineys had taken the stand, but this, too, had been blocked out of his memory. Yet he knew that in the lunch break following, he had had a lobster roll with too much salt in it.

Surely Dr. Trask must have been a witness. Had he been? Freeman racked his brain, but certain pages had been torn from his book of memory. Why had he forgotten that, and not the ginger tomcat, moving fretfully in and out of the courtroom, looking for a place to nap?

Freeman was surprised at how little of his own testimony had remained with him.

"State your full name, please."

That "full" startled him and caused him to reply, "Freeman Thaxter Osborn."

Jacqueline was startled as well. She had never heard him use Thaxter, his mother's maiden name.

"Where do you reside?"

"Cooke Street, Edgartown, Massachusetts."

"What is your occupation?"

He paused before making his considered response.

"I am retired. I *was* a registered pharmacist."

An objection. Sustained. He is confused.

Chuck looked down at him and, in all friendliness, suggested, "Just say 'Pharmacist,' Freeman."

"Pharmacist," said Freeman.

It was all he could do to suppress a smile as Dana, the clerk, droned (just like in the movies), "Do you swear to tell the truth the whole truth and nothing but the truth so help you God?"

And his response (just like in the movies), "I do."

Was he in a movie? Was it *all* a movie? Or a dream? Whatever it was, it was certainly happening in black and white, not in color. This had happened to him before. When?

Coby elicited the long story of his training and experience: of his apprenticeship; becoming a partner; assuming ownership. Then his war service; his return; his experiments and their successful results. Finally Coby came to the crux of the matter.

"This brings us," he said, "to the day and the evening of the—the misunderstanding."

WITNESS: There *was* no misunderstanding.

THE COURT: May I ask the witness to confine himself to answering such questions as are put to him?

WITNESS: Okay, Chuck. I'll do my best.

THE COURT: You may proceed.

COUNSEL: Thank you, your Honor. We were on the point of examining the events on the day of the—mischance. Did Dr. Trask phone you at six thirty-five on that day?

WITNESS: On the day of the *mistake*, Dr. Trask called me at six thirty-five p.m., yes.

COUNSEL: May it please the Court, I must request a short recess for the purpose of a conference with my client.

THE COURT: I should think so. Granted.

Coby beckoned to Freeman, who stepped down from the witness stand, and to Jacqueline and Max, who came forward. The group went into a corridor behind the bench.

"I can't make a case, Freeman," said Coby, "if you won't help me. I can't do it if you insist on changing *mischance* to *mistake*. I know what I'm doing."

Freeman's face flushed with anger as he said, "And so do *I* know what you're doing. You're trying to put a better face on an ugly fact. And I don't want—"

"Freeman," said Coby patiently, "would you like me to step down?"

"No," said Jacqueline, "he wouldn't." She turned to her father. "Dad, won't you please just answer the questions?"

"No," said Freeman. "No, I won't. It's no good. This game goes against the grain. I know what happened, and I don't want to hide any part of it—certainly not behind language that doesn't mean anything. *Mischance!* I know what mischance is, believe me. I've known too much of it!"

His voice broke. He got out a handkerchief and blew his nose. Max got him a paper cup full of water.

"Thanks," he said, and drank it.

Coby sighed, and shrugged. "Well," he said, "I don't know *what* to do."

"Come on," said Freeman. "Ask away. I'll answer. Don't worry."

(Recess over.)

COUNSEL: Did Dr. Trask phone you at six thirty-five on the evening of the mischance?

WITNESS: Yes.

COUNSEL: And dictate a prescription for the infant?

WITNESS: Yes.

COUNSEL: Did you carefully commit this prescription to paper?

WITNESS: Yes.

COUNSEL: Did you then fill this prescription?

WITNESS: I did.

COUNSEL: Was it absolutely accurate to the most precise degree?

WITNESS: Absolutely.

COUNSEL: You swear to that?

WITNESS: I do.

COUNSEL: What happened then? Tell us fully, please.

WITNESS: Well, what happened then was exactly the way Ted told it. I've got nothing to add or subtract.

COUNSEL: We'd like the account from *your* point of view, please.

WITNESS: I was typing the label. He came in. Agitated at the delay—understandably. Anyone would have been. He grabbed the bottle, started out. I took it from him—it doesn't do to have medicine in blank bottles. We got into some fuss, raised a little sand. I finished the label fast. I kept worrying he might grab the bottle again—and he did, too, the minute I'd stuck the label on.

COUNSEL: Is this the label you typed?

WITNESS: Looks like it, yes.

COUNSEL: Is it?

WITNESS: Yes.

COUNSEL: What's wrong with it?

WITNESS: The decimal is missing, so it reads "twenty" instead of "two-point-zero."

COUNSEL: Can you explain the error?

WITNESS: No.

COUNSEL: Might it have been the result of the altercation?

WITNESS: Might.

COUNSEL: You were upset. Thrown. Rattled. Disturbed. Perturbed. Unnerved. Flustered.

WITNESS: Yes.

COUNSEL: How many prescriptions have you filled? I mean you personally.

WITNESS: Well, I knew you were going to ask me that, so I looked it up. Thirty-three thousand, seven hundred and twenty-seven. Including this last one. The MacAlliney.

COUNSEL: Had you ever made an error before?

WITNESS: Yes.

COUNSEL: When was that?

WITNESS: My second year in the store—

COUNSEL: What happened?

WITNESS: I was in a tearing hurry and left the codeine out of a cough compound.

COUNSEL: So we have a grand total of two errors in thirty-three thousand, seven hundred and twenty-seven prescriptions.

WITNESS: Pharmacists make very few errors. I don't consider my record outstanding.

COUNSEL: That will be all.

Cross-examination followed. Freeman waited for the question regarding the elapsed time between the doctor's call and Ted's arrival. He was ready with his "I don't know" answer, but the question never came. The prosecutor was ill prepared, his grasp of the case, as a whole, faulty. And he was polite—*over*polite. Coby had done such an outstanding job of character building that the prosecutor was reluctant to lose the jury's sympathy by treating Freeman harshly. Then, by accident or luck, in the fourth hour of cross-examination came the question which brought a vital disclosure.

PROSECUTOR: Sometime earlier this morning, Mr. Osborn, your attorney used the words *misunderstanding* and *mischance*, and you used the word *mistake*. How *do* you yourself characterize your act?

WITNESS: I would call it—criminal negligence.

Coby sprang to his feet, then realized he had nothing to say.

The prosecutor said, "Thank you, that's all."

There were other witnesses, but their testimony no longer mattered. The summations came. The prosecutor's, brief; Coby's, desperate. There followed the judge's charge to the jury. The jury retired and, apparently sensing Freeman's desire, returned in less than an hour to oblige him with a verdict of guilty of involuntary manslaughter as charged.

Early on the morning of the final proceedings Freeman had asked Jacqueline to phone Judge Whiting and ask if he was going to request a statement before sentencing. "Well, it's customary," the judge had said, "but I won't if he doesn't want me to."

"No, no," said Jacqueline. "That's just the point. He wants to make sure he can say what he has to say. He's been up all night preparing it."

The moment came. "Does the convicted wish to make any statement before sentence is passed?" the judge asked.

"Yes, your Honor."

"You may proceed."

Freeman took some folded sheets of yellow paper from his breast pocket, unfolded them, put on his reading glasses, and began to read.

"I wish to state that I have never before been involved in a court proceeding, and I have been greatly gratified to observe our form of justice in action. I believe that my trial was fair, the judge considerate, and the witnesses truthful. The prosecutor seemed to me to be seeking no more and no less than the truth, and my own counsel, Mr. Coburn Saltonstall, represented me in the most exemplary possible manner.

"I made an unforgivable mistake, and I should indeed be punished. My regret and remorse and sense of guilt are, I fear, beyond my power to express. To the parents of the infant whose death I inadvertently but surely caused, I offer my abject apology. No term in prison can restore life to that hapless infant; yet I mean to serve it, as a reminder, I trust, to others of my calling, of how often we hold life and death in our hands, and with what unrelenting care and caution we must perform our duties. No amount of money can make up to the parents for their child, yet I intend to turn over to them a part of my estate. . . . The suspension of my license is, in many ways, the most painful part of this ghastly misfortune, yet I must accept it as just. I shall dispose of my establishment here and shall never again practice pharmacy. . . . My good counsel has recommended an appeal of this verdict. With all due respect to him—and to you, your Honor—I do not wish that to take place. I only want to pay my debt. Thank you."

Judge Whiting was astonished. He looked at Coby, who shrugged. Finally, in no little confusion, the judge said, "This is, of course, most unusual. One would have thought . . . However, it is my painful duty to sentence you, Freeman Thaxter Osborn, to a term of penal servitude in the state prison at Walpole not to exceed twelve months from the date of your incarceration, and to pay over to the clerk of this court a fine in the amount of one thousand dollars. Are there any questions? Is there anything further? If not, this case is closed. The court is adjourned." . . .

WATCHING an exceptional sunset from the porch of the Falmouth Sunset House, Freeman was remembering his life with Sheila. Had they been two parts of a single entity? Of course. Did this, then, explain the continuing sensation of his being something less than whole throughout his life without her?

Their exchange had been a living thing, filled with growth and surprise. He recalled the exquisite smile that often suffused her face, the times of laughter.

And right to the end they had never quarreled. Well, once. About the mistakes in the Adlai Stevenson campaign. That wasn't a quarrel. That was a political debate. Very well. What does it matter now? What does anything matter? They had once discussed never quarreling. The St. Regis. Was there anyone else in his life about whom this was true? Why not? The attempt to find answers to these two questions occupied him for hours.

Quarreling was probably a habit, he reflected. A contest. Like card playing or tennis or prizefighting. A game presupposes a willingness on the part of the players, an adherence to the rules. There are those who quarrel to win, others who quarrel to quarrel.

He himself had often enjoyed the ones with Colette. They made it possible for him to relieve himself of pent-up feelings, criticisms, objections and corrections.

He had had violent disagreements with his father, although, on the whole, they were fond of each other. He thought his father narrow in political views and mean in business. "Near with a dollar" was his town reputation. It was in these areas that their bouts most frequently occurred.

Jacqueline, too, had often been an adversary. In her rebellious periods she appeared to take perverse pleasure in attacking her father's weak spots. Freeman did not take these battles seriously. He considered them common parent-offspring adventures. Still, he mused, they *were* quarrels.

With his lawyers? Yes. And doctors and business connections and customers—even with the rector of St. Andrew's.

Never with Shelia.

The circumstance fascinated him. Once, toward the end, he had asked her (not for the first time)—

The end.

The end. He had not known how near it was.

The end.

Was there anything he could have done to delay it, forestall it? No. Nothing. Nature is whimsical, unreasoning, cruel, harsh, insane, unnatural. What? Nature is unnatural?

He smiled at the twist of thought, moved back a few moments in time, picked up the thread of his remembering.

Once, toward the end, he had asked her, "Why do you suppose it is that we never quarrel?"

And she had replied, "Because we don't have the time, my love. It takes time. Think how little we have together. Wouldn't we be foolish to waste any of it in bickering?"

He is kissing her, in memory, for a timeless time. He is looking at her, into her. "Were you a happy child?" he asks.

"I suppose so," she replies. "Although it's only now, looking back, that it occurs to me. I had two doting brothers, and we lived in nature—the best way, isn't it?—and were always involved somehow with the animals and crops and seasons. I was thrown from a horse once, broke my collarbone." She laughs. (That laugh!) "I certainly wasn't a happy child *that* day. But, on the whole, yes—a happy child. Were you?"

"I wonder. I was an only—and my mother was gone by the time I was five, and my father was a tough Yankee with pretty fixed notions. Knowing nothing about children, he treated me like a grown-up. And I guess I became one pretty fast."

"And when did you discover girls?"

"Girls. Well, they were just nice frilly things all through grammar school. In high school, though, they were nervous making, and the most important subject in the curriculum. College was just talk, mostly, in my day. Bluff and bluster. Some experimentation. A good many false starts. Frustrating. The army made it all real, finally."

"Were you a good soldier?"

"No. A scared one."

She puts her arms about him. They stop talking. They continue to communicate, however. Freeman, looking back across the years, thought it remarkable how, without constraint, they had found themselves always able to express what they felt, to say whatever came to mind. Her complete openness was one of her most endearing traits. There were times when she would guide him, carefully and gently, into new avenues of exchange. There were times when he would lead and she would follow. They had owned each other, proudly, happily. . . .

SEVEN

Freeman served seven months, two weeks, and two days of his sentence. He found the prison experience not unpleasant, but never conveyed this fact to anyone for fear of being thought capricious. He thought his companions an amiable enough crowd, although, for the most part, they seemed bewildered men.

While in prison Freeman read newspapers more often and more fully than ever before. A headline on page three of the Springfield *Union* caught his eye one evening:

SENATOR VAN ANDA WED IN WASHINGTON
Recently Widowed Senator and Secretary
in Quiet Nuptials

Washington, Sept. 14—Thomas Van Anda, United States Senator from Indiana, and Mrs. Gina Martucci Roos were married here today before a small gathering at the home of friends, by Rev. Arthur Lathrop of St. Thomas' Episcopal Church.

Senator Van Anda, whose wife died a year ago, and Mrs. Roos, a divorcee, will defer their honeymoon trip until the congressional holiday adjournment.

Mrs. Roos has been associated with the Senator as private secretary since her divorce from Arthur Roos, assistant to the Secretary of the Interior.

Freeman read the story; then read it again and again, after which he tried to read what lay between the lines. The images that assailed him kept him awake for many nights to come. That telephone call in London. "Mrs. Roos, my secretary. She's going with me, of course." Of course.

In time he was able to dismiss it from his mind. He would never know the facts. He must come to grips with the here and now. He laid out a program of activity for himself and followed it rigorously.

From the Old Corner Bookstore in Boston he ordered, by mail, a library of current books about Japan. From the bibliographies of these he found other, older titles and acquired as many as possible.

At Freeman's request Jacqueline brought him, on the first of her monthly visits, a conversational course in Japanese, with a record player and earphones. On another occasion she brought him *kanji* cards: Japanese symbols and pictures on one side, the English translation and phonetic pronunciation on the other.

In between Jacqueline's visits were Coby's. There was much to do. Freeman transferred his interest in All-Off to the MacAllineys, who, by means of a single signature, became wealthy.

Freeman studied maps and travel books. He made plans, seeing the truth in the saying, "Happiness is mostly looking forward." His spirits were, all things considered, high. He sold the store to a Vineyard Haven pharmacist, but retained ownership of the building it occupied and assigned its title to Jacqueline and Max.

And he planned a trip—seven months in Japan—a span of time almost equal to his servitude. A repayment, as it were, from the bank of time.

Jacqueline brought him, from his vault at the Edgartown National Bank, a locked strongbox. It contained information he had gleaned from some of Sheila's letters—her numerous references to Japan. He wrung from his memory what she had said to him about certain places and persons. He sifted these and larded them into his itinerary. What he was going to do was to make a trip to Japan with Sheila.

In the fifth month of his imprisonment he met Tomoyuki Saito, a fellow inmate. Freeman had wandered into the recreation room and saw, in a far corner, a trim young Japanese reading a magazine. He hesitated, wondering if he dared try out a phrase or two. He approached the young man, who looked up at him apprehensively.

"*Konnichi wa,*" said Freeman carefully.

The young man giggled, and said, "*Konnichi wa.*"

Freeman thought, then said, "*Watakushi wa Osborn desu.*"

"*Hai. Watakushi wa Tomoyuki Saito desu.*"

The young man rose and bowed three times. Freeman extended his hand. The young man took it awkwardly and shook it once. They sat down.

"Mr. Saito–" Freeman began.

"Call me Tomo. That's short for Tomoyuki." They talked for the forty minutes that remained of the recreation period.

Tomo was a Nisei, born in the Napa Valley in California. In 1941 he was sent with his parents to an internment camp in Utah. They were herded into a guarded camp and treated like enemies. Yet his three older brothers had been drafted and were serving in the United States army. It had not made sense to him then. It did not make sense to him now.

After two years, having reached the age of eighteen, *he* had been drafted and moved from the internment camp to Brownsville, Texas, training—because of his small stature—to be a B-52 tail gunner. He had been terrified of the exposed bubble on the rear of the lumbering bomber, but the war ended before he had flown a mission. The occupation of Japan had begun, and since bilingual men were needed he was offered a commission.

"I tol' 'em to stuff it," he said in gutter English. "The way they handled me, treated my folks an' all—my mother got arthritis in that camp—and as soon as I could, I grabbed my discharge. I didn't go back to the valley, though, because I met this Joe in the service, see, and he–"

The bell clanged, signaling the end of the period.

Freeman and Tomo agreed to meet again the next night. They became friends, and Freeman engaged Tomo to give him lessons in Japanese for an hour each evening.

"We'd make quite a team over there," Freeman said to him one evening. "I know all about the place, and you know the language."

"Take me with you," said Tomo.

"Maybe I will."

And he did. Freeman thought he would get more out of the trip this way than with pickup interpreters. Jacqueline questioned the idea.

"He's a good kid," said Freeman, "but he's had a bad time. Fell in with some men who got jobs at different airports and then—using faked invoices, bills of lading, and labels—filched a lot of stuff. They went too far—and made him take the blame—easy because he's Japanese, and you'd be surprised how many Americans haven't signed the peace treaty yet."

"I'm one of them," said Jacqueline, and provoked a row.

But Freeman had his way. He and Tomo flew to San Francisco, where they spent three days testing photographic equipment and tape recorders. Freeman carried, in addition to his letter of credit, sixty thousand dollars in traveler's checks, since it was his intention to arrange shipment to Martha's Vineyard of all that was needed to construct his Japanese house.

The flight to Tokyo was splendid, and Japan was again a revelation, a dream, another beginning.

Tomo was thoughtful and efficient, and possessed the valuable gift of getting along with everyone they met. Moreover he was sensitive to Freeman's need for privacy and did not intrude. There were periods when they would separate for days, before meeting at the next point on their itinerary.

Freeman was seeing all that Sheila had wanted him to see. He was coming to know something of the strange and profound ways of the Japanese. It was all, he thought during a particularly beautiful sunrise, revivifying.

After his visit to the Osaka teak works, where he ordered flooring, there was one side trip he wanted especially to make alone—to a country inn, Mingei-Ya.

"It's where we're going to spend our honeymoon," she had said. "Of all the lovely places I've known, there's none lovelier. It has no chic—it couldn't be more simple—but it's of the earth and exudes the good of life. Food and wine and comfort and conviviality. Human contact is so easy there, so open. There are no locks on the doors. People wander about, being congenial. Everyone does everything. The girls who make the beds play the koto in the morning and the samisen in the evening. The chef paints portraits of the guests and gives them away. The valet writes haiku and recites them at odd times. It's utterly romantic. Life—not as it is, but as it could be, should be."

Freeman's anticipatory excitement peaked as the Mingei-Ya date approached. He carried a single bag, his briefcase, a pocket camera, and a small recorder. Tomo shepherded everything else to Nara, where he was to make arrangements for a pilgrimage the following week to the Horyu-ji Temple. This great structure, Sheila had explained, was the original wood concept, the basis of all Japanese architecture.

Mingei-Ya. Freeman was not disappointed. In fact Sheila had failed to do justice to the place—a dream of beauty and atmosphere. As the first day progressed it occurred to him that she might have done so purposely, in order that she might not deprive him of his own joy of discovery. Sheila. Had there ever been anyone like her? As he strolled reflectively through the ancient rock garden, tears came to his eyes.

In a diminutive teahouse, built to hold no more than two, he found himself talking aloud—not to himself, but to Sheila. He stopped, shaken and troubled. He left the teahouse and continued his walk. Why was he so disturbed? He had often talked to himself. During the time he was working on his formula he did it frequently. True, he thought, but that was talking to *himself*. Here he had been talking to Sheila. Was he all right? Was this the first step toward—well, maybe not madness, but incompetence?

He sat down beside a clear, dark pool and looked into it. His mirrored image stared back at him. Here he was: Freeman Thaxter Osborn, sixty-three; retired pharmacist; ex-convict; inventor of All-Off; father of Jacqueline. Former husband of Colette (alive); former lover of Sheila (dead). What was he doing in this remote place? Another land, another world. He had come here because of

Sheila. Was she here, other than what he had brought in his mind? She seemed to be materializing all about him. Was it part of the magic of the place? Or was he indeed losing his mind? As he began to walk back toward the inn his reason took the upper hand. Of course. Sheila had created so vivid a projection of them together in this place that it had become real, even though it had never happened. He felt giddy, heard the sound of her laughter. The scent of her wafted across his path—that well-remembered, unmistakable fragrance that was hers alone. His feet did not seem to be touching the ground as fantasy enveloped him again. Was she here in some way? Was this a meeting, prearranged? He struggled to return to reality as one tries to break out of a difficult dream. But had not the renowned philosopher William James given serious consideration to afterlife communication? He sat down again, obliterated his imaginings, and rested.

Reality returned solidly during dinner. He sat cross-legged on the tatami, to the friendly amusement of the girls serving him. He had consumed two carafes of sake with the delicate *sashimi* and was now savoring the hearty peasant *shabu-shabu*. He had not ordered beer, but here came a beautiful waitress, bringing it in a small pail that called to mind the picture of himself as a little boy, trudging home from the corner saloon, swinging a similar receptacle for his father's supper.

As he reached the end of the *shabu-shabu* the manager, who had been hovering about, approached him, knelt, and bowed. He was about forty, moonfaced. "I greet you," he said in careful English. "I am Iwasa Ito, son of the innkeeper."

They shook hands.

"May I join you for a moment?"

"Of course," said Freeman.

Ito sat opposite him. "Is all satisfactory? As you wish?"

"Mr. Ito, this is heaven."

Ito, embarrassed, laughed. "Mr. Osborn, we have a problem. My father, I fear, has misunderstood some of your correspondence. He thought that Mrs. Van Anda would be with you."

Freeman paused before saying, "No."

"Oh. He is *most* disappointed. He has exceptional fondness for her—for so many years. She came here often, as you know. I, too, have fondness of the same degree. She is my friend from boyhood. She has taught me my first English word—'lovely.'"

Freeman felt stricken, trapped. The moment of revelation lay irrevocably ahead, like a whirlpool in the rapids. It could not be avoided. He dreaded its coming, tried to slow time.

Ito went on reminiscing, laughing—but Freeman no longer heard the words. Tell him *now!* he commanded himself. The longer you wait, the worse it will be. Yet he could not bring himself to convey the news. What if not at all? He would be leaving the day after tomorrow. Perhaps he could, after all, spare himself—and them—the agony.

His attention returned to Ito, who was saying, "She was the first object of my love. I left flowers for her and wrote horrid poetry. I learned English in order to speak to her. I had not yet learned that in this matter language is not important. Tell me. Is she well?"

The serving girls were clearing away, chattering. Suddenly one of them became aware of the enveloping mood, touched the other's shoulder. They scurried away.

"She is dead," said Freeman with obvious pain.

Ito rose to comfort him, then uttered a phrase in Japanese that Freeman failed to catch.

"Please," said Ito, his face contorted. "When?"

"A little over a year ago—1955. In Crete."

"An accident? She was so young."

"No. Heart. She was fifty-eight," said Freeman.

"I do not know how to tell my father. He is not well. It will break him. She was his link to America."

"Why tell him at all?"

"Do I dare not?"

"Spare him. Of course."

Now Freeman stood, too. He did not want Ito to leave him. He did not want, for the moment, to be alone.

"A cognac, perhaps?" asked Ito.

"Well, something."

"Please do me the honor to join me." Ito led him to a small room off the lobby, apparently his private quarters. Like all Japanese rooms it appeared spare and impoverished. An illusion. A cabinet was opened, displaying an array of bottles from various parts of the world. The bourbon bottle looked like an old friend, and Freeman greeted it accordingly.

They drank for an hour. Freeman became loquacious. There was so much that had been pent up for so long that he wanted to talk about. He told Ito of his first meeting with Sheila, of their almost immediate involvement, and then incident after incident of their growing together.

He was talking about the war years when he found himself walking with Ito, arm in arm, following a flashlight's beam. The air was cool and bracing. After a time Ito said, "I respect your courage, telling me alone. Here, by custom, a death is always announced by two. We think it too lonely, difficult for only one."

A town. A shop. Snakes in baskets on a shelf. Was it happening? He had read of it, never seen it—the shopkeeper carefully removing a single snake; the flash of a blade; a gland pressed; a tiny glass filled with—well, snake juice. Another glass. Ito, demonstrating, knocks his back. Freeman does likewise.

They are on the road again, and by the time they approach the inn Freeman feels himself sobering.

They are in the bathhouse of the inn. Four women, two middle-aged experts and two young apprentices, scrub and rub, rinse and massage. Afterward small trays of food are brought. Ito explains that this is part of the *kaiseki* cuisine, in celebration of summer.

One of the older women leads Freeman back to his room. His bed is a colorful mat, called a *futon.* The woman helps him into his pajamas. He lies down on his back. She turns him over gently and rubs the back of his neck. Now his feet are being massaged. He relaxes. He is spent, physically and emotionally. He is asleep.

The next morning he was awakened by a young apprentice, who brought him a breakfast of broth, ginger-flavored scallops, and black tea. Later she added *mikan:* a sweet, tangerine-like fruit.

He encountered Ito during midmorning. They chatted pleasantly for a few minutes, then Ito said, "I have not informed to my father. As you have suggested. But there is difficulty. He asks especially to see you before you depart."

"All right," said Freeman. "I can lie."

Later in the day he did so, but it was not as easy as he had thought. The elder Ito sat propped up on his *futon*. He spoke. His son interpreted.

"You are friend to Sheila Van Anda?"

"Yes."

"How sad we are she did not come."

"She will come soon."

"Alas, I am near my end. I have hoped to see her once again. She is a goddess."

"I agree."

"Will you tell her that, in my last hours, among my thoughts were those of her ineffable loveliness; that although absent she has helped to ease my pain. She was a true friend, that rarest of all creatures."

Freeman swallowed before he said, "I shall tell her. Good-by."

The old man raised a hand in salute, tried to bow, fell forward. In order not to embarrass the elder Ito, Freeman, who had begun to understand Japanese decorum, left the room as the son began to minister to his father.

An argument ensued when Freeman was refused a bill. He insisted that he wished to pay. Young Ito threw open his arms in appeal and said, "My father has instructed me. There is *nothing* I can do. And in any case, it is small. As we say here, 'no more than a sparrow's tears.' "

They said good-by after Ito had promised to come one day to Martha's Vineyard and after Freeman had promised to return.

In the crowded train to Nara he considered that, if for no other reason, the journey to Mingei-Ya had made this trip to Japan worthwhile.

In Nara, misfortune awaited him. Tomo had failed to appear. The hotel had held the reservations, but had had no word from Saito-san. Only fragmentary English was spoken here, and Freeman was in trouble. He telephoned the American consul in Osaka and explained his predicament: he suspected his traveling companion, a Japanese-speaking American citizen named Tomoyuki Saito, had gone off with his belongings, including some fifty-one thousand dollars in traveler's checks.

A whistle.

"Were they in your luggage?" asked the consul.

"No. I'd handed them to him for safekeeping."

"Do you have the numbers?"

"Yes."

"Phone them in at once, although I'm inclined to believe it's too late."

"I agree," said Freeman. "This lad is sharp."

"We'll do what we can, but he'd find it easy to go underground. He's made his fortune now."

Jacqueline had been right about Tomo, but Freeman was determined not to let a crook ruin the trip of his life. He was off to Horyu-ji. He wanted to see it for his project.

He could manage financially on the letter of credit, but the strain of replacing essentials, revising his travel plans and attempting to track down Tomo—claims, interviews, police—wore him down. Low in resistance, he succumbed to a stomach virus. He was flown back to the United States in the company of a nurse arranged for by Iwasa Ito.

JACQUELINE took over in San Francisco. After a month in the hospital there, Freeman was brought to Denver, where he spent three additional months in the hospital and four more in a convalescent home. Jacqueline prevailed upon her father to remain in Colorado, since she was in the midst of a difficult pregnancy and would not be able to travel east for some time. When Freeman left the convalescent home he went to live with Jacqueline and Max, but could not invent a life for himself there.

Jacqueline's second baby was born by cesarean section. Another boy, named Max, Jr.

Freeman returned to the Vineyard. It was changing. Television.

Dr. Trask was dead. Fewer sails and more motors. Loud music. Motorcycles. Campsites and condominiums. The kids were growing up and taking charge.

A New York blowout with Jacqueline and Max marked his sixty-fifth birthday.

The MacAllineys were divorced. Each remarried.

Freeman found himself sleeping more, drinking less, reading. Why poetry? It had never much interested him. Now it was somehow strengthening. He enjoyed form.

Jacqueline bought him, for Christmas, an album of recordings of modern poets reading their work. "Although," she said, "I can't understand your interest in it."

"Well, it's like A. E. Housman said a while ago:

"And since to look at things in bloom
Fifty springs are little room,
About the woodlands I will go
To see the cherry hung with snow.

"Do you see what I mean?"

"No."

"I'm sorry, but thanks for the records. They're grand."

He sold his house and took a small apartment across from where Dr. Andrew Lucas, his physician now, lived and worked. He bought a forty-two-foot cabin cruiser. He took it once around the island. He sold it. He went often to Squibnocket Pond and meditated, waiting for the thrust of energy that would complete the action he had so long envisioned.

He planned another trip to Japan. Jacqueline did everything in her power to dissuade him. He knew he was not thinking clearly, but this mission had become the main purpose of his life. In a suite at the Huntington Hotel in San Francisco he told his daughter to save her breath, that he was going. "But by sea, this time," he said.

"Why?"

"Because it takes longer, that's why."

Another hour of fruitless argument, serving only to make each of them cling more firmly to previously held views.

Resigned, Jacqueline said, "Will you take someone with you? A nurse, a companion?"

"You and Max come along. It'll change your life. For the better."

"We can't. You know that."

"Then I'll go alone. You've got to try and see it my way. Look here. I don't know what kind of father I've been to you—"

"First class. The best."

"Well, maybe. The final score isn't in yet. But you know I tried, don't you?"

"Of course."

"And the one thing I tried to get you to be—beyond anything else—was resourceful. Independent. Without that, you can't have dignity. Remember what a bore I was about having you learn shorthand and typing?"

"You certainly were. But I'm grateful to you for it."

"Sure. It's a skill. You can always make a living with a skill. And that may lead to something else. Everything in life leads to something else. And there comes a time for each person when he's on his own. You've got to know how to handle that. Everybody ought to be able to make a bed, cook a meal, sew a button, bandage a wound, beat off a dog, fix a toilet, shuck a clam, apply mouth-to-mouth resuscitation—there's no end to the things we ought to learn to do."

She touched his hand. "It turned out exactly the way you said it would, Dad. I took the shorthand and typing, and that's how, after the awful time in Texas, I got the UNESCO job and traveled and met Max and found a life. Yes. You were right."

"You do understand, then, why it's important for me to make this trip? And alone? Time goes by; more and more's done for you; you begin to lose your sense of resource. There comes a time you've got to let your kids take their first bus ride alone. The same goes for fathers."

He went off to Japan alone, but returned with a companion: Gaisha Muto, an elderly, well-known architect, who had accepted

Freeman's invitation because he wanted to see, before his life ended, as many as possible of the works of Frank Lloyd Wright.

From San Francisco they set out for the east coast in a hired car, with two drivers, making dozens of side trips during which Muto studied and photographed dozens of Wright structures. The cross-country trip took them five months.

It was during this excursion that Jacqueline began to have further concerns about her father's mental state. She and Max consulted a close friend, Gary Feld, a psychiatrist. They had compiled a list of the many odd, unexplainable activities in which Freeman had been involved since the MacAlliney tragedy: the trips to Japan; buying and shipping back masses of materials; the involvement with Tomo; the plans for building the Japanese house; the transfer of a fortune to the MacAllineys; and, earlier, the seven thousand dollars to Diana Boyle, a stranger; his new interest in poetry—the list went on and on. Looking for trouble, they had found it. It had escaped them that they had picked only his strange actions, and that the normal ones outweighed these.

Dr. Feld analyzed the material and suggested that Freeman was suffering from the complications of deeply felt guilt. This explained his profligacy and his desire to rid himself of his money. Considering Freeman's age and actions he could very well be committed, at least for observation.

Jacqueline rejected the idea. But the following summer she invited Dr. Feld and his wife to spend two weeks on the island with Max and her. During this time she arranged several events that gave Feld an opportunity to study her father. One of these took place at Squibnocket Pond, where Freeman and Mr. Muto described the plans for the house and garden that were soon going to be built there.

Later that night, over beers with Jacqueline and Max, Feld said, "Beats me. He could pass any test ever devised, and yet I'd swear he's a bit off."

"About the tests," Max said. "How do you know?"

"Because," said Feld, "I've given him the larger part of three. In talk. In questions. Did you think I was that interested in dimensions and stresses and strains? Or bird comparisons? Or color identifications? Or dates or times?"

Jacqueline and Max may not have been aware of Feld's method, but Freeman, discussing him the next day, said, "Nosy, that Feld, isn't he? Or is he giving me a secret sanity test?"

Ten days later, however, when the Felds had gone, Freeman called on Jacqueline and Max. They sat out on the back porch. "Maybe I'll have to give up the house," he said. "Gaisha tells me it would take three years to get it right. And he's worried about the craftsmen. It's a whole different ball game. We could bring a crew of ten or fifteen over, I suppose. But that really *would* be crazy, wouldn't it?"

"Yes," said Jacqueline.

"No," said Max. "Hell, no! Not if you want to do it. Sorry, puss. I'm on *his* side. We've meddled enough. Dad, if you want to build a Japanese house on Squibnocket Pond, go ahead and do it. I'm sure you've got a good reason."

There was a long silence. Jacqueline left the porch and came back, carrying a tray. They drank tea and munched on her blueberry muffins.

"Yes," said Freeman. "I *have* got a good reason. The most important reason in the world. In my life." They waited. "But I'm not going to tell you what it is. I can't. Believe me. I've got to do it before I die. What I mean is, I can't die until I do it. I don't *want* to, and I'm not *going* to!"

"All right, Dad," said Jacqueline. "More tea?"

Gaisha Muto returned to Japan, and the river of time flowed on for Freeman.

ONE Christmas he said to Jacqueline, "I never cared much for Christmas. Too artificial. But I'm glad of it now. It's one of the few times I'm sure of. I mean I know it's where it is."

"Yes, Dad," said Jacqueline quietly.

"Otherwise, these days I hardly ever know what day it is. Or what month. I ask people, and they tell me, but even *that* gets to be confusing. I asked Dr. Lucas once what day it was, and he said Friday. So I went downtown to get a *Gazette*, and when I got there, Irving said, 'I'd've thought you'd know by now it comes out only Fridays in the wintertime.' 'Well, this *is* Friday, you ol' coot,' I tell him. And he says, 'I'll give you a good bet it's Monday.' Well, I got back and said to Dr. Lucas, 'It's Monday. Why the hell'd you tell me it was Friday?' 'I told you it was Friday last Friday,' he says. 'You didn't ask me today!' Well, y'know, things like that can make you real nervous."

"Don't worry about it. Easy to understand, in a way. All your days are pretty much alike, aren't they?"

"Yes, but then the seasons. I get *them* mixed up, too. Do you suppose the time has come? The coming unglued?"

"Not a chance, Dad."

There came a lengthy period when Freeman found he was sleeping by day and walking around or reading by night. When had this reversal taken place? He could not remember. It took him months to return to a normal routine.

A year or so later a new problem arose. He discussed it with no one. He was increasingly vague as to whether certain memories were real or if they were merely unfulfilled wishes and dreams that had become, by repetition, a part of his remembrance. His attempts to find his way through the labyrinth of images and sounds perplexed him and often led to severe headaches. When lucid, he realized that he was too frequently disoriented.

He spent nights, sometimes whole days, in reminiscence. Their first visit to the pond. Yes. That had happened, he was sure of it. Tanglewood. Had they gone there together or only talked about it, planned it? The latter. London. Of course. All that *had* happened. Had they been together in Japan? Yes. No. No? What about their honeymoon at Mingei-Ya? No. They had never been in Japan together. Strange. How did that happen? Not happen.

Television finally captures him, and he sits hypnotized, days and nights. The "Today" show. Daytime serials. Game shows. News. Movies. Talk shows. Funny stuff. The performers grow old before his eyes and are replaced by younger, louder ones.

Jacqueline bore another son. Named, at last, Freeman Osborn

Tarloff. More like it. This one was Freeman's favorite. Bright as a button.

Freeman was living now in two rooms at the Daggett House and owned four television sets—all color, except the tiny Sony he kept beside his bed. Life had become a spectator sport. The record player. The music of Charles Ives. Great stuff, he thought. Before its time.

He found himself standing, one afternoon, in the entry of the main dining room of the Harborside Inn. He looked about, thought hard, then ran his tongue over his teeth. Face it. Ask. "Have I had lunch yet?" he asked the headwaiter. "I don't know if I'm on my way in or on my way out. And I'd like you to tell me."

The headwaiter touched his upper arm and led him to a corner table. He lunched quietly while he worked out a new plan.

He went to his room, packed a bag, and called a taxi. He went to the airport and waited for the first plane to Boston. At Logan Airport he bought passage to Denver, and telephoned Jacqueline.

"I'm on my way to see you," he said. "Don't be alarmed. I'm phoning ahead because I didn't want to walk in and startle you. I'm in good health, but I want to see you and Max."

They met him at the airport. "Let's go somewhere and eat," he said. "I'm starving. Can't eat that airplane muck. Someplace jolly. Is there a place with music? Or dancing girls? Some kind of a nightclub? It doesn't *have* to be topless, but on the other hand—"

"Yes," said Max. "Several. I couldn't vouch for the food, though."

"I don't care," said Freeman. "I'm not very hungry."

Jacqueline and Max exchanged a look. Hadn't he just said, "I'm starving"?

They went to Laffite. The music was loud, the entertainment raucous, and the steaks surprisingly good. Cocktails. Draught beer. Brandies. "This is fine," said Freeman. "Perfect."

When they got home he said, "We'll talk in the morning," and went to his room.

After breakfast and a visit with the children they assembled in Max's study.

Freeman told them of the incident at the Harborside Inn. "I think that does it," he said. "I've got to make other arrangements. I've gone—cuckoo, we used to call it. Do you still?"

"You're not cuckoo," said Max. "You may be overfatigued or having blood-supply-to-the-brain trouble, and there's treatment now for that."

"*Whatever* I am," Freeman insisted, "I'm not right. And I need looking after. I don't trust myself anymore."

"Dad—" Jacqueline whispered.

"Now, the thing I'd like to avoid," he continued, "is being institutionalized. I wouldn't like that. I'm told there are several fine retirement homes over on the Cape. I hate leaving the island, but we don't have one there. I want you to pick one and set me up there. I'm calling Coby to arrange the documents. I'm turning everything over. The fact is I'm not competent. Not anymore. So you'll have to manage things."

Jacqueline was weeping softly.

"Whatever you say, Dad," said Max.

"Don't cry, Jackson. I've had a good life—you, lately Max, and a great love. I'll tell you about it someday. When you come east. I couldn't tell you here. She's part of there. So you see, I'm far more fortunate than most."

EIGHT

THE stack of morning papers was brought to Freeman's room with his breakfast at the Falmouth Sunset House. He had, of late, taken to reading ten or more newspapers daily. And, of course, on the days it appeared, the *Vineyard Gazette*. This was one of those days, and as was his habit he put the others aside to consider the *Gazette*. Over the masthead there was a poetic line, a regular feature of the paper, which he had come to think of as an American form of haiku. Today it read: *Blackberries! Thick on stickery canes, Where wild vines grow rank, In tangled abandon, They dangle from branches.* Not bad. His eyes scanned the headlines: 48TH ANNUAL REGATTA HAS MIXED YACHTING WEATHER. As usual. G. C. WUERTH: CAME TO ISLAND IN 1913. Oh, dear. Another friend gone.

Then, suddenly, another headline came up from the page with such force that he literally flinched.

A sound, somewhere between a moan and a gasp, escaped him. He closed his eyes hard for a time, reopened them, and read again:

JAPANESE HOUSE TO RISE ON SQUIBNOCKET POND
AUTHENTIC WOOD REPLICA ALREADY
UNDER CONSTRUCTION

A story followed, but he did not read it. He got out of bed and showered, but could not shave because his hands were trembling. He dressed hastily, settling on a turtleneck shirt when he found he could not knot his necktie. He drank a cup of coffee, sat down, and made a firm effort to collect himself. His behavior of late had been exemplary. There had been a single lapse when he had reversed the to and from addresses on a letter to Jacqueline and was surprised to receive a letter from himself. As to his own pond project, he had long since put it out of his mind. What could this announcement mean, if indeed it was an announcement and not his sick imagination at work? He had learned by now that deterioration is neither neat nor ordered. Mind and body do not wear out in tandem. He knew that either his physical being or his mental capacity would give out first. He had hoped it would be his body. He decided to look at the paper once again to make certain. He picked it up. There was no mistaking it: JAPANESE HOUSE TO RISE ON SQUIBNOCKET POND.

His next thought was that it was all an elaborate joke of some kind. Who would perpetrate it? He could not think. It *was* a joke. A single copy with this inserted. They do things like that these days.

He walked to Falmouth, to the newspaper store. He looked at the stack of *Gazettes.* All the same. There it was.

He went to the dock and boarded the *Island Queen.* An hour later he got into a taxi and was driven to Squibnocket Pond. He instructed the driver to wait, and walked into his wood. Nothing. The hatch door that had, an eternity ago, held picnic supplies, had been pushed aside and the locker ransacked. Kids? Who cares? But the story in the *Gazette* was a fabrication. He knew it.

He became aware of the vibrant music of carpentry. Rhythmic hammers and a counterpoint of singing saws. His imagination again? He grasped his head, covering his ears. He sat on a stump for a long time. When he released his head, the sounds were still in the air, and he knew, beyond doubt, that they were real.

He made his way, pulled magnetically, toward the sound. It proved to be a long journey to the opposite side of the pond. He moved through brambles and thorns, fell into a marsh, slipped on a cluster of mossy rocks and hit his forehead, but went on.

He reached a hedgerow. Beyond it, activity could be discerned. On his hands and knees he crawled through, stood up, and saw it. A Japanese house, under construction. He fell to his knees and regarded it. It was larger than the one he had once planned, but lovely in proportion and line. The gardens around it, still in layout stage, would be beautiful.

He shifted his attention to the workers. There were six. Three men, two of them bearded, all of them long-haired, wearing the briefest of denim shorts. The other three were girls, also in shorts, also stripped to the waist. Were they? Yes. All six people in efficient action. He stood up and moved toward them.

One of the girls saw him and screamed. The sounds stopped. The workers froze.

"All right, all right. Cool it. I'll handle it. It's nothing. Some old bum. Lost, probably." A man stepped forward. "Lookin' for somebody, Pop?"

"I'm Freeman Osborn. I'm the owner of the property across the pond."

"Yuh?"

From afar: "What does he want?"

"Nothing. Get back to work." To Freeman: "So?"

"How does it happen," asked Freeman, "that you're building a Japanese house?"

"We're all Japanese, that's why."

A girl approached. "Go *'way*, mister. We're not dressed!"

"What is so strange," Freeman said calmly, "is the fact that *I* was going to build a Japanese house on this pond. I have the materials for it—imported—in storage right now. I went to Japan and bought them myself. It was the dream of my life."

"Is that so?" the young man commented. "Thanks for dropping in, Pop. Now drop out."

"Did you ever hear of Gaisha Muto?"

"No."

"A fine architect. Great, maybe. He came back with me from Japan. I'd love to show you his plans and specifications."

"I can hardly wait to miss 'em," said the young man.

"Good," said Freeman. "I'll bring them over."

"The guy's a riot," said the girl.

"I wonder," said Freeman, "if someone could give me a lift to my taxi?"

"Sure," said the young man. "Come on."

Freeman got into a jeep with the young man. As they drove, Freeman talked about the Horyu-ji Temple at Nara, but the young man did not seem interested, so he stopped.

The taxi driver was shocked when he saw Freeman's condition. "What happened?" he asked.

"Nothing," said the young man. "But keep an eye on him, will you? You keep letting him loose and he'll get himself hurt."

The driver started back to Oak Bluffs, but Freeman insisted on Edgartown. He went directly to the Edgartown National Bank. When his friend Olive Hillman saw him she took him at once to a doctor friend. She telephoned Falmouth and explained the situation. Freeman spent the night at the doctor's house.

In the morning, provided with fresh clothes from Brickman's and a razor from the Colonial Drug Store, he was ready to proceed with his mission. He went to his vault at the bank and selected a number of large envelopes containing material pertinent to his Japanese-house project. He went to Coby's office and, from his files there, took further plans and photographs and specifications.

In an Edgartown taxi he made the trip back to the pond. Was he in the right place? A fence had been erected overnight, with a locked gate. A sign read:

COMMUNE

KEEP OUT!

O-U-T

THIS MEANS YOU!

Y-O-U

RING BELL IF YOU HAVE A REASON

BUT YOU DAMN WELL BETTER HAVE A REASON

Freeman pressed the bell. In the distance he heard it ring loudly. A few minutes later the jeep approached. Freeman waved his roll of plans at it. It stopped. The driver, not the one he had met yesterday, seemed angry as he asked, "What do *you* want?"

"I was here yesterday," said Freeman. "I talked to your friends. I have these plans I want to show you people. The Japanese house we were—I was planning to build on Squibnocket Pond. We."

"Look, fella. We're busy here. We're working."

"I meant it in the friendliest—"

"Sure, sure—but who's got the time?"

"It's really a remarkable house. Ours was. Is."

"Two cheers," said the young man. He got into the jeep and backed it into the woods at breakneck speed.

Some weeks (months? days?) later, in Falmouth, Freeman, tired out, sat in his accustomed rocker and found himself considering, reconsidering that adventure.

They were right, he *had* been a nuisance. They were at work. They would finish it someday. He would still be a land neighbor. He wondered if they would ever invite him in. He would love to see the interior. And then again, he might not. Depended. On what? Who knows? Sheila. He watched the slow sunset.

He would tell her about it tonight. He was now talking to her nightly. Some people might think that crazy, but he wasn't crazy. He knew Sheila was dead—to everyone, but not to him. He would tell her. He smiled.

The porch door behind him slammed, jarring him. "Beautiful night, isn't it?" someone said.

"Yes, it is."

Freeman returned to his thoughts. Why had they been so rude, those young people at the pond? He had only been trying to help. They might have learned something. He might have given them all the building materials he had stored if they had been civil. The countless hours that had gone into *his* house—time and travel and money. Those damned young mugwumps—and didn't one of them call him an old bum? And that one with her bare chest. What did *she* have to be so sassy about? He'd seen better.

What was that they used to say? Something funny. What's the difference? The difference is the terrifying chasm that lies between remembering and not remembering. Try to recall it. Try. Harder. No. No use. Wait. Boopers. Yes! "There are subnubbins, nubbins, boopers, droopers, and superdroopers." He laughed, not so much at the line, but delighted that he had been able to remember it. What did *she* have to be so fresh about? She and her subnubbins. And their house wouldn't be a patch on the one he— Sheila. Sheila appeared before his eyes. Perfection. So beautifully proportioned, her body full and bursting with life. He was getting dizzy. Damn!

What if he went ahead and built the house after all? Wait. Hadn't everything been turned over to Jacqueline? Yes, but he was sure she'd see him through. He would tell her what the doctor—one of the doctors—had told him the other day (last year?): "There's nothing more important for you, Mr. Osborn, than activity. Physical, mental, emotional. Exercise. Walking. Do you ride a bike? Try it. More important still is the memory muscle—not a muscle, of course, but I like to call it that. I notice you read poetry. Do you ever memorize any? You should try. And learning. Anything. Some skill. Manual or otherwise. We should, all of us, never stop learning. It keeps the vital functions resilient—the way walking keeps the leg muscles and the circulatory system in shape. Mrs. Roosevelt, I read somewhere, started piano lessons at seventy-three. Stay involved, Mr. Osborn. In geriatrics, these days, we say: 'Add life to years, not just years to life!' Isn't there some project that would interest you? Why not undertake it? Action!"

Freeman felt his skin tingling. What was it Ed Tyra had last told him about the total cost? A hundred and ten thousand dollars. Impossible. His own estimate had been just under thirty thousand.

Yes, but that was in the beginning, a long time ago. That was—when? What is it now—1950 something? No—1960. It is 1973 . . . 1974? His head was beginning to ache. He got up out of the chair and started into the lobby.

He closed the screen door quietly and went up to his room. There, with some difficulty, he pulled the footlocker out from under his bed. He had emptied the vault at the Edgartown bank—too hard to get to—and now had his things here. All that was left of his life, he reflected, contained in one tin box and his head. He found the folder marked SQUIB PND, removed it, and returned the footlocker to its place.

He took the Squibnocket material to his writing table, adjusted the reading lamp (a birthday gift from his eldest grandson), put on his glasses, found his magnifier, and began to pore over the documents. His determination increased, his confidence swelled, and he felt stronger than he had in a year. Aloud he spoke a familiar maxim: "Resolve to perform what you ought; perform without fail what you resolve."

He became deeply immersed in the sketches and revisions and specifications and estimates and plans. Plans. Hours (days?) passed. His eyes tired. He should put these back into the footlocker. He *had* put them back and taken them out again, more than once. Time had passed. How much? Put them back, they can always come out again. No. He had not done with them. Leave them where they are. No need for all this endless in and out. Safe here? Of course. Who would be interested in any of this junk? Junk? No. He looked at the alarm clock beside his bed. Late. Whatever day it was, whatever season, it was long past his bedtime, but he was far from ready for bed. He would go down and watch the sunset. No. It had already set. Oh, well. There would be another.

He would go down anyway. Perhaps the sunrise. That was more in line with his present mood, in any case. Yes. The sunrise. Sheila was especially fond of sunrises. They had shared many. Not enough, but some. The one in London after the V-E Day all-night celebrations. The world of reason being reborn before their eyes. And that one in Japan—had they been together? He could not be certain, dredged his memory, decided affirmatively. But the best was the one that had awakened them the first night they spent at the pond. That one, too, suggested rebirth, but of them as a pair. *Any* sunrise was worth waiting for, worth living for. He went downstairs, moving hurriedly.

"Still up, Mr. Osborn?" (An unrecognized person.)

"Still up."

He returned to his rocker. He squinted at the sky, which was powdered with stars. He estimated a couple of hours to sunrise. He knew from sight and sound, the state of the dew, the touch of the atmosphere on his skin.

Spring had turned to winter. (More than once?)

He was alone on the porch. It was still. A faraway owl, hooting mournfully, shared his vigil. Was the owl, too, remembering?

Freeman picked up the broken thread of his thought. Plans, he brooded. Plans. His whole long (too long?) life had been largely plans. Did any of them pan out? Plan out? No, *pan* out. Did any of them happen? Come to—what's the word? Damn! Come to—like food—an *f*—harvest—fruit—*fruition!* Did any of them come to fruition? Not many. Some. Small ones. Mosquitoes. His discovery. What was it called? Something something. Two words. Which two? Hell with it. None of the big plans made it. Well, the planning was life, too. He and Sheila on the floor with the blueprints. The excitement. Blueprints? The ones in the vault—no, *upstairs!* Yes. And now our plan has materialized, come to—fruition. A Japanese house on Squibnocket Pond. Yes. But not mine and Sheila's. Does it matter? Probably not. *Certainly* not! The fact is, there it is.

He had seen it, done, finished, beautiful. Had he?

He looked up at the moon. It was full. Does it matter, in the end, who first sets foot on the moon? Name or nation? (Hadn't there been something on TV and in the papers about someone doing just that, not long ago?)

The point is—*someone* gets to the moon. *Someone* builds a Japanese house on Squibnocket Pond. That is the point.

Sheila.

He smiled, then laughed softly. A moment later he began to cry.

"Are you all right?"

It was the voice of Mrs. Weidenfeld, the night attendant. He waved her away. "Shouldn't you be in bed?" she persisted. "What are you doing out here anyway?"

He turned to her and bellowed, "I'm laughing and crying! Now go away! Go to bed yourself!"

He kept his eyes on her as she went through the screen door—it slammed like a gunshot—and saw her approach Petey, fat and mulled, playing solitaire at the desk.

Freeman listened.

"*He's* not long for this world," said Mrs. Weidenfeld.

"Who?"

"Old Osborn."

"Oh, *he's* okay," said Petey. "Leave him alone."

Freeman turned back to the sky. The sun was coming up. He stopped laughing, and, a few minutes (months? years?) later, he stopped crying.

Garson Kanin

The author of *A Thousand Summers* is the renowned writer-director of the award-winning Broadway comedy *Born Yesterday,* director of *The Diary of Anne Frank, Funny Girl* and scores of other hit plays and movies, and most recently author of the best-selling *Tracy and Hepburn.*

In 1972 Kanin and his equally famous wife, actress and writer Ruth Gordon, bought a house on Martha's Vineyard, where they had often spent vacations. *A Thousand Summers,* set on the Vineyard, "came as a result of our moving permanently to Edgartown," Kanin recalls. "I was cut off from urban existence. I had just reached my sixtieth birthday, and that was a kind of milestone, too. But the book really grew out of the beauty of the island, which started me thinking in new categories.

"Late last spring I got a notion about a love story. It was not meant to be a novel at all, but began as a short story. Then the whole phenomenon of love began to course through my head, and I soon saw I could not contain it at that length. In it I am saying that love is not something reserved for the very young—that it has to do with the capacity for feeling and can exist at any age."

Kanin has a passion for Japan, a country he has never seen. When he was casting about for a title for his novel, he came upon the last line of one of his own poems written in the Japanese three-line verse form known as haiku; his poem is quoted in full on the novel's title page. He also collects *kokeshi* dolls, likes Japanese food, and when he speaks of Japan it is in Freeman's voice: "I *live* to go there. I think about it all the time."

The longed-for trip will have to wait. Kanin is just finishing a book on his years in the movies, *The Leaping Tintypes.* He expects it to be his last nonfiction for a long time.

"I'm off on a new life now," he says. "I'm very anxious to continue writing fiction. I hope to write many plays and films, too."

Where does this perennially youthful vitality come from?

"It's expressed in a remark of Picasso's," he says. " 'It takes a long time to become young.' "

PHOTO BY ALEX GOTFRYD

SHIPWRECK

MORRO CASTLE

SHIPWRECK

The Strange Fate of the Morro Castle

A CONDENSATION OF THE BOOK BY

Gordon Thomas and
Max Morgan Witts

PAINTINGS BY CHARLES LILLY

"All the News That's Fit to Print."

The New York Times.

LATE CITY EDITION

Section 1

VOL. LXXXIII....No. 27,987. NEW YORK, SUNDAY, SEPTEMBER 9, 1934. TEN CENTS

MORRO CASTLE BURNS OFF ASBURY PARK; 200 TO 250 ARE LISTED AS DEAD OR MISSING

GORMAN PROPOSES STRIKE ARBITRATION IF ALL MILLS CLOSE

Union Leader Would 'Avoid Murders' While President's Board Settles Issue.

BUT WIDENS WALKOUT

Calls Out 50,000 More Workers as Employers Plan Mill Openings Tomorrow.

HOSIERY STRIKE ORDERED

Labor Chiefs Direct 50,000 to Quit Wednesday—Green Confers on Textile Peace Plan.

Sailor Missing 12 Years 'Found' on Morro Castle

5 LOST IN STORM WHEN BOATS UPSET

3 Missing, 5 Washed Ashore Off Jersey—Two on Tug Drowned in Bay.

4.8 INCHES OF RAIN HERE

Floods Disrupt Land Travel—Ships Torn From Moorings by Wind in Hudson.

AN AIR VIEW OF THE BURNING LINER MORRO CASTLE OFF THE JERSEY COAST.

MANY BURNED IN CABINS

Flames Cut Off Escape of Tourists Returning From Cruise to Cuba.

STORM HAMPERS RESCUERS

Darkness and Pounding Seas Add to Death Toll—Captain Had Died Shortly Before.

SWEEPING INQUIRIES SET

Speed of Conflagration and Cause a Mystery—Crew Is Praised and Scored.

Rescue Liners Pick Up 157; Craft Near By Speed to SOS

Four Large Vessels Put Out Lifeboats to Circle Water With Coast Guard—Many of the Saved Are Injured.

List of Victims in Sea Disaster and Survivors

SURVIVORS.

Survivors Tell of Leaping Into Sea to Escape Flames

Many Sang and Prayed on Decks—Reluctant Women Pushed Overboard or Into Boats —Ship's Plates Red Hot.

For all these years this disaster has remained a mystery. The sudden death of the captain . . . the possibility of arson . . . crew negligence . . . delayed SOS . . . Communist conspiracy . . .

SHIPWRECK: The Strange Fate of the Morro Castle presents startling answers to a multitude of questions. Its record of shocking blunders, uncertain motives and suspected villainy is an absorbing sea story in the great tradition.

"*Shipwreck* is a superb piece of crime reporting. . . ."
—FORT WORTH, TEXAS, *MORNING STAR-TELEGRAM*

PROLOGUE

In 1884 an editorial in the *Daily Spray,* a journal circulating in the Asbury Park area of New Jersey, suggested one way for Asbury Park to improve its resort status.

> We want a first-class shipwreck. Why? To make Asbury Park a famous winter resort. There is a very comfortable berth for a big ship between the fishing pier and the Asbury Avenue Pavilion.
>
> She should strike head-on, so that her nose would ram the Baby Parade grandstand, and her tail might hop around even with the end of the pier.
>
> We could accommodate her all winter.
>
> Pontoon or suspension bridges could be built from the pier and the pavilion, so that the ship could be used as a casino.
>
> We need a spectacular ship.

Fifty years later, almost to the day, the newspaper's demands were fulfilled.

This is the story not only of how it happened, but of why.

HAVANA: September 5, 1934

SOMEBODY on board wanted to kill him.

Robert Wilmott, captain of the *Morro Castle,* a cruise liner shuttling between New York and Havana, Cuba, had come to this conclusion by the time the ship docked in Havana on September 4, 1934.

Wilmott, ponderously firm and earnest, lacked imagination. To the passengers aboard the *Morro Castle,* however, he epitomized the enchanted world of a sea cruise. In an era when many passengers expected a liner captain to be either a Valentino or an old sea dog, he had chosen the latter role. He was big-boned, with a face crimped by the weather, deep-set eyes and a head of graying, close-cropped hair. For the well-to-do he was the worldly-wise cosmopolitan, yet he could always act the hick inside the dinner jacket to accommodate any wealthy farmer. He regaled passengers with tales of rounding the Horn and roaring through the China Sea. It was not all myth: in September 1933 he had spent seventy-five continuous hours on the bridge steering the *Morro Castle* through a hurricane.

Wilmott had left his native England in 1902 as a deck boy on a freighter. He had climbed the promotional rungs of the Ward Line with dedication, and was rewarded in August 1930 with command of the company's flagship, the *Morro Castle*. Three years later, at fifty-five, he married a first-class passenger, the recently widowed Mathilda Howell Reed. They usually spent some time together on Saturdays, when the *Morro Castle* docked in New York.

For four years Captain Wilmott's ship, launched in 1930, had been the playground of the Eastern Seaboard smart set, a haven for those eager to avoid Prohibition and forget the Depression.

On this, the 174th voyage, her reputation as a floating gin mill remained intact.

But in the summer of 1934 a series of events had endangered both the *Morro Castle* and her master. On July 29 a meal had been served to him that made Wilmott ill enough to suspect a plot to poison him. It was a dish of finnan haddie, which was on the first-class menu. Yet none of the passengers complained of it. On August 4 an attempted strike had threatened to wreck the liner's tight schedule. On August 27 a fire had started in number five hold, which contained high explosives.

On the present run these incidents had become linked together in Wilmott's mind. Since the ship's departure from New York on the afternoon of Saturday, September 1, he had shunned virtually all social obligations on board and had confined himself to his cabin, not eating, drinking only bottled water. Apart from the first officer and chief engineer, who reported regularly, his only caller was the chief radio officer bringing messages from the radio shack. The captain's absence aroused speculation on board—even among the tourist passengers—in spite of the ship's officers' bland reassurance that there was nothing to worry about.

THE *Morro Castle* berthed at a Ward Line pier in Havana on Tuesday. By midmorning on Wednesday, September 5, Eban Starr Abbott, the chief engineer, was bathed and dressed carefully in an immaculate white uniform with gold braid and epaulets.

For four years the boxlike cabin between the ship's two smokestacks had been his home at sea. At the end of the last voyage, his 112th on the *Morro Castle,* Abbott had removed the photograph of his wife, Ada, from his cabin. Packing for this voyage he had told Ada why he was leaving her picture behind. "There were goings-on in the ship that he didn't want me to be part of," Mrs. Abbott later recalled. "The passengers were a fast crowd, he said."

Abbott, son of a seaman, was raised for the sea. In 1909 he got his chief engineer's license and joined the Ward Line. For twenty years he sweated through the tropics or buffeted across the Bay of Biscay on cargo boats. Then in 1929 he was told he was being promoted to chief engineer of the new *Morro Castle*, the fastest turbo-electric vessel afloat. He quickly learned the caprices of every generator, the position of every circuit breaker. On her first trip to Havana she clipped twelve hours off the record.

Only one thing marred the situation for Eban Abbott: the ship's first officer was William Warms. Since the maiden voyage the mutual dislike between the two had deepened to the point where Abbott openly referred to that "worm on the bridge," and Warms talked of that "stuffed tailor's dummy in the engine room."

Abbott hurried ashore. Waiting for him on the Havana pier was the ship's surgeon, Dr. De Witt Van Zile. The two men headed toward Sloppy Joe's, the most famous tavern in the Caribbean.

DEEP in number five hold, Storekeeper William O'Sullivan and Seaman John Gross sat on a pile of sacking and watched Cuban stevedores stack a cargo of bananas, eggplants and peppers. The laborers worked fast, keeping pace with the derricks and winches that lowered the cargo into the hold. Ever since the fire, the one that Captain Wilmott now believed to have been arson, O'Sullivan and Gross had been detailed to guard the huge steel-lined hold whenever it was open. From where they sat they could clearly see the scorch marks on the bulkhead near where the fire had started a bit over a week before. The *Morro Castle*'s smoke-detecting system had alerted the bridge; the flames were extinguished by a mechanism which pumped pressurized carbon dioxide into the hold. The incident had been over in moments.

Suspicion of arson was supported by several clues: a small train of charred pieces of cardboard led away from the initial fire point, and the heat generated was unusually intense, suggesting the use of a chemical agent. The fire had been extinguished only a few feet from crates marked SPORTING GOODS, a regular consignment in the *Morro Castle*'s Havana-bound cargo.

O'Sullivan's bunk was only a few feet from the crates of "sporting goods" and, in his words: "They contained enough guns and ammunition to blow the ship all over the Atlantic!"

The storekeeper understated the situation. For a whole year

the *Morro Castle* had been a floating arsenal. Certainly none of her passengers had any inkling of this; neither did the Bureau of Navigation and Steamboat Inspection of the U.S. Department of Commerce, nor the American Bureau of Shipping. Built with a low-interest government loan of $3,422,181, the liner had been designed for conversion into a troop carrier in the event of war. At no time had the Ward Line or its parent company, Atlantic, Gulf and West Indies Steamship Lines, informed the government that the vessel was going to be involved in gunrunning.

The arms carried by the *Morro Castle* were to support the Cuban government. There are strong indications that the shipments were organized by powerful U.S. business interests concerned that the growing Communist influence on the island would pose a threat to the handsome profits coming from Cuban tobacco and sugar.

In one month, August 1934, the *Morro Castle* carried over 100 crates of assorted weapons—high explosives, drums of gunpowder, and ammunition—to Havana. This arsenal was always unloaded at night by soldiers of the Cuban army.

Storekeeper O'Sullivan had stumbled on the arms traffic in July 1934, when a longshoreman had revealed the contents of the cargo to him. Since then O'Sullivan had kept a careful tally of weaponry going to Cuba.

To him the motive for starting a fire near the "sporting goods" was clear. Somebody was desperate enough to risk sacrificing a whole ship's crew and passengers to prevent these explosives from reaching Cuba; to murder, if necessary, up to 750 people. As to who would take such chances, O'Sullivan hazarded a guess. "Communists," he told Gross. "They're the ones behind it!"

Gross listened and made a decision: when the *Morro Castle* berthed in New York three days later he would sign off the ship. Better to be unemployed than run these risks.

COMMUNISM had had a toehold in Cuba for some years before the *Morro Castle* was launched. In May 1919 a handful of professional revolutionaries from Haiti slipped ashore at Guantánamo Bay. They came to Cuba to spread a "workers' revolution," which they had declared months earlier against American domination on Haiti. They preached the doctrine that Cuba, like Haiti, belonged to the people.

Since 1903 American interests had exercised virtually complete control over Cuba's political and economic affairs. The United States rented military bases at Guantánamo and Bahía Honda, but did little to improve conditions for the Cubans. In 1920 there was only one doctor for every 3000 people; the per capita income was two dollars a month; six out of ten rural children never went to school; 75 percent of the arable land and 90 percent of the telephone and electric services were controlled by U.S. companies.

Dedicated to the abolition of colonialism, the revolutionaries' immediate goal was to overthrow the corrupt and repressive regime of President Machado; their ultimate hope was the removal of American influence from the island.

In the interests of stability successive American administrations openly supported the dictatorship. In turn Machado raised no awkward questions of independence.

SEAMAN Joseph Spilgins had made a discovery. The twenty-six-year-old deckhand had sailed on the *Morro Castle* for three trips. On the second run down from New York he was put in charge of the six starboard lifeboats. He had found that several of the boats had rusted buoyancy tanks. Where the rust had become severe it had been covered with a slick of paint.

Spilgins believed that the boats would be useless in an emergency. In his words: "Taking a chance in them would be as bad as jumping into the water." He did not voice his fears to any of the ship's officers, lest criticism cost him his berth.

FIRST OFFICER William Warms had gone to sea at the age of twelve, at wages of two meals a day and a dollar a month. He had immersed himself in sea lore to cushion some of the hard knocks that a turn-of-the-century sailor had to take. He had sailed with captains who carried Bibles under their arms and forbade drinking, gambling or "going with dirty women."

Those wrathful skippers had molded Warms into a God-fearing man who had little enthusiasm for fancy living—which was one reason he disliked Eban Abbott. He believed that Abbott was a man "who liked the uniform and not the job."

William Warms was intensely proud of his own climb up the promotion ladder. In 1918, after nine years of service, the Ward Line made him captain of a fruit boat. In 1926 he became master of a small passenger liner named the *Yumuri*. He worked the crew as hard as he drove himself. Yet, unaccountably, he ignored the cardinal rule of sea captaincy: take every precaution to ensure the safety of passengers and crew. He never held any lifeboat or fire drills on the *Yumuri*.

Following a complaint filed by three members of the engine-room staff with the Bureau of Navigation and Steamboat Inspection, Warms lost his license for ten days, and the line "beached" him. After an agonizing year ashore he was given command of the Ward cruise liner *Agwistar*. In 1928 two fires mysteriously broke out on board. Once more the issue of proper fire precautions came under scrutiny; again Captain Warms lost his command, was demoted to first officer and forced ashore. To his dying day he would maintain he had been a scapegoat.

In 1929 he returned to sea on a Ward Line freighter, and within a year had established a reputation as probably the best cargo officer in the American Merchant Marine. It was this reputation that influenced Captain Wilmott. With the cargoes the *Morro Castle* carried, he needed a first officer who knew how to load a hold—and how to keep his mouth shut.

What Robert Wilmott had not banked on was a personal clash between his first officer and chief engineer—two key men in any emergency. After four years of increasing tension Captain Wilmott told Warms he planned to recommend that Abbott be transferred to the Ward Line's other turboelectric liner, the *Oriente*.

AT 11:30 a.m. that Wednesday in Havana, George Ignatius Alagna, the ship's first assistant radio officer, received a message from his employers, the Radiomarine Corporation of America, saying that he was to be relieved of his post when the voyage ended. There was no mention of a new assignment. At the age of twenty-two the dark, handsome Alagna faced a bitter lesson: his concern for the welfare of others had probably cost him his future.

Alagna had joined the *Morro Castle* in June. He was leased to the ship by the Radiomarine Corporation, which had a virtual monopoly on radiomen within the American Merchant Marine. The pay, $80 a month, was good compared with the wages received by the crew. Ordinary seamen earned $35 a month; firemen, $52; quartermasters, $55; engine-room oilers, $60. The senior officers were in a substantially higher bracket. Captain Wilmott received $300, First Officer Warms, $180, and Chief Engineer Abbott, $220. Alagna was one of three radio operators on the *Morro Castle*.

The junior member of the communications team was a heavily muscled, nineteen-year-old blond Finn named Charles Maki. Off duty his favorite pastime was to trade sledgehammer blows with a fellow Finn until one of them collapsed. Between these frequent contests of strength Maki would lie on his bunk contemplating the bulkhead overhead, which he had covered with pictures of muscle men clipped from body-building magazines.

Stanley Ferson was chief radio officer when Alagna first joined the *Morro Castle*. Ferson was taken ill shortly before the ship sailed on one trip. She left for Havana with only Alagna and Maki, and Alagna was designated acting chief radio officer. On the next trip Maki became ill. Ferson returned, taking over again as chief, and a newcomer was drafted into the radio room. To Alagna's fury, he was reduced to the most junior post. Only one thing stopped him from making a heated protest—the sympathetic attitude of the newcomer, George White Rogers.

On his first night aboard Rogers had taken Alagna aside. "He said he was specially assigned by the Radiomarine Corporation to get information allowing them to sack Ferson and myself," Alagna stated later. "I gathered that somebody on board had stuck a knife into us. Before acting, the Radiomarine wanted positive proof that we were no good. That was why Rogers was there." It was extraordinary, but to the inexperienced Alagna it was believable.

Rogers had tapped a well of resentment in Alagna, who angrily spit forth a catalogue of complaints: the food was little better than pig swill; working conditions were appalling; the officers seemed to have stepped out of the nineteenth century.

Rogers suggested a simple solution: "Organize a strike just before the ship sails on the next trip from New York. You will get all the backing you want." Rogers said he would be unable to participate. His involvement might compromise his "undercover work" for the Radiomarine Corporation.

Exactly a year before, in August 1933, the crew of the *Diamond Cement* had staged a sit-down strike, demanding higher wages and better working conditions. They were backed by East Coast waterfront workers, and the shipping line finally capitulated. It was a great victory for the seamen. The foundations for that strike had been carefully laid; the reinforcements to sustain it had been readily available. George Alagna had neither of these advantages. All he had was his enthusiasm.

On August 4, 1934, Alagna, clutching a copy of the *Marine Workers' Voice*, the official organ of the Marine Workers International Union, approached a number of the crew and junior officers an hour before sailing time and urged them to walk off. The officers looked on Alagna as a dangerous radical willing to risk their livelihoods in an era when ships' officers would sign on as watchmen to make a living. The deck crew was not much more sympathetic, and the call to strike was a total failure.

Captain Wilmott wanted to fire Alagna at once, but the Radiomarine Corporation said it was impossible to find a replacement at such short notice. Alagna, temporarily reprieved, was shunned by all the officers and crew, except Rogers.

On August 11 Stanley Ferson walked off the *Morro Castle* when she docked in New York. With his departure Rogers became chief radio officer, Alagna regained his old position as first assistant radio officer, and Maki returned to complete the team.

Alagna found it difficult to relax. He believed somebody was trying to waylay him for the trouble he had caused. "I thought several times that I heard footsteps behind me in the shadows of the deck. But each time, when I swung around to investigate, the deck would be vacant."

It may have been this stress which finally sealed Alagna's fate. On this trip, as the *Morro Castle* steamed through the Straits of Florida on her way to Havana, Alagna had been on radio duty. Suddenly he raced to the bridge and accused the watch officer, Second Officer Ivan Freeman, of tinkering with the radio compass, jamming the main transmitter.

It was a ridiculous allegation, and Freeman complained to First Officer Warms, who reported the incident to the captain. Captain Wilmott sent a signal to the Radiomarine Corporation demanding the removal of Alagna on the ship's return to New York.

CREW troubles had plagued the *Morro Castle* since her second voyage. Her schedule allowed only seven hours in New York every Saturday. In that time the crew had to refuel and load supplies, cargo and a fresh group of passengers. Only officers were allowed ashore. Crew members wishing to leave the ship had to sign off, thereby giving up their jobs in an era of unemployment.

This led to acrimony and dissension, and over the years the *Morro Castle* increasingly drew only seamen of poor quality. Already scheduled for dismissal after this trip were six dining-room stewards, two cabin stewards, an electrician, five deckhands, radioman George Alagna and Chief Radio Officer George Rogers.

AFTER a visit from the Havana chief of police, Captain Wilmott locked his cabin door. Captain Oscar Hernandez had confirmed Wilmott's worst fears: his life and ship were threatened.

Captain Hernandez had warned the captain to be on the watch for a Communist agent. He had received information suggesting that the Cuban Communist Party wanted to sabotage the ship because she was aiding the lawful government. It seemed probable that an agent had been placed on board.

When Captain Wilmott recounted the details of the mysterious fire, poisoning attempt and the strike threat, Oscar Hernandez pronounced them all "classic symptoms of the presence of Reds."

Captain Robert Wilmott, master of the Morro Castle

The captain accepted the police officer's diagnosis. What is more, he believed that Alagna was the Communist agitator, ready at any moment to sabotage the *Morro Castle.* Wilmott wasted no time. He picked up the telephone and called First Officer William Warms. "Bill," he said, "there's a Red in the radio shack. Get some irons."

Although both men disliked Alagna, Warms argued against clapping him in irons. It would mean bad publicity for the line; the possibility of the Radiomarine Corporation's demand for an independent inquiry; and undue concern among the passengers.

As an alternative Warms suggested keeping a "close watch" on Alagna until the ship reached New York, at which point the radioman would become somebody else's problem.

Captain Wilmott finally agreed.

THE ship's cruise director, Robert Smith—Smithy to the crew—was the front-desk manager, the man in the blue blazer and raffish cap who was always staging some new amusement. Smith spent a great deal of time sizing people up. Almost intuitively he could sift the important passengers from those who went on a cruise to pretend they were important. On this trip there were 318 passengers. Thirty-two of them, mostly Cuban, were using the ship simply as a means of transport to Havana, and Smith had left them to their own devices. Another, larger group on board consisted of the 102 members of the Concordia Singing Society of the East New York district of Brooklyn. They were a self-contained group, dining, playing and dancing as a bloc.

That left the cruise director with just under 200 people to amuse for six days. On this particular Wednesday noon he was gathering most of them on the pier at Havana. He would address them for a few minutes on the delights ahead, bundle them into a flotilla of cars, wave the drivers on. Then he could go back on board for three hours' sleep before the convoy returned.

With a glad-eye smile for the ladies, Smith watched the group assemble. They were representative of the American urban middle class. A few were obviously rich. Many of the unattached women were searching—in earnest—for husbands. Robert Smith calculated that the single women outnumbered the bachelors by about two to one.

The trip itself was not very expensive. Most of the passengers had spent between $80 and $120 round trip; a few had splurged $160 for a deluxe cabin.

With the air of a man who had paid for it all out of his own pocket, Cruise Director Smith outlined the conducted tour. "Now listen to this! First, a visit to a typical Cuban farm. An amazing revelation, folks, of tropical luxuriance. Sugarcane, pineapples, coconuts, tobacco and, for the ladies, a world of flowers. On the way back you will visit the world-famous Tropical Gardens, drive down the Avenue of Bamboo Trees and the Royal Palm Drive to the Country Club Park, La Playa, the Yacht Club. On to Old Havana, with its winding streets and balconied houses, then back on board ready for sailing time—and new games!" Most passengers had no idea what they were missing of the real Havana.

They shouted approval, climbed into the open cars and thundered away from the pier. Smith watched them go, beaming happily. Not a single passenger had reminded him that his speech was memorized word for word from a Ward Line brochure which had been available to them in New York travel agencies.

For Dr. Joseph Bregstein the 1168-mile run to Havana had been exactly fifty-eight hours and forty minutes of bitter disappointment. The thirty-four-year-old widowed dentist had paid over $200 for a first-class twin-bedded stateroom for himself and his nine-year-old son, Mervin. Apart from being a holiday, the trip was also intended as an opportunity for Joe Bregstein to face one of the most difficult situations any father faces—preparing to introduce a stepmother into a close-knit family unit.

Two years had passed since the tragic death of his wife. The scars were still there, but in recent months there had been a visible healing process. Joe had fallen in love again, and he and his fiancée wondered how Mervin would react. In New York there had not been a real opportunity to find out.

As the *Morro Castle* headed toward Havana, father and son had gone for an early dinner. They sat virtually alone in the dining room full of white tables glittering with institutional silverware. The white-coated stewards, Bregstein thought, seemed distantly polite.

The food, when it came, was hardly first-class fare. "The sort of stuff you would get in a summer hotel," Bregstein recalled later. "There was turkey and duck, both with the kind of stuffing which tastes like kitchen soap. The salad dressings seemed to have been bottled years before." Mervin couldn't eat any of it, so Bregstein asked for a couple of lamb chops. "The waiter said they weren't on the menu. I reminded him this was first class. He shrugged as if he couldn't have cared less. I insisted, so he went away and eventually returned with the chops. In one of them was a nail which had obviously been slipped in after the meat was cooked. I called the headwaiter, and he apologized and said there was always trouble with waiters."

Other things disturbed the dentist. There were no life jackets in his cabin; there had been no lifeboat or fire drills. He also noticed that some crew members doubled up on jobs: deckhands would don stewards' jackets to help out during the cocktail hour.

Thus preoccupied, he had not found an opportunity to bring up with Mervin the subject of his forthcoming marriage. Nor had the sojourn in Havana offered an appropriate moment. As soon as father and son stepped ashore they were surrounded by a bevy of guides eager for their business. In the end they took a conducted tour of the city designed to take the tourist for his last cent.

On the second day in Havana the Bregsteins broke through the

Ward Line brochure advertising New York–Havana cruises aboard the Morro Castle

Acquainted

...with your Cruisemates

Every afternoon the ponies gallop over a measured course with all the thrill and suspense of a horse race on the turf.

ask parties will be another gay feature. ere you may show your genius in costume designing.

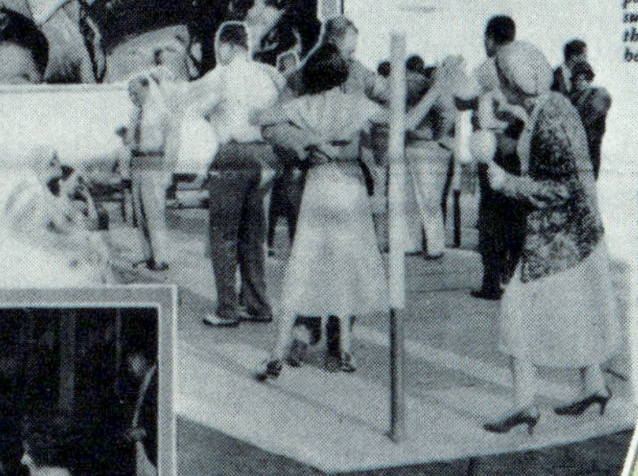

Who doesn't like to dance? The Dancing Deck is ideal, and in the moonlight it's simply gorgeous!

he attractive Tea Room is the ideal place to entertain your friends

Many pleasant minutes will be spent watching for porpoises, sailfish and other denizens of the deep.

ring of guides crowding the pier, fended off hawkers and pimps and lost themselves in the Havana the brochures ignored.

Whenever Joe Bregstein tried to raise the subject of the future, Mervin drew his father's attention to some new sight. Bregstein decided to wait for the heart-to-heart talk until they were back on board and on their way to New York.

PASSENGER William Price was a thirty-eight-year-old New York police patrolman on vacation with his wife, Mary. On the morning of September 5 they had spent several hours ashore, buying cigars, perfumes and souvenirs. Now they leaned over the ship's rail, watching men and boys diving for coins in the foul water between the pier and the black-hulled ship.

The Prices were about to go to their stateroom when a shrill whistle sounded on the port side. There was a pounding of feet, and somebody shouted, "Break out da hose, break out da hose!"

Warning his wife, who was crippled, not to try to move from where she was, Price raced across the promenade deck, unbuttoning his sports jacket as he ran. The shoulder holster and pistol he wore strapped to his body were in clear view. For a moment Price stood there, hand hovering around the gun butt, taking in a most unusual scene: the *Morro Castle* was having its first fire drill in three months.

First Officer Warms had given the order. It is almost certain there would have been no fire drill if Captain Wilmott had not confined himself to his cabin. On June 16, 1934, in violation of the regulations of the Bureau of Navigation and Steamboat Inspection, the captain had banned all further fire drills. Wilmott had acted in what he believed to be the Ward Line's best interests. In May, during a fire drill, a woman passenger had fallen on a deck wet down by a leaking hose connection. She fractured an ankle and hired a good lawyer, and the Ward Line settled out of court for $25,000.

After a visit to the shipping line office Captain Wilmott had ordered the *Morro Castle* deck fire hydrants capped and sealed; 2100 feet of fire hose was locked away, along with nozzles, outlets and wrenches. Whether the captain received instructions from an executive of the line or whether he acted independently is not known. But as a result of Wilmott's order one of the fastest and most luxurious liners became, from that moment on, a floating fire hazard in all but its cargo holds. If a fire started in any of the passenger areas, the only pieces of equipment readily available to fight it were 73 half-gallon portable fire extinguishers and 21 carbon-tetrachloride extinguishers.

How this extraordinary situation could possibly have gone undetected can be explained in part by the fact that the required annual government inspection of the ship had been carried out on May 16, 1934, a month before Captain Wilmott issued his order.

But other questions raised after a routine reinspection by another team of government inspectors on August 4, 1934, remain largely unanswered. Crew members insisted later that the inspection was little more than "a walk around and then a drink with the captain." Officers maintained it was a "thorough going-over." If it was, why were the secured fire hydrants not noticed? Why did the ship's officers and crew remain silent?

The reports on the reinspection no longer exist. But remarks made years later by Third Officer Clarence Hackney and Seaman John Gross may provide a clue. "When making a living means not being difficult, then you are not difficult."

THE fire drill ordered by William Warms was a charade. He refused to allow any water to be used—in case another passenger should slip, be injured and collect damages from the Ward Line. Without water there was no way to test the single 42-foot length of hose he ordered removed from the ship's storeroom for the drill.

Taking their cue from such lax leadership, the men on the hose treated the drill in carnival spirit. They did not couple the hose to a hydrant; instead they ran up and down the deck, lugging it along. Ports, deadlights, convention valves, deck baffles, fireproof valves and watertight doors—none were tested. And during this pantomime off-duty stewards lay around the deck sunning themselves, reading books.

In Suite 107 on B deck honeymooners Charles and Selma Filster slept, oblivious to the fire drill, happily exhausted after four days of almost nonstop revelry.

The voyage had surpassed the Filsters' wildest expectations. From the moment they boarded, JUST MARRIED chalked on their luggage, they had been caught up in a honeymoon euphoria. By day the couple sunbathed and played shuffleboard and deck tennis. In the afternoon they could be seen waltzing at the tea dances, and in the evening attending the gala balls. Whenever they paused there was a waiter on hand with an ice bucket and a bottle of champagne. It was the perfect honeymoon in all but one respect. Charles Filster still awaited the promised invitation for his bride and himself to dine at the captain's table.

Embarrassment, more than anything else, made Raymond Aloysius Egan, a twenty-seven-year-old bachelor, reluctant to return to the ship before he had to. It meant facing another round of well-intentioned prodding for him to pick up one of the single girls on board and have a "good time." Raymond Egan did not choose to explain, although his reason was simple enough. He was a Roman Catholic priest, and he had an idea that vacationers were ill at ease when a clergyman was aboard.

The only two symbols of his calling he had brought with him were his clerical collar and a Daily Office. Both were packed away in his trunk.

For Dr. Charles Cochrane the cruise was his first vacation in three years. He was accompanied by his sister, Catherine, a woman of delicate health who, he believed, would benefit from the sea breezes.

Despite the presence of other doctors on the passenger list, few on board knew Dr. Cochrane was one of New York's most distinguished physicians. He was chief of the urological staff at Kings County Hospital in Brooklyn. From previous experience Charles Cochrane knew the inevitable problems which would arise if it were generally known he was a doctor. "A doctor is somebody to be consulted at the first rumble of pain," he told one of the passengers. "People do so without a second thought–though they would never dream of consulting a banker about financial problems if he was on vacation with them."

Tall, elegant and naturally reserved, he had ensured privacy for his sister and himself by booking the most expensive pair of suites on the *Morro Castle,* staterooms one and two on A deck. Each cost $160. Forward of all other passenger accommodations and immediately beneath the navigating bridge, their location provided a superb panoramic view of the ocean ahead.

Apart from the absence of the captain from their dinner table the cruise so far had been what Dr. Cochrane expected. Catherine looked better than she had in years, and he had finally been able to relax. On the other hand, the rumors about the captain did concern him. Dr. Cochrane was disturbed by the captain's almost complete seclusion in his cabin and his strained look during his few public appearances. Such obvious signs of stress in a man charged with the safety of all on board were not reassuring, especially since the physician had the impression that few of the crew were competent to handle an emergency.

On September 5 at 5:00 p.m. Dr. Cochrane and his sister were alone on the sun deck watching the last hold being loaded with salted hides. The stench was awful. Catherine Cochrane wondered whether the smell would spread to the rest of the ship.

Third Officer Clarence Hackney had just received orders from Captain Wilmott on how to control the odor. He had been instructed that once the hold with the cargo of skins was sealed the ship's smoke-detecting system was to be turned off and was to remain off until the last passenger had disembarked in New York.

In twenty years at sea Hackney had never been given such a baffling command. The system, the most sophisticated early fire warning then available, was composed of 27 lines of piping leading from the cargo spaces to a detector cabinet in the wheelhouse. An exhaust fan drew a continuous sample of air through each pipe to the cabinet. The system was so sensitive that, Hackney knew, "anybody having a smoke in the hold would be spotted at once."

At 5:15 p.m. he shut the valves in the cabinet tubes.

At about that moment Rogers, the massive chief radio officer, lumbered ashore. When he returned he carried two small bottles. One contained sulfuric acid, the other nitric acid.

Dr. Emilio Giro and his brother-in-law, Rafael Mestre, both Cuban, had planned to travel to New York with another line, but were unable to get berths. At the last minute they had found a vacant double stateroom on the *Morro Castle*.

The tall, dark-eyed Mestre was twenty years old, rich and single. His infectious laugh and his enthusiasm for life charmed everyone. As he bounded up the gangway he checked the number of pretty, unattached girls on board. Mestre was in luck: there were plenty to ensure him a good time all the way to New York.

Emilio Giro was thirty-four years old, well-off, married, with an infant daughter, Sylvia, named after his wife. Firmly established as Cuba's outstanding specialist in the field of endocrinology, Dr. Giro was going to America for two months of research.

He approached the *Morro Castle* as if she were a patient. First he formed an overall impression: black-hulled, rising gracefully to a towering white structure, the ship was quite the largest he had ever traveled on.

Next he inspected the stateroom. It was compact and planned with care. On the back of the door Dr. Giro read a framed notice in English and Spanish:

TO ALL PASSENGERS

The necessary number of life preservers for adults and children will be found in each stateroom.

Directions for Use:

Slip the arms through the shoulder straps and secure the belt across the body and under the arms.

Your lifeboat is No. 10.

Your lifeboat station is B deck.

Emilio Giro located a life jacket under each bed. Then he set off to find lifeboat number ten.

ACCORDING TO HER SHIPBUILDER, the *Morro Castle* was a "three-deck, complete superstructure type, with combined forecastle head and long bridge forming a flush deck forward; double-bridged, with an overhanging promenade deck of steel." Her gross tonnage was 11,520; displacement, 15,870; length overall, 508 feet; total cargo space, 335,000 cubic feet; type of machinery, twin-screw turboelectric drive; shaft horsepower, 16,000; boilers, 6 watertube.

For their part the interior designers had succeeded in eliminating any hint of the sea in the passenger compartments. The decor mixed something called Olde English with the wilder moments of the Italian Renaissance. In the mood of Elizabethan England, lutes and mandolins hung on the walls of the first-class smoking room. The first-class lounge resembled the drawing room at Versailles during the time of Louis XVI. Satinwood, ebony and rosewood provided false walls, ceilings and doors. Traveling first class on the *Morro Castle* was like putting to sea in the Waldorf Astoria.

Tourist-class accommodations for 95 passengers were located well aft on C, D and E decks. Here the rich paneling and carpeting gave way to paint and linoleum. Plain wall fittings replaced diffuse lighting. The ventilation system, which pumped sea air into the first-class areas, here carried the aroma of engine-room oil and cooking fat.

DR. Giro located lifeboat number ten on the port side of A deck. He guessed it would hold 50 people (its actual capacity was 70). At first he was puzzled that his embarkation station was below on B deck, the promenade deck. Then he realized that for easy access seamen would lower the boats to the level of the deck below, where the passengers could "just step in."

Satisfied with his inspection Dr. Giro went below to the promenade deck to watch the final preparations before departure. He was not in time to see the huge waddling figure of Chief Radio Officer Rogers puffing his way toward the wireless shack. Dr. Giro was probably the only man on board qualified to recognize Rogers for what he was—the victim of an unusual disease, adiposogenital dystrophy, a pituitary disorder which frequently produces social maladjustment. Of all the officers and crew in responsible positions, the chief radio officer was probably the least suited for his responsibility.

George White Rogers was born with the pituitary disorder on June 9, 1901, in New York City. His mother, Lulu, suffered from a similar glandular disturbance.

This gave her a rotund figure, poor equipment for husband catching. It appears also to have affected her personality: she had a self-defensive reserve. However in 1897 she had met George Rogers, Sr. They married in the fall of that year. He was a reticent man with strong religious convictions. During the week he drove a dray; on Sundays he read aloud from the Bible. There was very little communication between the two, and the arrival of baby George four years after their marriage did nothing to help.

In August 1906 George Rogers, Sr., took his family West to San Francisco, attracted by newspaper reports that there was big money to be made in rebuilding the city shattered by earthquake and fire. The reports proved to be untrue. There was work, plenty of it, but there was no fortune to be made hauling rubble.

In the spring of 1907 George Rogers, Sr., died of a chest infection, and a few weeks later Lulu Rogers joined him in the municipal cemetery of San Francisco. George was taken to live with his maternal grandmother in nearby Oakland.

At the age of seven he developed an alarming symptom. In a month he gained almost 50 pounds, concentrated in the abdominal region, around the hips and thighs, the upper arms and the back of the neck. The disproportions were accented by the thinness of his lower arms and legs.

Taunted increasingly by the neighborhood children, George Rogers must have been a pitiful sight—an enormous boy, wearing cut-downs of his grandfather's clothes. By the age of twelve he weighed 170 pounds. His knock-knees, flaring hips and soft facial features made him even more susceptible to ridicule.

He had also become painfully aware of the classic symptom of his illness: he was sexually underdeveloped. His hairless skin seemed inordinately feminine, and his voice never deepened into a manly register. The psychological effect of all this was devastating: the fat child became a secretive and reclusive adolescent.

He also turned to crime. His first known crime was stealing skates, a pointless piece of thievery. For fourteen-year-old George was far too clumsy to balance on any rollers. He had stolen to get even with the children who tormented him.

George was let off with a warning, but nine days later he burglarized a house. This time he was committed to a reform school, the Good Templar's Home in Vallejo.

During adolescence his psychotic tendencies became more deeply rooted. He committed a series of petty thefts in the home. The superintendent reported that young Rogers was also "untruthful; his influence on the other children of the home was bad; he would not work." And, finally, he was a "moral pervert."

In March 1915 Rogers was committed to the Boys and Girls Aid Society in San Francisco, a place with a policy of firm discipline. But punishment did not arrest the development of the boy's disturbed personality. Extended silences alternated with an intolerant, often domineering manner. The conflict between his inner world and the world around him grew.

Not once during the troubled period was he seen by a doctor. Even a cursory medical examination would have indicated physical abnormality, and a psychiatrist would have recognized his psychotic characteristics.

Instead the San Francisco society found him a job—as assistant wireless operator on a schooner sailing out of San Francisco. By chance it was a job Rogers actually wanted. He was paroled, and on May 12, 1917, he went to sea.

He then worked his way through a series of jobs as a telegraphist. By the time he joined the *Morro Castle* he was literally obsessed with his sexual immaturity. Although he had married, the union had been a disaster. That failure had increased his hatred of his body, which now weighed 250 pounds; the cruel teasing by neighborhood children had become a painful memory in adulthood.

Rogers equated respect with love, happiness and power. Respect could compensate for the cruel trick nature had played on him. At numerous stages of his life his craving for recognition went out of control. In 1929 he became fascinated with the possibility of murder in which the evidence is totally destroyed. Arson fell into that category. Rogers collected scientific books and magazines on the subject and started experimenting. He made a number of fountain-pen bombs filled with acid which ate down into a combustible powder through a thin membrane of copper.

In March 1929, while he was employed by the Wireless Egert Company in New York, a mysterious fire broke out at the plant. Police files noted: "It was Rogers' custom to arrive for work at 8:30 a.m. The morning of the fire he was on the scene at 7:30 a.m. He unlocked the door and let the firemen in."

By then the blaze was burning fiercely. Salvage experts concluded it had been started by a chemical timing device. Rogers was questioned for days. A set smile never left his lips. In the end he was released. The police file stated that Rogers was "suspected of arson." The police could have found the evidence they needed in Rogers' home in Bayonne, New Jersey; a back room contained timing devices powerful enough to destroy a dozen factories.

In March 1934 Rogers decided to return to sea. Radiomarine Corporation officials had no inkling of his record of crime and mental disturbance when they hired him. Nor did the Ward Line. Rogers might have appeared to be an oddball, but a lay person could not know he was genuinely disturbed.

He liked the *Morro Castle*. It took him away from America, away from the police. As chief radio officer his salary was $120 a month. But this was not enough for Rogers. He started to pocket charges to passengers for radiograms. However he overlooked the fact that at the end of each voyage inspectors from the Radiomarine Corporation checked the books against the money handed in. Rogers failed to doctor the books and was found out.

Now, after three months on the *Morro Castle*, the Radiomarine Corporation had told him that this was to be his last trip. His dismissal followed a confidential investigation by the corporation.

Rogers believed—mistakenly—that a number of people on the ship had been questioned during the inquiries. On the voyage to Havana, believing himself the victim of injustice, he had allowed his paranoiac fantasies free rein. When he slipped ashore forty-five minutes before sailing time to obtain two bottles of acid, he was ready to act.

AT 5:50 p.m. Captain Wilmott appeared on the bridge. Moments later he was joined by the pilot. Two tugs were made fast aft and forward, and the cables that held the liner to the land were loosed. The ship's whistle blew a long, sharp blast. The bridge telegraphs rang. The tugs nudged bow and stern, and the gap between the *Morro Castle* and the pier steadily widened.

AT SEA: September 5 – September 7, 1934

BY 6:30 p.m. life on board the *Morro Castle* had returned to its normal cruise pattern.

Aft on B deck the ship's orchestra was playing hits from the 1920s. Its efforts elicited intermittent applause from Charles and Selma Filster. They were particularly happy: on their way to the deck ballroom the ship's headwaiter, Carl Wright, had told them they were to be the captain's dinner guests the following night. It would be Captain Wilmott's first dinner with his passengers in three days.

IN stateroom number one a steward served cocktails to the four people seated on the overstuffed chairs. Dr. Cochrane and his sister were entertaining Dr. and Mrs. Theodore Vosseler. The two doctors knew each other by reputation. Dr. Vosseler often referred patients from his thriving private practice to Dr. Cochrane at Kings County Hospital.

Chief Engineer Abbott dressed carefully. He was thinking about Captain Wilmott's polite suggestion earlier that evening that he transfer to the Ward Line's *Oriente*. Eban felt strongly that Wilmott didn't want him to go, but that for unexplained reasons the captain had to please Warms.

At about the same time First Officer Warms decided to check the radio shack. As he came to the door he saw that George Alagna was on duty. Suddenly the bulk of George White Rogers filled the doorway. Rogers called out softly, "Mr. Warms? I'd like to see the captain."

"Why?"

"I have some information for him."

"About what?"

"Best I tell the captain first."

During the conversation a fixed smile remained on the chief radio officer's lips. It was that, more than anything he said, that Warms found disturbing.

The first officer promised to arrange an interview after dinner. Only much later did he realize that as a ship's officer Rogers did not need permission to call on the captain.

George White Rogers knew that within three days his career at sea would be terminated unless something dramatic changed the course of events. Rogers had a plan to ensure that change. He had placed the bottles of sulfuric and nitric acid on the shelf above George Alagna's bunk.

During the evening he casually strolled over to the shelf, removed the bottles and turned to Alagna. "What are you going to do with these, George?" he asked.

At precisely 7:30 p.m. William Warms and Eban Abbott arrived in Captain Wilmott's cabin. The predinner meeting was a ritual at sea, a chance for the ship's three senior officers to discuss informally the day's run.

The cabin was furnished with sofas, easy chairs and tables. Along one bulkhead stood a cabinet which converted into a bar. A connecting door led to the captain's night cabin. It held a double bed, bath and toilet. A speaking tube above the bed was connected to the bridge. A telephone stood on a side table.

The chief engineer's report was short: the engine room and his men were working normally.

The first officer reported five stewards logged for drunkenness and a fight in the forecastle between two deckhands. All would be sacked in New York. Warms made no reference to the fire drill he had authorized, and the captain did not mention his order to seal off the cargo smoke-detector system.

At 7:45 p.m. the three men began their rounds—a brisk tour to show both passengers and crew that the ship was under effective command. Their inspection of the bridge required only a few moments. The complex of equipment seemed to be in order and indicated that the *Morro Castle* was on course and on time.

The three proceeded to the promenade deck, which was enclosed at the forward end with storm windows. The glass swept back to midships, where it gave way to open rail lined with deck chairs. Beyond lay the deck ballroom.

After a brief look into the veranda tearoom the captain's party strode down to D deck. Captain Wilmott wanted to check the galley area. Neither of his fellow officers could recall ever before having made such a digression from the normal evening rounds. It seemed proof to Eban Abbott that the captain was still preoccupied by the apparent attempt to poison him on July 29.

The main galley, pantry and mess spaces were located just aft of the first-class dining room. Captain Wilmott, followed by Warms and Abbott, walked quickly past the bank of ovens, broiler and roasting spit to the zinc counters covered with servings of the chef's specialty, a crabmeat cocktail. Headwaiter Carl Wright, who had come into the kitchen the moment he was alerted to the captain's presence, hovered in the background. When the inspection party finished their rounds he moved forward.

"Captain, sir, is everything in order?"

The master of the *Morro Castle* nodded, and picked a dish of the crab hors d'oeuvre at random. "Serve me this one at dinner," he ordered Wright, and proceeded into the dining room.

SEVENTY FEET FORWARD of the first-class dining room, with its silver-and-gilt baskets of fruit, the deck crew used stale bread to sop up the last of the greasy stew.

The air in the crew's mess reeked of sweat, cigarette smoke, dirty clothes and liquor. This jungle of bare steampipes was a world into which few ship's officers ventured. Thieving from the line, drug running and bootlegging were commonplace. So were fights—with fists, knives and wrenches. During the *Morro Castle*'s four-year history a number of men had been taken off the ship with severe wounds.

The crew formed small groups and aired their complaints over their tin plates at mealtime. Storekeeper William O'Sullivan, seamen John Gross and Joe Spilgins discussed the lack of proper safety drills and precautions on the *Morro Castle.* Watchman Arthur Pender described the situation as "catastrophic."

In sixteen years at sea Pender's concerns about safety had made him unpopular with more than one master. On the *Morro Castle,* as on other ships, he had compiled a "potential disaster dossier." He had discovered that the fire doors were not equipped with sirens or bells, standard in all first-class passenger vessels. In port the men on gangway watch had never been instructed where the nearest fire alarm was located ashore. He noted that most of the crew had no actual training with fire hoses, and the fire-screen doors were never closed during the rare fire drills.

Four of the ship's lifeboats were virtually useless. They were the first two forward on either side. In an emergency lowering they would come down outside the enclosed promenade deck and it might well be impossible to open the heavy glass windows in order to get into the boats. The plugs in the lifeboats were not chained or fastened to the boats. In the port lifeboats the Jacob's ladders were heavily coated with paint; the shackles were useless.

Pender also discovered something that dismayed him even more. The ship's Lyle gun—a line-throwing apparatus—and the drum of powder to fire it were originally stored on the bridge. Captain Wilmott ordered it moved elsewhere, as "it might get some Cuban excited into thinking we were an armed ship."

Third Officer Clarence Hackney discovered an empty compartment between the ceiling of the first-class writing room and the deck above. He ordered the Lyle gun and the drum of powder placed in the space. There it would be easily accessible from the bridge in an emergency. He overlooked the fact that all that was between 25 pounds of dangerous explosive and the writing room below were thin sheets of board covered with plaster.

The seamen who stowed the gun and powder barrel carried the apparatus past the wireless room. When Chief Radio Officer Rogers stopped them to ask what they were doing, they told him the purpose of their mission. He expressed interest and said he never knew the compartment existed.

Discussion in the crew's mess reached a new intensity over the fire drill held earlier that day. "I just hope I get off this ship before anything happens," insisted Seaman Gross.

"Well, if you're going, don't take a lifeboat," said Spilgins.

In the first-class dining room Captain Wilmott's presence after three days caused an understandable stir, not least of all among the physicians present. Dr. Emilio Giro, two tables away, observed that Wilmott ate very little and sipped only ice water. The two doctors at the captain's table, Charles Cochrane and Theodore Vosseler, were both aware of a seeming nervousness in his conversation. He appeared preoccupied. The captain told his table guests that the "pressure of work" had been responsible for his absence during the outward-bound voyage.

At the table of First Officer Warms, when the Right Reverend Hiram Richard Hulse, missionary bishop of Cuba, mentioned that the captain looked excessively tired, Warms directed the conversation to other topics.

The food continued to appall Joe Bregstein. The dentist, who had become popular on board, had perceived that many of his fellow passengers didn't seem to be having the good time described in the brochures. In spite of the efforts of the cruise director, passengers were left to their own resources a great deal.

The ship's orchestra was grinding out the sort of schmaltz one could hear in any second-rate summer hotel. So after dinner Joe Bregstein went into the first-class lounge, sat down at the piano and hammered out honky-tonk renditions of "My Gal Sal" and "Let Me Call You Sweetheart." His performance was greeted with appreciative applause.

After dinner Captain Wilmott excused himself and went to his cabin to keep his appointment with Chief Radio Officer Rogers.

AT 8:45 p.m. George Alagna tuned the receiver in the radio shack to the 600-meter frequency, the distress wave band for the mandatory three-minute "listening-out" period observed by all ships at sea fifteen minutes before and fifteen minutes past the hour.

At 8:48 p.m. Alagna adjusted the apparatus to maximum sensitiveness—standard procedure before transmitting—and turned it over to Maki to send a handful of passengers' messages. For a moment Alagna watched Maki working. When he was satisfied that the Finn was on the proper frequency he went into the adjoining room where the three operators slept.

Two things had bothered Alagna all evening. How had those bottles gotten onto the shelf over his bunk? He was positive they had not been there until Rogers had returned from his trip ashore. And why had Rogers insisted that they contained acid? There were no labels on the bottles. Alagna had unstoppered them earlier; the contents were odorless; he understood that acids gave off a distinctive smell.

He was struck by something else. The porthole above his bunk was closed; for a stranger to reach the shelf he would have had to come through the radio shack. There had been no callers that day. There seemed to be only one answer: either Maki or Rogers had placed the bottles there. And the two bottles were now gone.

AFTER dinner William Warms left the bridge to "walk the ship." Everything appeared normal. Subdued chatter, laughter, the rattle of trays and the sound of the orchestra emanated from the public rooms. Yet he had a vague feeling of uneasiness.

ROGERS HAD PLANNED his story with care for his interview with Captain Wilmott. For weeks, he told Wilmott, he had suspected that Alagna was capable of stirring up trouble. Now he had proof: the discovery of the two bottles of dangerous acids.

The captain was so shaken that he accepted without question the chief radio officer's statement that he had thrown the bottles over the side immediately. "I think the man is crazy!" Wilmott ranted. "In New York he started a riot because he wanted to get off the ship without having his crew pass stamped by the immigration authorities." The more Captain Wilmott talked about Alagna, the more irrational he became. Alagna was now the epitome of every Communist agitator the captain had ever heard about.

Rogers listened gravely. He had no need to do anything else; the captain's fears were now firmly established.

The captain finished his tirade: "Mr. Rogers, I want you to take the key to the emergency room and put it in your pocket. I do not want that key anywhere that man can get it."

Precisely what damage George Alagna could do to the radio compass, which was the only item of importance kept in the emergency room, Captain Wilmott did not explain.

The captain already had Alagna under surveillance by Warms. Now the chief radio officer had effectively established his own role as the captain's contact within the radio shack, reporting regularly on the operator's activities.

As Rogers left, the captain thanked him again for disposing so promptly of the two bottles of acid. He had no reason to suspect that the chief radio officer had retained them for his own use.

AROUND 11:00 p.m. the orchestra slowed down the tempo in the deck ballroom. A medley of romantic numbers announced the end of the evening's entertainment.

Charles and Selma Filster planned to retire to their stateroom, which was equipped with a loudspeaker offering a selection from the ship's record library. As they left the ballroom Charles asked a steward to send down a bottle of French champagne. At $1.50 a bottle, the honeymooners rated it the best value on board.

As the orchestra played the last dance the chief engineer whirled one of the beautiful young female passengers around the dance floor. Like many ship's officers Abbott had long understood the fine difference between easy familiarity and inappropriate intimacy, and a few harmless flirtations relieved his boredom.

The Prices were playing cards with Charles and Annie Menken. Menken, like Price, was a New York policeman, but the two men had never met before. They were discussing life insurance. William Price revealed that if he were to die that night he would leave his wife $1400 plus what she would get as a policeman's widow. Charles Menken wondered aloud how an insurance company calculated something as involved as the coverage of a ship.

Joe Bregstein played one last tune on the piano and left the lounge for a stroll around the deck before turning in. He leaned over the port rail, peering into the night. Far in the distance a light broke the darkness. Bregstein wondered what it was.

Farther down the deck Father Raymond Egan was also watching the light. The priest had returned to the ship that afternoon tired and depressed and had gone to bed early, without dinner. He had slept fitfully, awakened often by the sounds of music and laughter coming from the public rooms. He hoped a stroll around the deck would relax him.

"Miami."

Father Egan turned around, startled. Standing behind him was George White Rogers. The chief radio officer explained that the light came from Miami, ten miles away on the Florida coast, and the next landfall would be Port Everglades.

Nodding good night, Rogers proceeded down the deck. Father Egan marveled that such a big man could move so quietly.

At midnight the ship's bell on the bridge announced a change of watch. A new squad of oilers and firemen scuttled down to the engine room. On the bridge Fourth Officer Howard Hansen assumed command. The barometer was dropping; the wind was shifting and stiffening. Bad weather was on the way.

From where he stood far in the stern, Watchman Arthur Pender noticed that the ship had increased speed. Apparently a decision had been taken to push the *Morro Castle* hard through the night.

Pender made his rounds, pausing at regular intervals to punch a time clock. Except for the muted throb of engines or the hum of a ventilator, everything seemed quiet. At around 1:00 a.m. the watchman came to the first-class area. The public rooms were still filled with drinking parties, and stewards moved in and out carrying drinks to the cabins.

Pender was shocked to see that the two other watchmen, who should have been on deck, had been drafted to help with cabin service.

The *Morro Castle* was now protected by only four men: Fourth Officer Hansen, the officer of the watch; a helmsman; the bow lookout; and Watchman Pender. Pender regarded this as the most flagrant breach yet of the rules governing safety at sea.

Another violation of those rules kept First Officer Warms awake in the early hours of Thursday morning: the lack of boat drills. Lifeboat drills had been suspended by Captain Wilmott because the captain insisted they "upset passengers." As a reminder of the potential cruelty of the sea, they were not in keeping with the balmy world of the pleasure cruise.

The memory of his own suspension in 1928 for failing to carry out similar drills haunted Warms. He had a premonition that the situation could repeat itself, and that along with Captain Wilmott he would again face censure. As he lay there in his bunk he decided that rather than risk another such censure he would take a gamble. When the ship docked in New York he planned to confront Captain Wilmott with the dangerous situation the captain had allowed to develop. If that failed to set things right, he thought of laying all the facts before the Ward Line itself.

Within moments after Warms drifted off to sleep, wind, rain and waves were thundering against the *Morro Castle*'s starboard freeboard.

Chief Engineer Abbott awoke with a start as a burst of spray flew through his cabin porthole. He listened for a moment to the sounds outside, then reached for the emergency speaker tube linking him with the engine room.

From below a voice told him what he wanted to know: the bridge had ordered reduced speed. Abbott closed the porthole and went back to sleep.

Fourth Officer Hansen had awakened the captain shortly after 3:00 a.m. with news of the tropical storm. Now, on the bridge, Hansen plotted the new zigzag course Wilmott had ordered, which brought the ship head on toward the wind and seaway, then reversed the process a few moments later. The maneuver reduced the roll considerably. By 4:00 a.m. the storm had blown over.

Dr. Emilio Giro awakened early from habit. He looked out of the stateroom porthole; the ship's progress along the Atlantic swell was almost imperceptible. He dressed quietly, anxious not to disturb his brother-in-law, Rafael Mestre, who was sound asleep after a long night of dancing and drinking.

At 7:00 a.m. Dr. Giro stepped out on deck. The sun was coming up behind a bank of clouds. In spite of its warmth he shuddered, remembering his fear during the storm. Lying in bed, he had suddenly realized he couldn't swim. He wondered what would happen if the ship sank. Now he found himself walking down A deck toward lifeboat number ten. The boat was still there, still intact.

Feeling relieved and just slightly foolish, Dr. Giro began a leisurely stroll around the decks.

By 7:30 a.m. Cruise Director Smith was putting on a brave show of losing a game of shuffleboard to Mrs. Thelma Hulse, wife of the missionary bishop of Cuba. Smith was probably one of the best players on the Eastern Seaboard—but he knew when it paid to lose. Farther down the sports deck Charles and Annie Menken played a fast and skillful set of deck tennis before a growing crowd of onlookers. Father Raymond Egan stopped to watch for a moment, then went to the first-class dining room, where he told his waiter he felt like eating his way through the whole menu.

The dining room filled rapidly.

At 9:00 a.m. Smith's voice came over the dining-room loudspeaker: "Good morning, everybody. This is your cruise director speaking. Are we happy? Everybody? Good, good, good!"

First he gave them the weather forecast: it looked like a wet day. Never mind, there was plenty to do: miniature horse racing, bingo, indoor quoits. For the ladies, the beauty parlor was open all day. And "Don't forget, folks, tonight there's the grand elimination dance with lots and lots of prizes!"

THAT morning Captain Wilmott locked himself in his cabin. He opened it only to First Officer Warms, to whom he announced: "Acid—that's what they'll use. Acid to destroy me with!"

Warms beat a hasty retreat, convinced the captain was having some kind of breakdown. If he continued to behave like this, the Ward Line was bound to retire Wilmott. For William Warms that could mean a real chance of sewing an extra stripe of gold braid around his cuff.

To Joe Bregstein the voyage was becoming increasingly unbearable; his feelings about the food had long since been overridden by his worries about safety. When a number of seasoned passengers remarked on the absence of boat drills, it heightened his apprehensions.

Bregstein felt worried enough to question the first ship's officer he came across, Chief Engineer Abbott. When the dentist told Abbott what some of the other passengers had said about boat drills, the chief engineer smiled reassuringly. He asked if this were Bregstein's first trip, and when he told him it was, Abbott nodded and said the dentist's fears were very natural among first trippers. There was absolutely no need for worry: "The *Morro Castle* is the *safest* ship afloat." As a measure of good faith he offered to take Bregstein on a tour of the ship the following morning. Bregstein agreed. The excursion would be a surprise for his son, Mervin.

At many of the tables lunchtime gossip focused on Captain Wilmott's absence. The passengers theorized that either the captain was not well or he was on the bridge, plotting the fastest possible course to New York to avoid the worst of the weather.

When the radio room received a meteorological report warning of a gale, force seven, bearing down in a wide sweep from Newfoundland, the news was conveyed to passengers by Cruise Director Smith. "But," he assured them, "that won't spoil the fun. A tea dance, bingo and miniature horse racing are still scheduled."

At the table hosted by Dr. Van Zile, the ship's surgeon, news of approaching bad weather, the captain's absence and bingo sessions made little impact. By the end of lunch his guests had worked their way through several pitchers of planter's punch and interminable toasts to a "wonderful time."

"I did the best thing possible by dumping them overboard, George, the best thing all around. You've got to believe that."

Alone, sitting on his bunk, George Alagna recalled the words of the chief radio officer. They did not make sense. Alagna had not brought the bottles aboard, nor had he known of their contents. There was only one way to interpret Rogers' statement: in dumping the mysterious bottles the chief radio officer had implied that he had helped Alagna—and at the same time accused him of intending to commit a crime. The longer Alagna thought about it, the more upset he became.

When George Rogers went to Captain Wilmott's cabin to make his first report of the day on Alagna's activities he knocked and found the door locked. When he knocked again and identified himself, Captain Wilmott ordered him to go away and stay away. For whatever reason, Rogers' role as the captain's informer was over.

Rogers found himself in an all-too-familiar situation. When he reached New York he would be out of a job and would again face police harassment. If anything could turn his mind once more to thoughts of revenge, the moment when Captain Wilmott ordered him away was tailor-made.

IN THE VERANDA TEAROOM Selma Filster was having phenomenal success at horse racing. By the end of the afternoon she collected $25—exactly the weekly salary of Cruise Director Robert Smith, who paid over the winnings. When the races broke up, rain was falling steadily from a leaden sky.

ON the bridge the watch changed. Third Officer Clarence Hackney made up the log and handed it over to Second Officer Ivan Freeman. The rpm indicator showed 145, giving a speed of about 20 knots. With the weather closing in, it was too fast for passenger comfort. Freeman ordered a reduction to 17 knots.

THE reduction in speed came too late for Catherine Cochrane. The plunging and pitching had finally made her sick. Her brother prescribed sips of salted ice water and rest in bed.

Other passengers relied on different remedies to combat the seasickness brought on by the gale. William and Mary Price chose a large brandy apiece; the Menkens settled on whipped egg with a dash of rum. Selma and Charles Filster lay in their bunks willing the sickness to go away. They knew it scotched their plans for dinner at the captain's table.

The gale was a relief to Headwaiter Carl Wright. It reduced the number he could expect for dinner and provided a cast-iron story should the captain continue to be absent from meals.

THE gale, in fact, brought Captain Wilmott out of his cabin.

When he joined Warms on the bridge, the first officer gave him the latest weather report, and Captain Wilmott authorized a further reduction in speed. For a while he stood staring ahead into the storm. Then he turned to Warms and said, "I don't feel good. I will take an enema and lie down." He went back to his cabin and locked the door.

AT midnight the watch changed. Fourth Officer Howard Hansen ordered an increase in speed from 16.2 to 18 knots: most of the passengers were probably in bed anyway.

Watchman Pender welcomed the rain because it excused him from a regular chore: he usually had to help wash down the decks between patrols. Tonight he passed his free time in the comfort of the ship's pantry, sipping hot coffee and wishing life could always be so peaceful.

Fourth Officer Hansen ordered regular course corrections. At 5:00 a.m. the most treacherous stretch of coastline lay ahead. The Cape Hatteras Lighthouse had still not been sighted when Hansen handed over the watch to Third Officer Clarence Hackney and went below for breakfast and a morning's sleep.

After breakfast in his cabin First Officer Warms called on Captain Wilmott. The captain complained of a backache and tiredness. He had seen the ship's surgeon that morning, and Dr. Van Zile had prescribed "some medicine."

Warms reported that surveillance of the radio room continued, and that Alagna had done nothing untoward. He now suggested—in a curious reversal—that the radioman should be locked up. The captain—in an equally curious reversal—resisted the idea. "No, we will get rid of him in New York."

Perhaps Warms should have pressed the captain for an explanation for his change of attitude. He did not. It might have provided an opportunity for Warms to divulge his doubts about the chief radio officer.

By noon the *Morro Castle* had less than fifteen hours of normal living left.

"In the event of collision, five electrically operated watertight bulkheads seal off the ship. They just press a button on the bridge!" For an hour Joe Bregstein and his son listened as Chief Engineer Abbott recounted an endless stream of "safety facts." He told them the decks were covered with about 67,000 square feet of Selbalith, a fireproof lightweight sheathing laid on the plates. An electric fire-detecting system was installed in all staterooms, officers' and crew's quarters, with thermostats to warn of any temperature increase. There was also the smoke-detecting system; and 74 steel cylinders of carbon-dioxide gas, located at strategic points around the ship, fed a complementary smothering system through which the gas could be pumped under pressure.

Abbott did not know that Captain Wilmott had ordered the smoke-detecting system turned off. Nor did he tell the Bregsteins that the fire-detecting system did not extend to the public rooms.

Eban Abbott was impressive. In addition to the lifeboats, with a total capacity of 816 passengers, there were a dozen balsa-wood floats, each capable of carrying 17 people; 18 ring life buoys, each capable of supporting two people; and 851 life preservers, of which 78 were designed for children.

The chief engineer reserved until last the tour's climax—the engine room. He led them across catwalks and down steel ladders, pausing briefly for a lecture on the generators that supplied electricity, air conditioning and refrigeration.

To Joe Bregstein it seemed a different world from the one he saw topside. It was a hot and noisy place and, he thought, the men had the honest look which comes from a hard day's toil.

He probably would have retained that image of the engine-room crew, but for one incident: he noticed a Cuban, with an open paint pot, painting a pipe adjacent to an open furnace door. It was an obvious fire risk, he pointed out to Abbott. The officer looked unhappy and said he couldn't really say anything. "I just don't start up anything with these people," he told the dentist.

Bregstein wondered how Abbott would face a crisis, if he found it so difficult to exert his authority in a simple situation.

By Friday afternoon the continuous rain and wind had produced almost universal gloom among the passengers. Many had missed lunch, their appetites gone because of the pitching and tossing of the ship. The tea dance had been a gelid affair; the bingo and horse racing were poorly patronized. Cruise Director Smith tried musical chairs, prize dances, mixed piggyback races, *anything* that encouraged contact between sexes. All failed.

By 5:00 p.m. he was reduced to making regular announcements: "Remember, folks, this is Friday—the *last* day! There is still one last grand fling left—the captain's farewell dinner and gala ball. Come one, come all, to the crowning event of your week—the end of an epoch in your life."

At exactly 5:15 p.m. Captain Wilmott undertook a social obligation he could not avoid—the traditional farewell cocktail party for a few favored first-class passengers. On this trip there were only four: Dr. Cochrane, his sister and Dr. and Mrs. Vosseler. It was a restrained affair. Catherine Cochrane was still recovering from seasickness. None of the guests had come to know the captain as well as was normal on such cruises. Furthermore, none were great social drinkers. Captain Wilmott apologized for his continued absence, but pleaded that weather conditions made it imperative for him to remain on the bridge. He repeatedly assured his guests that no storm could be as bad as the hurricane he had faced a year before, when the waves had been up to 65 feet high. The party broke up around 6:00 p.m.

Chief Engineer Abbott was about to dress for dinner when the engine room called. Assistant Engineer Antonio Bujia reported that one of the fire boilers had a fuel blockage.

"Can you clean it?"

"Not without shutting down."

Abbott climbed into a boiler suit and stepped out of his cabin and into the express elevator which took him down to the engine room. When he stepped out of the elevator he noticed that the buffeting from the sea sounded like not-so-distant artillery.

The blockage was in number three boiler in the forward fireroom. After checking the burners and the fuel regulator, the chief engineer realized it would be necessary to strip down the feeder system, something which could be done only in port. He ordered the faulty boiler closed down. It would mean that the *Morro Castle* would not be able to reach 20 knots for the rest of the voyage. Nor would the engine room be able to meet a call for maximum water pressure to the fire hydrants.

He telephoned the captain's cabin. There was no reply.

He called the bridge. Second Officer Freeman told him Captain Wilmott was not there. Again Abbott dialed the captain's cabin. He could hear the number ringing. After a few minutes he called the bridge and reported the loss of boiler pressure. He also said he could not get a response from the captain's cabin.

In the engine-room log he noted the closing down of number three boiler. Eban Abbott went back to his cabin, washed and dressed. Then he set out to discover why Captain Wilmott had not replied. It was exactly 7:45 p.m.

Moments later First Officer Warms stood in the captain's night cabin, shocked and horrified.

Slumped over the side of the bath, half dressed, lay Robert Wilmott, his eyes open, obviously dead.

WARMS closed the captain's eyes. He looked at his watch: it was 7:48 p.m. About three minutes had passed since he knocked on the cabin door. Receiving no reply he had pushed it open, walked into the night cabin and found the body.

Eighteen minutes earlier—at 7:30 p.m.—Warms had seen Captain Wilmott alive. He had gone to the captain's cabin with a weather report and found Wilmott, apparently in good shape. Nearby was a tray of food that Wilmott had picked over: a slice of melon, scrambled egg, toast, coffee and a pitcher of ice water. Warms delivered his weather report: "It is a little thick, but I am here, everything is all right." When he asked the captain how he felt, Wilmott assured him that he felt "all right."

Warms had then gone back to the bridge, where he discovered the weather had worsened. In addition to the heavy rain there was fog. Second Officer Freeman suggested reducing speed. Warms agreed, and ordered Freeman to blow the foghorn as well. When Warms returned to the captain's cabin to report further on the ship's progress, he had found Captain Wilmott dead.

Now Warms called the bridge and was answered by Fourth Officer Hansen, who had reported early for watch. Warms ordered him to locate Robert Tolman, the ship's purser, and to come with him to the captain's cabin immediately.

While Hansen sought the purser, Warms telephoned the ship's surgeon. He ordered him to the cabin, adding, "Bring your bag."

At that moment Abbott walked in and began to explain. "One of the boilers has gone. I'm looking for the old man—"

"He's dead. In there." The first officer motioned toward the night cabin.

Abbott walked across the day cabin. He stopped short when he saw Wilmott's body. "Maybe he's just fallen—"

"He's dead! I'm taking over command. Everybody, including *you,* will take orders from me."

Warms, as senior deck officer, would automatically assume command, even though Abbott outranked him. But it seemed to Abbott that he was making a special point of emphasizing his new authority.

Abbott's feeling was reinforced by the arrival of Purser Robert Tolman, followed by Fourth Officer Hansen and Dr. Van Zile. The only reason Warms has the purser here, the chief engineer thought, is to swear him in.

Dr. Van Zile knelt beside the body and felt for a pulse. He ordered Captain Wilmott to be lifted onto the bed. At this stage the purser remarked on the change of color of the body. "It's quite blue." Dr. Van Zile ignored this as he filled a hypodermic syringe and injected a colorless liquid into a vein in Wilmott's arm.

What the injection was is not known; it may have been Adrenalin. The ship's surgeon probably was attempting to revive the captain. Finally Dr. Van Zile announced, "The captain is dead." It was 8:15 p.m.

Purser Tolman turned to William Warms. "I will prepare the necessary papers placing you as master."

Warms nodded, murmuring, "Very good." He stepped to the bedside and glanced briefly at the body. "God bless his soul." Turning to Hansen he said, "Lay him out and dress him up."

Then he ordered Abbott to stay and close up the room. "Leave everything as it is. Turn out all the lights and turn the key over to me."

The new captain walked from the cabin followed by Dr. Van

Zile and the purser. In the corridor he turned to the ship's surgeon and asked, "What was the cause of death?"

"He died of indigestion and heart failure," the doctor replied. Without an autopsy it would have been difficult for Van Zile to have been more explicit, but his reply was only a statement of symptoms, not a real answer to Warms's question.

Warms, troubled, said, "I believe there are other doctors on board. Why not get them to confirm your findings?"

FOLLOWED by the purser, Warms walked to the bridge. "Wilmott is dead," he said to Second Officer Freeman. "I have assumed command. You are promoted to first, Clarence becomes second, and Howard, third. Go below and tell every member of the crew you see that I am now the master and to obey my orders."

Next Warms ordered the purser to notify the Ward Line.

The purser wrote out two identical messages, one to Thomas Torresson, the line's marine superintendent, the other to Victor M. Seckendorf, its passenger traffic manager.

WILMOTT DECEASED 7:45 P.M. ACKNOWLEDGE. WARMS.

Warms initialed the radiograms and told the purser to take them to the radio room for instant transmission. Turning to the business of sailing the ship through the appalling weather, he told the men on the bridge, "I'm not leaving here, come what may."

IN the night cabin Eban Abbott and Howard Hansen completed laying out Robert Wilmott's body. Resplendent in his uniform, his arms folded, he lay in the center of the bed. A steward removed the captain's dinner tray, saying news of the captain's death had stunned the kitchen staff. Why Abbott allowed the tray's removal, particularly in view of the suspected previous attempt on Wilmott's life, is not clear. Undoubtedly the chief engineer, like his colleagues, was under great emotional stress.

Howard Hansen wondered, as he noticed the captain's face turning black, whether the surgeon's diagnosis of the cause of death was satisfactory.

George Alagna awoke with a start. Rogers was shaking him. "George, George," he said to Alagna. "The old man's dead."

It took a few seconds for the words to penetrate. When they did, Alagna noticed the excitement in Rogers' voice. Suddenly desperately afraid, he looked up at the chief radio officer and noticed that Rogers seemed to be smiling.

"Go back to sleep," Rogers said soothingly. "You can't do anything. We'll be in port tomorrow by this time, thank God." He showed Alagna the message Purser Tolman had brought to the radio shack.

When he left, Rogers called over his shoulder, "Looks like a busy night for me."

Father Egan sensed a growing tension among the diners around him. At first he put it down to the ship's motion. The stewards performed ballets of equilibrium as they carried away trays of uneaten food.

Some of the guests wore costumes, but the majority of first-class passengers were in evening dress, a tradition for the captain's farewell dinner. Father Egan wore his clerical collar. He still believed the passengers would be uneasy in the presence of a cleric on a "fun cruise." On the other hand he wanted to do what was "fitting" for such a special occasion. His appearance in the dining room had caused a momentary flutter, which was quickly superseded by something more significant.

For some moments all had been aware of the fact that neither the captain nor any of his officers had yet appeared for dinner, and it was, after all, the captain's farewell dinner. Attempts to question the waiters about it proved fruitless.

Coffee was being served when Headwaiter Carl Wright appeared from the kitchen, white-faced. Shortly afterward Dr. Van Zile entered the dining room and whispered something to Dr. Cochrane and Dr. Vosseler, both seated at the captain's table. They rose with apologetic smiles and followed the ship's doctor out of the room.

It was a little after 8:30 p.m.

By 9:00 P.M. Eban Abbott was accustomed to the ritual: there would be a knock on Captain Wilmott's cabin door, it would be pushed open and Dr. Van Zile would lead another distinguished-looking passenger into the night cabin where the body lay. Abbott, seated in a corner of the day cabin, had not stirred from there since he and Hansen had laid out the body. The death of Robert Wilmott seemed to have induced a severe trauma in him.

During the time he sat in the cabin, half a dozen doctors had come and gone. Later those who attached any significance to the discoloration of the body ascribed it to a condition sometimes found after a severe heart attack. Although it was an acceptable medical deduction, it was not necessarily the right one: poisoning could also produce discoloration.

If the doctors noticed the silent chief engineer sunk in a chair in the corner, they made no comment.

News of the death was brought to the engine room by an oiler carrying a case of Cokes down from the kitchens. It was discussed in snatches over the thunder of machinery, but the boiler-room crew had a more immediate problem: maintaining speed with one boiler out of commission. Very few of the men believed it would make any difference to their work whoever commanded the ship. Bearings, housings, condensers, gauges, compressors and pumps were far more dependent on the engine-room crew than on any captain on the bridge.

Acting Captain Warms peered through the bridge windows. There was nothing to be seen except black sea streaked with white. But the ship no longer pitched and tossed so violently. She had returned to a rhythmic rolling to starboard and back again.

Warms turned to his new senior officer, Ivan Freeman.

"All hatches battened down and ventilators and everything secured about the deck?"

"Yes, sir."

"Is she washing salt water on deck?"

"No, sir."

"All watches at regular strength?"

"Yes, sir, plus a lookout forward."

Satisfied, Warms nodded.

THE change in command had a profound effect on the seamen in the forecastle. Among the older hands the death was regarded as a bad omen. Several said they would sign off and try to get a berth on another ship for a trip or two until the danger had passed. Others agreed with Storekeeper O'Sullivan that it might mean an extra day's stopover in New York while "things are tidied up."

Inevitably the conversation veered to the kind of captain Warms would be. No one doubted that Warms would be confirmed as captain, but there was a division of opinion as to the first officer's fitness for command.

Some, like O'Sullivan, wondered whether he had that "magic thing with the passengers." Others, including John Gross, believed Warms would be a hard taskmaster. "He's bound to make for a better ship," was Gross's verdict.

Joe Spilgins hoped the new captain would reintroduce proper safety rules. "Half the guys on the ship never even raised or lowered a lifeboat." Spilgins drew a chorus of approval when he said if it was a choice between a captain with personality and one who observed a stricter adherence to safety standards, he'd take the latter every time. "Hell"—he grinned—"if they want a personality as a captain they should stick Smithy on the bridge!"

WHILE the discussion between the seamen grew more intense, Smithy—Cruise Director Robert Smith—took it upon himself to stop further speculation in the first-class dining room. On hearing of Wilmott's death he marched briskly to the captain's table. The room was suddenly still as the cruise director clinked a spoon against a glass. His voice was flat, almost emotionless. "Ladies and gentlemen. A great tragedy has befallen us. The captain is dead." He paused. "Captain Wilmott passed away earlier this evening. First Officer Warms has assumed command." Again he paused. "There is no cause for alarm—only sorrow. I request, out of respect for Captain Wilmott, that all the scheduled activities of tonight be canceled."

Before any questions could be asked the cruise director left the dining room to repeat the news to the tourist-class passengers.

At 10:28 p.m. the tension in the radio room was broken by an incoming radiogram addressed to Robert Tolman, ship's purser:

PLEASE CONFIRM QUICKLY MESSAGE SENT BY WARMS TO SECKENDORF REGARDING WILMOTT GIVING DETAILS. WARDLINE.

Rogers looked at the message intently, then shook his head. "They don't trust him," he said. He handed the radiogram to Maki to deliver, and said to Alagna, "It's bad, George, bad for Warms. When they cable the purser for more news it's going over the head of the man in command."

At 10:40 p.m. a priority radiogram was sent to the Ward Line:

CONFIRMING MESSAGE FROM WARMS. WILMOTT DECEASED ACUTE INDIGESTION AND HEART ATTACK 7:45 THIS EVENING. ALL PAPERS FOR ENTRY IN ORDER. TOLMAN PURSER.

Was Robert Wilmott murdered?

In the months following his death suspicion fell upon the Cuban Communists, who murdered Captain Wilmott, it was said, as a gesture against the Ward Line for shipping arms to the island's dictatorial regime. Even today Cuban exiles living in Florida produce faded clippings from Havana newspapers speculating that Communists were responsible for Wilmott's death. Captain Wilmott was probably not murdered for political purposes. It would have been pointless: the Ward Line would simply have replaced him and the arms traffic would have continued.

Numerous investigations seem to lead to one significant probable cause of death: poisoning. It must be added, however, that the question of whether Captain Wilmott was in fact poisoned is impossible to prove. A more careful investigation by Dr. Van Zile on the scene might have provided a more concrete basis for this hypothesis. But medical authorities today emphasize the virtual impossibility of determining the cause of sudden death like Captain Wilmott's without an autopsy.

Later speculation on who might have murdered Captain Wilmott revolves around the figure of George White Rogers.

The three volumes on the case compiled by Police Captain Vincent Doyle of Bayonne, New Jersey, and exhaustive investigations by Captain Wilmott's lifelong friend Captain George Seeth provide evidence of Rogers' responsibility.

As far as is known, Doyle and Seeth never met. Yet somewhat astonishingly both came to the conclusion that Rogers poisoned Captain Wilmott as a deliberate act of retaliation.

The evidence presented by Doyle and Seeth differs in certain details. In Doyle's version the radio officer sought revenge because he believed Captain Wilmott had discovered the evidence which would result in Rogers' dismissal.

Seeth believes Captain Wilmott had discovered Rogers' involvement "as a key member of a smuggling ring among the members of the crew" and that "Rogers murdered him to avoid discovery."

The ring had operated from the first voyage, smuggling drugs and liquor out of Havana into New York. From time to time New York customs officers arrested crew members caught moving contraband off the ship. On at least two occasions suspected informers in the crew had met "accidents." One had disappeared overboard at sea; the other had been crushed under a load of cargo. Seeth thinks that Rogers was responsible for transmitting and receiving details of contraband to an accomplice ashore.

According to Doyle, Rogers obtained the poison used against Wilmott during the ship's stopover in Cuba; he does not indicate what type it was. The Doyle documentation on the *Morro Castle* case is fragmentary, and unfortunately the police officer is no longer alive to support his contentions or to suggest how the crime was committed.

Seeth believes the poison was an irritant which in ordinary circumstances would not have been fatal; but Rogers knew it was powerful enough to kill the captain, who had a weak stomach. He suggests that Rogers got to the captain's food tray during one of his visits to the galley for coffee, and had simply slipped the poison into the master's coffee or scrambled egg. It is possible: the kitchen crews were in the middle of final preparations for dinner. The sight of the chief radio officer pouring himself another coffee would cause no comment.

In the veranda tearoom Rafael Mestre was keeping time to a rumba record with a set of maracas, watched by an admiring group of girls. The session was brought to a sudden halt by Cruise Director Smith, who appeared to be hunting down any sign of frivolity in the public rooms. When the cruise director confiscated records, player and maracas, Mestre smiled and walked away with the girls.

On the promenade deck members of the Concordia Singing Society were drinking beer and singing at the tops of their voices. The cruise director cut them short in mid-chorus.

By around 11:00 p.m. most people understood that parties were not appropriate. All the same, a number of passengers made an attempt to sustain a festive atmosphere. This was the last night of the voyage. Inhibitions began to dissolve as the drinking continued.

Stewards Sydney Ryan and Daniel Campbell, at the bar, wanted the party to break up early. They would have a great deal of work afterward. The public rooms had to be gone over with the buffing machine for the new passengers who would board the *Morro Castle* the next day. But the party showed no signs of abating.

Chief Engineer Abbott finally left Captain Wilmott's cabin and went to his own. He undressed, then telephoned the engine room and was told "All okay down here." He fell asleep wondering why Warms had made no attempt to contact him.

Chief Stewardess Lena Schwarz awoke from a troubled sleep. It was unbearably hot in her tiny cabin. She adjusted the air vent. The merest whiff of smoke was being blown in through the duct.

For several minutes she waited for another scent. It never came. Puzzled, she went back to sleep.

Nearly 100 feet forward of her cabin Father Egan also smelled smoke. He wondered sleepily if it might be coming from either the engine room or the kitchens.

AROUND midnight George White Rogers had handed over the watch to Maki, saying he would "take a breath of air." Twenty minutes later Rogers returned.

There is strong circumstantial evidence that during this absence Rogers prepared an incendiary device—or several such devices—designed to set the *Morro Castle* on fire and threaten the lives of all its crew and passengers.

Rogers would have had no trouble hiding the materials he needed in the emergency room beforehand: the unlabeled bottles of acid, an innocent-looking fountain pen and a strip of copper wire. With his knowledge, the twenty minutes he was absent from the radio room was ample time to make several incendiary devices. A fountain-pen bomb—of the type he had made in the past—would be totally self-destructive, leaving no clues.

A locker in the deserted first-class writing room contained spare jackets for the stewards. It was a perfect site for an incendiary bomb. The locker was immediately below the space into which Rogers himself had watched the seamen move the Lyle gun and the barrel of gunpowder. The gunpowder would make a perfect trailer to spread the fire.

Another trailer was even closer at hand. Near the radio room were two gasoline tanks, used to run the transmitting equipment. It would be a simple matter to uncouple the feed line, allowing the gas to trickle along the deck.

Watchman Arthur Pender, who passed near the tanks, smelled a strong odor of gasoline which he did not report to the bridge, thinking the smell must be the result of late cleaning on the eve of the ship's arrival in port. If Pender had reported it, even a cursory investigation might have revealed the preparations for sabotage. But he did not.

FIRE AT SEA: September 8, 1934

AT midnight Clarence Hackney, newly promoted to second officer, came on duty. He was surprised to find Warms still peering into the night, totally absorbed. Hackney could see no cause for concern. The threatened gale had either bypassed them or blown itself out. A northeaster was skimming squalls of rain over the ship.

Hackney saw that Warms looked tired. "Have a break, sir."

"Later, Clarence, later. Plenty of time to sleep when we dock." Warms's eyes kept moving back and forth from the mass of instruments to the darkness outside. Hackney thought the captain "appeared to be on the watch for everything, as if nothing was going to escape him while he had command." In spite of his watchfulness Warms failed to notice that the ship's smoke-detecting system was still switched off so that the smell of raw hides would not disturb the passengers.

DURING his rounds Pender paused for coffee in the galley pantry. He was disturbed to hear cabin stewards discussing "wastebasket fires" in some of the public rooms, caused by discarded cigarettes. He poked all the wastebaskets he came across—no trace of fire.

At 1:00 a.m. he and another night watchman, Harold Foersch, reported to the bridge that all was quiet.

At 2:00 a.m. Clarence Hackney reported to Captain Warms that the *Morro Castle* was thirty miles south of Scotland Light. Soon the ship would turn into the relative shelter of Ambrose Channel and then up into New York Harbor.

Warms carried out his own swift inspection of the ship, returned to the bridge and told Hackney that all was in order below.

By 2:45 A.M. THE PARTY around the bar had dwindled to two women in trailing evening gowns and their escorts in tuxedoes.

Stewards Campbell and Ryan were collecting glasses. Campbell looked sourly at the quartet. "If you're planning to get some sleep before we dock," he said, "you'd better get to bed."

One of the women giggled. "Who wants to go to bed? I'm not going to bother." Her companions agreed.

At exactly 2:50 a.m. Sydney Ryan paused in his glass collecting and turned to Campbell. "Dan. You smell it?"

Campbell wrinkled his nose. "Come on," he said.

Both smelled smoke—coming from the forward section.

At 2:51 a.m. Watchman Foersch reported to the captain that he had just seen and smelled smoke coming out of one of the small ventilators on the port after side of the fiddley. The fiddley was a galvanized-iron duct supplying fresh air to the first-class writing room on B deck, among other rooms.

Warms rushed to the fiddley. A trickle of smoke emerged from the opening. He ran to rouse his first officer.

"Ivan! Get up! Fire!"

Back on the bridge the acting captain ordered Hackney: "Go down below, find the source of the fire and let me know the situation *fast*."

As he ran from the bridge Hackney grabbed a fire extinguisher.

At that moment Campbell and Ryan reached the writing room, puffing slightly. Low-lying smoke carpeted the room.

"It's in that locker!" Campbell shouted.

Opening the locker he saw a mass of flames inside. Quickly he slammed the door, blistering his hands in the process.

As both men ran from the room to raise the alarm they passed a fire extinguisher on the wall near the door—the first mistake by members of a crew poorly trained in fire drills and rescue operations. If Campbell and Ryan had turned that extinguisher on the fire *at once*, it might have made a critical difference.

Three vital minutes passed before Clarence Hackney arrived. He yanked open the locker door and a wall of flame rushed out.

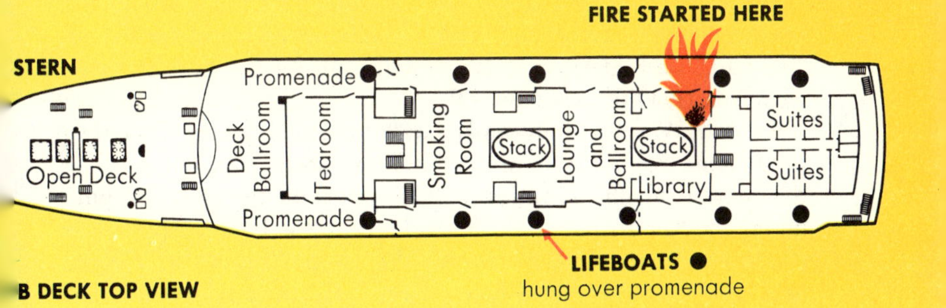

Hackney backed off and emptied his fire extinguisher into it, but a dozen extinguishers could not have contained the inferno now raging around the locker. Stunned, he watched the flames lick across the false ceiling. It was he who had given the order for the Lyle gun and its deadly powder keg to be placed immediately above. Choking from the smoke, he ran from the writing room.

He had made the second fatal mistake. Solid-steel fire doors had been built into entrances to the public rooms to deal with just such an emergency. It would have taken Hackney only a few moments to isolate the writing room by lowering its fire door. Instead he ran through the first-class lounge to the telephone near the smoking-room entrance. He dialed the bridge.

"It's pretty bad," he told Warms. "We better get water on it."

"Break out the hose and I'll get you the men," Warms ordered. "Get all the fire hydrants uncapped—fast!" Then he called down to the engine room. "I want all water pressure possible."

"We've got a boiler still out," a voice replied. "What do you want the pressure for?"

"Fire," retorted Warms. "Get all the pressure you can!"

On the bridge the sounds of a new storm breaking against the ship drowned out conversation. Warms ordered a textbook change of course, heading the ship into the wind to reduce the effect of the squall. He also ordered the bridge lookout to rouse the seamen in the forecastle. It was 2:55 a.m.

At that moment Ivan Freeman arrived on the bridge. He had gone straight from his cabin to B deck—to be met by a wall of smoke billowing across the lounge. Behind it he could see flames. "It's bad," he told Warms. "We should run for the beach in case we have to get the passengers off."

Captain Warms calmly walked over to the automatic fire-detecting system. Each light represented a thermostat in a stateroom or the quarters of officers and crew. The system did not cover the public rooms. Not a single light flashed red on the board. Apparently reassured, Warms told Freeman, "We are not going yet. We can hold her. Get down and take charge." He then telephoned the engine room to get steam on the main fire pump, and left word for Chief Engineer Abbott to call him the moment he got there.

Warms turned to the helmsman and checked the course: the *Morro Castle* was cutting through the Atlantic at the fullest speed possible with one boiler closed down, on a heading of two degrees, almost due north, into the storm.

Then Clarence Hackney rushed onto the bridge. "It's getting worse! We'll need every man on the hose!"

Warms did not hesitate. He set off the general fire alarm. "Get all the passengers out," he told Hackney. "Use tin pans! Anything you can get hold of to wake them!" It was 3:00 a.m.

THE quartet of drinkers at the bar moved toward the lounge doorway, sipping their highballs. Suddenly stewards Campbell and Ryan and Watchman Pender rushed past them, clutching fire extinguishers which they turned on the smoke. But it was futile. Even if hoses had been brought to bear on the flames, it would have made little difference: the engine room was unable to provide sustained pressure because of the closed boiler.

"Can't you stop all that smoke?" shouted one of the girl passengers. "It's going to ruin my dress."

"You best all get on deck," Campbell said. "Report to your lifeboat stations."

"Why? It's raining outside. Anyway, I want another drink." The man's drunken demand faded as flames darted out from the smoke. "Run for it!" he shouted. "The ship's going to go down!"

Panic had arrived on the *Morro Castle.*

Father Raymond Egan had put on his clerical garb so that in the crisis people would know his office. The moment he stepped out of his stateroom people turned to him. The corridor was filled with half-dressed passengers awakened by stewards hammering on their doors. But before the priest could act the lights flickered and went out, leaving them in total darkness.

"She's sinking!" a voice screamed.

"She's not!" Father Egan roared. "They're just switching the power supplies." The conviction in his voice stilled the panic around him. From farther down the corridor came shouts and curses, as passengers became bottlenecked at the foot of the stairs.

Father Egan forced his way along the corridor, deflecting groping hands and stumbling over feet. "Stay still! All of you! Wait until the lights come on!" he commanded.

The bedlam died away and the lights returned, revealing men and women sprawled up the stairs. The scene was terrifying. Ordinary, sensible people had turned into a pathetic rabble. The priest took charge quickly. He told the passengers to return to their cabins, dress in outdoor clothes, put on life jackets and go to their boat stations immediately. "And don't panic," he admonished.

Eban Abbott, awakened by the alarm ringing above his head, walked to the cabin next door, occupied by his assistant, Antonio Bujia. Bujia was struggling into a boiler suit. Abbott muttered dazedly, "When the bell rings there is a fire?"

Bujia finished dressing and left without saying a word.

Abbott returned to his cabin and carefully changed to his dress uniform. Then he telephoned the engine room.

Bujia answered. Three pumps were working to supply water for the fire-fighting crews. By then the smoke was drifting down into the engine room and "every minute seemed like an hour."

"Do the best you can and see that everyone is down there and keep things going," Abbott said. He put on his cap with its gold braid and straightened his jacket. Sartorially satisfied, he stepped out of his cabin.

Walking past the express elevator that would have taken him directly down to the engine room, he made his way to the promenade deck. There he watched a fire crew, supervised by Storekeeper O'Sullivan, struggling to couple a hose to one of the hydrants.

"Open the valve! Open the valve!" Abbott ordered.

But the water pressure was low.

"Permission to throw deck chairs overboard?" asked Seaman John Gross. "Something to cling to if we have to jump."

The chief engineer nodded, and the fire fighters abandoned their hoses and started to hurl the chairs over the side. Caught by the wind the canvas furniture flapped clear of the boat, dropping into the sea well astern.

Abbott, still shocked, walked down to C deck, where a group of girls from the Concordia Singing Society asked what they should do. He told them to go up to the boat deck and wait there.

Moving down to D deck he continued his unhurried journey, keeping to the crew stairways. Coming up one stairway was Bujia. Abbott peered at him. "What are you doing? Where are you going?"

"To the bridge. I called you and got no answer. Everything is running good. But we cannot stay down there much longer."

The two men looked at each other. Wisps of smoke were drifting around the staircase. "Go back and stand by. I'll go to the bridge," said Abbott. With those few words he changed his whole future; he would regret them all his life.

Bujia had brought Abbott head on with reality: the engine room, in his assistant's estimation, had shortly to be abandoned. There was only one proper course of action open to Eban Abbott. It was to go down to check out the situation himself.

Abbott was charged with the responsibility to ensure that the men in the engine room performed their duties in operating the fire pumps, lights and power to steer the ship through the growing crisis. He abandoned this responsibility when he ordered Bujia back down below and climbed to the safety of the open deck.

After the first sharp whiff of smoke Dr. Emilio Giro knew there was trouble. He smiled encouragement at his brother-in-law, Rafael Mestre, as they made their way up to the boat deck. Mestre grinned back, but Dr. Giro could see the fear in his face. Near the first-class lounge the two Cubans watched as the fire ran along the paint, wood and chintz. There was no one there to stop it.

"Remember, if we get separated, we are in lifeboat number ten," Dr. Giro repeated. Mestre nodded and crossed himself.

On C deck, Cruise Director Smith found near-panic among members of the Concordia Singing Society as smoke suddenly swirled overhead and down the corridor. He moved quickly among them. "Down! All of you. On your knees! Hold on to the ankles of the person in front of you. And keep your heads down!" He took position at the head of the crocodile, leading it in a painful crawl along the corridor under the smoke and up a stairway to the ballroom on B deck. "Get to your lifeboat positions. They'll swing the boats down to you," he said. Then the cruise director ran back to help other passengers up from below.

Storekeeper William O'Sullivan hefted a fireman's axe, swung it in a wild arc and smashed the window of stateroom number two on A deck. Behind him stood Dr. Cochrane and Dr. and Mrs. Vosseler. All three were nude under topcoats. Smoke poured out of the shattered window. At that moment First Officer Freeman appeared. "Up top. All of you!" he ordered.

"My sister is in there," said Dr. Cochrane.

"We can't get to her from this side, sir," O'Sullivan told Freeman. "I'll try from the other side."

"Very well. But the rest of you up top!" repeated Freeman.

Dr. Cochrane started to protest. Freeman cut him short. "We'll get her, sir."

Without waiting for further discussion Freeman followed O'Sullivan around to the port side of the luxury-stateroom complex. Barely able to breathe, the two men felt their way through acrid smoke to the cabin they believed Catherine Cochrane to be trapped in. Freeman lifted O'Sullivan through the window.

Inside, the storekeeper's flashlight was useless. He called out, but there was no answer. The bed was empty. He searched the floor of the stateroom and, finding no one, assumed Dr. Cochrane's sister must have escaped. O'Sullivan was almost unconscious by the time he got back to the window, and Freeman had to drag him out. The brave rescue attempt had failed. Unable to see, O'Sullivan had entered the wrong cabin. Catherine Cochrane had been overcome by smoke as she slept two staterooms away. Soon others would die with terrible speed as the fire roared down passageways and sealed them off.

On the bridge Warms looked on the smoke as an indication that the fire was being doused. As he turned to check the ship's course a light on the fire-detecting system flashed red: a temperature of 160 degrees Fahrenheit was being reported from stateroom number five. Suddenly the whole system flashed on.

"My God! They're all going," Warms cried.

Acting Captain Warms's first terrible miscalculation came when he executed the textbook turn into the wind to meet the storm. This brought the *Morro Castle* head on into the squall at a speed of 18.8 knots for over ten minutes. In that time the wind, gusting at over 20 knots, had acted as a giant bellows, fanning and speeding the flames the length of the ship.

Far below the bridge, on E deck, Chief Stewardess Lena Schwarz finally identified the strange sound she had been hearing: the *Morro Castle* was moaning. The noise of the fire seemed to her like a whimpering child. Since the alarm had been sounded Mrs. Schwarz and the other stewardesses had run from stateroom to stateroom, awakening passengers. Mrs. Schwarz's calm did much to reassure them as she offered a hand with life vests, guided people to the quickest route topside, repeating over and over, "There's probably nothing to worry about." But that deep, sorrowful whine sent a sudden chill through her.

"Help me!" The voice came from an outer cabin near the stern.

Lena Schwarz ran toward the voice, plunging from one empty cabin to another. As she got closer the cry seemed to come from outside the hull. The stewardess rushed to a porthole and opened it. A few feet away a woman was sitting on the rim of her cabin porthole, feet dangling over the sea, the wind tearing at her nightgown, abject terror on her face.

"Don't move!" the stewardess shouted. "I'll come and get you."

At that moment the ship lurched, catapulting the woman into the sea. Mrs. Schwarz caught a brief glimpse of the body bobbing in the ship's wake. Then it was gone. She turned, tears of fear and anguish streaming down her face.

The ship's lurch was the result of another command Warms gave to the helmsman: "Left wheel!" The *Morro Castle* rose and fell on the waves as she turned in toward the New Jersey coast. Warms hoped the maneuver would help contain the main fire in the area of the writing room, where he thought it was still localized. Although the lights were flashing on the fire-detecting system board, indicating intense heat as far down as C deck, he believed the lights only gave *warning* of impending danger.

"Hard to port!" Spray blew across the forecastle. The liner wallowed, broadside to, and then came onto her new course.

Suddenly a flash burst across the promenade deck near the writing room. The bridge rocked. The powder keg for the Lyle gun, hidden in the false ceiling, had exploded.

The explosion opened the door to full-scale panic. Passengers stumbled blindly or walked around in circles, spellbound by terror. Women screamed and men swore like maniacs. The ship was ablaze all across midships. For a moment her whistle cried. It was the most helpless and despairing sound Seaman John Gross had ever heard. The flames roared on hungrily. Gross could hear voices crying, sobbing, chanting prayers.

The seaman joined a group of crewmen with axes who were chopping apart deck chairs and tables and stacking them near the rails, where they could later be thrown overboard as floats. The men worked haphazardly with no officer present to direct them.

Dr. Joe Bregstein and his son reached the promenade deck moments after the explosion. The dentist saw general chaos all around. The crew here, panicking, pushed passengers aside—men, women and children. Bregstein's eyes smarted from the smoke. Red flames blazed into the sky. The heat on the deck was searing. Safety glass in the deck doors was melting; the metal doorframes began to buckle.

The wind appeared to be rising. Large waves, like hills, lifted the *Morro Castle* up, held her trembling for a moment, and then plunged her down again. Joe Bregstein, young Mervin clinging tightly to him, tried to retain his sanity. As father and son huddled near the open rail of the promenade deck, a gang of sailors appeared carrying ropes. They fastened them to the rail, then uncoiled them over the sides. The ends of the ropes trailed in the water. A seaman shouted that when rescue came passengers could scramble down the ropes to safety.

Joe Bregstein looked down at the water. It suddenly seemed much farther away than it had a few minutes before.

Down the deck another father and son had also been watching the sailors snake the ropes over the side. The man lifted his child onto his back and threw one leg, then the other, over the railing. For a moment he sat there, holding on with his hands, peering down at the sea. Then he let go of the rail.

Bregstein watched them hit the water. The sea closed over their heads. They seemed to go under forever. Then they shot to the surface. Somehow the boy still clung around his father's neck. The man snatched at a rope and held on to it, screaming, "Help, help, help us!" But there was nothing anybody could do. In the glare of the flames Bregstein could see the sea crashing the pair against the side of the ship. Finally a wave swept completely over them and they were gone. The rope hung slack.

Sickened and terrified, Joe Bregstein clutched his own son close to him and wondered how long it would be before rescue ships arrived. He assumed that the moment the fire had been discovered an SOS had been sent.

ROGERS sat calmly by the main transmitter, waiting for an official order to summon outside help. He had been sound asleep in his bunk when the fire alarm sounded. George Alagna had had to shake him quite hard to wake him. The two men had dressed quickly and joined Maki in the radio room.

Rogers tuned to the main 600-meter distress frequency and threw the switch into a position which would ensure that the transmitter would produce a very broad interfering path.

Evidence of fire was quite apparent from the radio shack. The radio room was filling with smoke. When Rogers went to the door he could see the reflection of the flames and hear shouting and confused commands. He signed the radio-room log, then, turning to Alagna, he said, "Go up to the bridge and see what orders the mate has to give you." It was just after 3:00 a.m.

Moments later Alagna returned, ashen-faced. "The flames are taller than the radio room," he told Rogers. "I tried to get to the bridge, but I couldn't make it."

Rogers took the news calmly. He tried to call the bridge by telephone—without success. He picked up the speaking tube, but all he could hear was a loud roaring noise.

Once more Alagna was ordered to go to the bridge and "obtain whatever orders it was possible to obtain." This time the smoke cleared momentarily, and he reached the bridge just in time to hear Warms give the course change for the Jersey shore and to see the helmsman frantically spin the wheel. Alagna yelled to Warms that he had been sent up to the bridge by Rogers.

Warms paid little attention to him. When he repeated what he had said, Warms finally answered, "All right." He appeared to be saying something else, but Alagna could not hear him in the confusion. Alagna assumed that Warms was too obsessed by the fire to answer him coherently.

Alagna was wrong. The sight of the radio assistant had brought to mind all the suspicions Warms had nursed on the voyage—suspicions that Alagna was a "radical," capable of any act, possibly even arson.

ALAGNA returned to the radio room and reported what had happened. Rogers shook his head. "Go back to the bridge and ask again for orders when we are to send an SOS," he said.

Alagna made a third journey to the bridge.

In the radio room the smoke was thickening. Maki shifted uneasily. "Shouldn't we do something?"

"We wait for orders. That's what the regulations say." Rogers settled back. Several minutes later he looked at his watch. Alagna had been gone for three minutes. He turned to Maki. "Go soak a towel in the washbasin so that I can breathe through it. Then go to the bridge and find Alagna."

Maki did as he was told and then left. He would never return to the radio room. For a while he would wander aimlessly around the deck; finally he would jump from the ship.

Alone, Rogers went to the doorway. The fire was spreading. Black smoke was everywhere. When he resumed his position in front of the transmitter he noted the time: 3:13 a.m. Thirteen minutes had elapsed since the general alarm had been given, and still no order had come from the bridge to transmit an SOS.

Alagna reappeared. "The whole place is on fire," he shouted. "We're going to be caught like rats in a trap."

"Are we to send the distress message?"

"I dunno. They're madmen up there, just running around—"

"Go back and ask the mate again," ordered Rogers.

Alagna began a fourth trip to the bridge. As he left the door, the transmitter crackled to life. Somebody else was using the 600-meter emergency frequency.

It was the radio operator aboard the freighter *Andrea S. Luckenbach*, steaming a parallel course ten miles seaward of the *Morro Castle*. At 3:14 a.m. her radioman contacted the U.S. Coast Guard station at Tuckerton, New Jersey. "Do you have any news of a ship burning off Sea Girt?"

"Haven't heard of any," came the reply.

The operator took the reply to the bridge, where the *Luckenbach*'s captain and first officer were peering west through binoculars. "That's the glow over there," said the first officer.

The operator reported his conversation with Tuckerton station. They lowered their glasses, believing they had made a mistake.

ROGERS SAT, TRANSFIXED by the exchange between the cargo ship and the Coast Guard station. The fire aboard was now visible ten miles away; in the critical situation the seriously disturbed chief radio officer could see the possibility of becoming a hero and saving his job. He had often contended that "heroes are never sacked."

Regulations governing distress signals at sea are strict: no SOS can be sent without the express order of the captain. But it would have been proper for Rogers to have sent a message such as, "Fire on *Morro Castle* off New Jersey. Awaiting orders from bridge." While not a formal SOS, it would nevertheless have been a standby call for help, confirming the *Luckenbach*'s sighting a serious fire. No one could later have criticized such a course of action.

At 3:15 a.m. the mandatory listening-out period for all radio operators at sea began. Instead of a distress signal, Rogers sent: "Standby. DE KGOV." KGOV was the call sign of the *Morro Castle.*

"KGOV wait three minutes," ordered Tuckerton radio station.

Rogers immediately stopped sending.

ON the bridge Alagna stood, almost mesmerized. Warms had just discovered Eban Abbott there, lurking in a corner. In his dress uniform Abbott looked as if he were going to the captain's ball. "What will we do?" he shrieked. "What will we do?"

"What are *you* doing *here?*" Warms screamed. "Why aren't you below to see that my engine orders are obeyed and fast—"

"It's too late—"

"Damn it, get below and organize things. We need water!"

"A hundred hoses wouldn't make any difference now—"

"Get below! And stay there until I tell you to come up!"

"Captain, the water pressure's gone!" Second Officer Hackney brought the news to the bridge. "It's hopeless down there!"

The lack of fire drills had produced a deadly effect. Seamen who had abandoned their hoses in the face of the flames had also failed to turn off the hydrants. The engine room's capacity to provide water was quickly dwindling. In twenty minutes the pressure had been halved, then cut to a third. Now it was only a trickle.

Warms turned to his chief engineer. "What's happened to that pressure?" he screamed. "*Answer* me! D'you hear, *answer* me!"

Horrified, Alagna watched as Abbott paced back and forth, saying over and over in a shrill voice, "What will we do?"

Warms continued to shout, "Answer me! Answer me!"

The radioman stepped toward Warms. "Mr. Warms. Do you have any orders for the radio room?"

"Orders? Can you send an SOS?"

"Certainly! That's what I've been coming here for—"

Warms turned his back on Alagna, preoccupied. Desperately, the radioman turned to Clarence Hackney. "What's our position?"

"Sea Girt. And get it off fast," ordered Hackney.

Father Egan estimated that the crowd of passengers huddled aft on C deck numbered nearly 100. Indifferent to the driving rain, their eyes were drawn to the raging fire. The priest moved among them, calming them, urging those who wanted to pray to do so.

"Father." A woman touched his sleeve. "My husband. He's still down there. He went back to get a coat for me—"

"Stay here. I'll go and look for him."

"I'll come with you, Father." The voice belonged to Steward Sydney Ryan. The two men started down. Ahead the fire crackled from port to starboard.

Near the barbershop a couple of stewards were kneeling beside a badly burned child whom they had pulled clear of a burning cabin. In places the child's flesh had peeled back to the bone. He kept on repeating, "*Mi madre! Mi madre!*" As Father Egan knelt to administer last rites the child died.

The priest rose. "Come on. Let's find that husband."

Even in his undershirt and shorts Headwaiter Carl Wright still retained much of the dignity of his office. He had organized a party of waiters on C deck. In twenty minutes they had evacuated a dozen passengers from their cabins.

Some passengers were openly resentful. One man threatened to report to the line the steward who awakened him. A young woman was quite put out at being taken from her boy friend's bed.

But by 3:20 a.m. the mood on C deck changed. Flames flashed suddenly through cabin door 226, situated directly below the writing room. Passengers started to scream. The lights failed. Wright flattened himself in a cabin doorway a split second before a tangle of bodies hurtled past him. People pushed and shoved like animals.

Forcing his way through the mass of bodies with the handle of his axe, Storekeeper O'Sullivan, with a handful of sailors carrying extinguishers, reached cabin 226 just as its ceiling collapsed.

Headwaiter Wright heard the piercing cry of a child. Bent double, he ran down the corridor. In cabin 234 he found a young girl cowering in a corner, too frightened to move. Wright picked her up and ran as the flames came roaring through the walls.

CHIEF Stewardess Schwarz and Stewardess Ragne Zabola climbed up to D deck. "I wonder where Sydney is?" Miss Zabola asked more than once. "I hope he's all right." She and Steward Sydney Ryan had been good friends since joining the ship.

"He's fine," said Mrs. Schwarz. "Probably up on deck waiting for you."

When they reached D deck they found themselves in a corridor ankle-deep in water. The spill was gushing from a couple of uncapped fire hydrants. Both women squinted their eyes against the smoke rolling down on them. The smarting pungency came from a combination of layers of heavy paint, laminated paneling in staterooms and highly flammable stain and varnish that had made the *Morro Castle* a thing of beauty and now helped turn it into a floating charnel house.

The women could hear the fire crackling overhead, interspersed with distant shouts. Lena Schwarz forced a smile. "Sounds like all the action is up top. Let's go and see!"

They were about to continue their climb when the chief stewardess stopped. "What about Mrs. Brown in five-oh-seven? She can't walk very well." Mrs. Schwarz turned and began to slosh down the corridor, finally reaching stateroom 507.

"Oh, Mrs. Schwarz, how good of you to come." Mrs. Brown might have been welcoming a late guest for afternoon tea. "I've been trying to get on my life jacket."

The stewardess fastened the straps, then led Mrs. Brown carefully back up the corridor. Suddenly behind them they heard a dull roar. The fire had reached D deck.

"WHICH way to lifeboat number ten?" Up on B deck Dr. Emilio Giro asked the question with polite diffidence.

A sailor shouted over his shoulder, "Forget the lifeboats! Jump!" Then he vanished into the smoke.

The doctor turned to Rafael Mestre. "Jump? But I can't swim."

"It's the only chance," his brother-in-law answered.

Dr. Giro considered the words carefully, as he might consider the opinion of a trusted medical colleague. "Very well. I will jump," he said gravely. The decision made, he took off his jacket, folded it carefully and placed it on the deck. Next he took off his shoes. He wondered whether he should also remove his shirt and trousers. He would find it easier to swim without them, but there were considerations of the cold and of propriety.

A few feet away a group of men and women knelt in prayer. "*. . . but deliver us from evil, for thine is the kingdom, and the power, and the glory, for ever and ever. Amen.*"

Turning his back Dr. Giro walked across to the rail. The sea was covered with bodies and pieces of debris. He started to weigh all the factors scientifically. He knew that his life vest alone would probably not support him in the storm. A piece of wood could become waterlogged. Then it occurred to him—he would need a body to hang on to. He stared down again into the sea. Then he turned to his brother-in-law. "Take care of Sylvia and the baby for me."

"You'll make it," said Mestre, embracing the doctor.

The two men stepped apart. Giro noticed that Mestre wasn't wearing a life jacket.

"It's okay," said Mestre. "I'll jump from lower down." He ran along the deck into the smoke. It was useless to go after him.

Dr. Giro walked to the rail and sat on it. He swallowed deeply, closed his eyes and jumped.

The coldness of the water was followed by another sensation—a pounding against his ears, the feeling that his stomach was being forced up and up into his chest, and then a terrible choking feeling, as if he were being strangled. He had expected this. Medically speaking, he was experiencing no unusual symptoms. As long as he didn't open his mouth he was still safe.

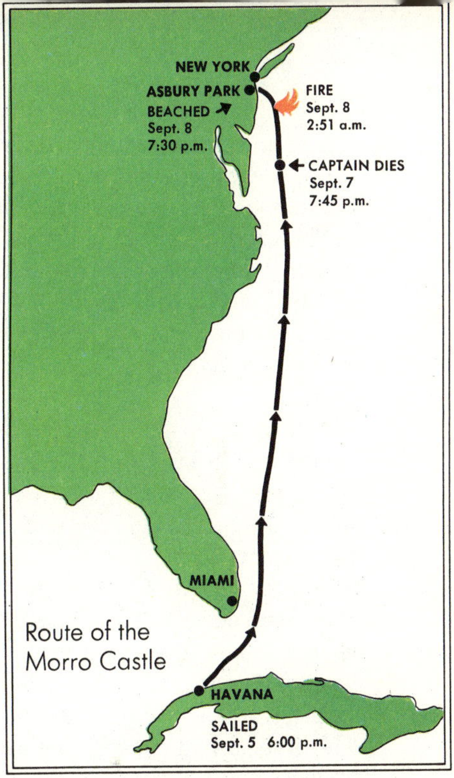

He shot to the surface, coughing and spitting, close to the ship. The black hull rose up like the side of a cliff. Coming down the cliff was the fire, showering the water with sparks. Giro could see people on the decks. They seemed to be dancing along the rail, little figures jumping up and down, waving their hands.

As the waves tossed him around the doctor felt as if he were being pulled down. He began to swallow seawater, then spat it out and closed his mouth. He kicked and flailed, repeating to himself, "You can't drown. There's Sylvia and the baby." Then he saw a corpse floating a few feet away, face down.

He reached out and got his arms around its neck. As the body turned over, Dr. Giro could see it was a man about fifty, dressed in pajamas. His face had been terribly burned. The doctor placed both arms around the body's waist and started to kick out with his feet, slowly and steadily. It was a long way to shore.

Father Egan and Sydney Ryan emerged from the furnace heat of C deck, unsuccessful in their search for the missing husband. Their eyes streamed from smoke.

The man's wife rushed toward them. She was on the verge of saying something when, with a scream of pain, she twisted forward. A great splinter of glass had pierced her back. She was dead before the priest could move to assist her.

The windows of the ballroom had shattered in the heat. Showers of heavy, smoke-blackened glass flew through the air.

"Duck under the thwarts!" a seaman shouted.

His warning was too late for some: a man and two women were cut down where they stood.

AMIDSHIPS on the port side Seaman Joseph Spilgins waited for twenty minutes to launch the first lifeboat. Then through the smoke straggled three young women passengers, a few stewards and a sailor. Spilgins helped the women into the boat. The others scrambled in after them.

Spilgins released the brake and dropped the lifeboat over the side. He knew that lifeboats are not lowered from a ship under way. But now it seemed essential to use any means of escape at hand. The wire falls whined in the sheaves as the boat shot down to the sea. The flames roared behind Spilgins. He looked down. The lifeboat had not dropped astern as it should have. It was being towed alongside the ship by one of the falls. Its hysterical occupants clung to the boat like leeches as it tossed and plunged. A man fell over the side and was hauled back on board by the sailor in the lifeboat as it scraped against the *Morro Castle*.

The sailor grabbed a hatchet stowed in the stern and slashed at the wire cable holding the lifeboat fast to the liner. The hatchet struck sparks from the taut wire. Another lifeboat, red-hot and flaming, came loose from its fastenings and pitched out over the ship's side. Then suddenly the hatchet cut the wire.

They were free. As they drifted clear of the liner the burning lifeboat crashed into the sea a few yards away from them.

ACTING Captain Warms's calmness of a few hours before was gone. It was understandable: he had never imagined his assumption of command would be under such circumstances; nor could he have expected his chief engineer to fail him at a crucial moment.

The helmsman spun the compass wheel to bring the ship onto a new course. "No response, sir!"

"Get her *around!*"

But the wheel spun slackly. The *Morro Castle*'s helmsman had lost control over her rudder.

There was one last option open to Warms. Going ahead on one engine and astern on the other could provide some control.

When Warms ran out to the wing of the bridge to check how fast the stern was swinging, the full enormity of the catastrophe struck him for the first time. A blast of heat scorched his face, singeing his eyebrows and hair. Tall columns of flame leaped as high as the mast amidships. Against this background Warms saw blackened figures run and plunge over the side.

For moments he peered aft, unwilling to believe his own eyes.

"Captain. Fire's totally out of control."

Warms turned at Ivan Freeman's words. "Ivan. They're jumping back there." Warms shook his head in wonderment. "Get forward and prepare to let go the anchor."

The two men ran back into the bridge, ignoring the chief engineer, still crouched in a corner. Eban Abbott was muttering, "It's too late. Too late. A hundred hoses wouldn't help. . . ."

At exactly 3:25 a.m. Alagna returned to the radio room shouting, "Okay, send it."

George Rogers began to transmit the SOS. "*Morro Castle.* Twenty miles south of Scotland Lightship. Ship afire. Need immediate assistance."

Alagna's and Rogers' versions of the events which followed are similar in detail, but Rogers' testimony is more melodramatic and puts him in a more heroic light.

Heroic he was, even though his motives may be questioned.

After dealing with a blaze in the radio room Rogers suddenly became conscious that his feet were so hot he couldn't stand it. He felt the floor with his hand and withdrew it quickly. "I had a wet towel over my face. I could hardly breathe any longer. I

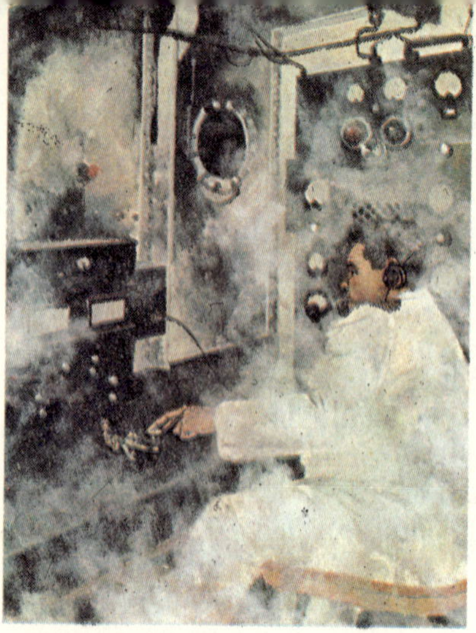

George White Rogers sends SOS

had gotten about halfway through the distress message when the corner of the radio-room table that housed the receiver batteries exploded." Rogers explained that the room became filled with sulfuric gas, probably because the hot deck was boiling the acid pouring from the batteries. "The receiver was completely out of commission. But I continued to send the SOS, realizing that the transmitter was still functioning.

"After sending the SOS," he said, "the . . . auxiliary generator . . . in the radio room suddenly stopped." Rogers staggered to the wall and hung on for several seconds. "Then I fixed up the connections and I heard the generator start again. . . . I was just staggering around. . . . My feet were burning bad. . . . I remember falling onto the towel and feeling the wet towel on my face. . . . The towel was already practically permeated with smoke. I could not hold out much longer.

"Then I heard an explosion in the auxiliary room and the radio generator stopped completely. . . . I felt Alagna shaking me and he was saying, 'Come on, Chief, get out of here. The whole damned place is on fire.'" But Rogers pushed him away and said, "Go back to the bridge and see if there is anything else!"

When Alagna returned to the bridge Acting Captain Warms ordered the radio room evacuated; the ship was being abandoned.

Then Alagna inquired, "Captain, what about Wilmott's body? Can I put it in one of the boats?"

"The living are more important than the dead," Warms said.

Alagna stumbled back to the radio room, where he found Rogers barely conscious and pulled him toward the door. They managed to get onto the bridge. The ship was covered by smoke and flames aft, and the pilothouse was completely afire. Rogers and Alagna paused, wondering which way to turn next.

On the port side of the bridge Warms struggled with a passenger, who was screaming: "Save my girl friend! She's trapped in a cabin."

Members of the crew swiftly disentangled the hysterical passenger. "Put him in a boat," Warms gasped.

The sailors bundled the man toward a lifeboat that had been prepared for lowering. Behind them came Chief Engineer Abbott. As the sailors dumped the passenger into the lifeboat, Abbott stepped into its stern. "Lower away," he ordered.

The kindest interpretation of Abbott's action is that he was still deeply shocked. But the fact remains that this lifeboat, with a capacity of 70, then held only eight people, six of whom were members of the crew. The chief engineer was not the only one who disregarded the safety of passengers. Of the first 80 people lowered away in lifeboats, 73 were crew members.

Acting Captain Warms shouted from the bridge, "Don't lower that boat! Keep it at the rail for passengers."

Eban Abbott continued to order the boat to be lowered, and as it slid down its davits he tore off his bars and gold braid.

Warms watched the lifeboat hit the water and drift into the night. "It was a moment of shame for all who believe in the tradition of the sea," he recalled later. Yet Warms himself was not without fault. The nearly thirty minutes he let pass between the discovery of the fire and the sending of an SOS has never been explained adequately. His explanation—that he didn't want to alarm the passengers by triggering a full-scale rescue operation—was accepted.

Some knowledgeable seamen have said that sending an SOS was the last thing a captain would do in those days. An SOS not strictly necessary could be expensive and attract undesirable publicity for the line. And a needless rescue operation would undoubtedly dim the promotion prospects of the acting captain.

Whatever the reasons, Warms ignored Alagna's repeated visits to the bridge to get permission to send out an SOS. If it had been somebody other than Alagna, he might have paid attention.

There is one inescapable fact: by the time the SOS *was* sent, the *Morro Castle* was beyond help.

ROGERS and Alagna picked their way to the forepeak, joining a small group around Warms, who held a flashlight.

"Hackney," said Warms to the second officer, "there is a ship off out there. See if you can raise her."

Hackney started to wink out the call sign of the *Morro Castle* to the steaming *Andrea S. Luckenbach.*

The freighter's blinker cut in: "Do you need assistance?"

Hackney flashed out: "Immediately. Five forty passengers."

"We will send a boat," came the freighter's reply.

Warms looked at the superstructure flaming aft from the bridge, virtually dividing the ship in two. In the forepeak were Ivan Freeman and Clarence Hackney, as well as Rogers and Alagna, Watchman Pender, Storekeeper O'Sullivan, a handful of seamen and Dr. and Mrs. Vosseler.

The wind which sent shivers through them also protected them from the blaze roaring through the rest of the ship.

"We'll all be safe soon. I got off the SOS," said Rogers.

C DECK, near the stern, was crowded with people. The cruise director was trying to calm them. Lena Schwarz had torn a bedspread into little pieces and wet them down so that the people could cover their noses to keep the smoke from choking them. Some of the men asked why she didn't jump. "I am *the* stewardess on the ship," Mrs. Schwarz said. "I must stay."

Steward Sydney Ryan and Stewardess Ragne Zabola had been holding hands by the rail. Mrs. Schwarz turned to give them strips of cloth, but they had jumped. Horrified, she rushed to the rail. Far below she watched the couple thrashing desperately to get clear of the stern. Then they were sucked under.

Headwaiter Carl Wright sensed that if he didn't jump soon, he and the little girl he still carried would die. But he knew the danger of jumping from the stern. He inched his way toward midships. It was a nightmare journey. A sailor's hand had been sliced off and he was appealing for help, trying to use his other hand as a tourniquet. A woman passenger lay face down on the deck, trampled to death or suffocated. Everywhere there was panic.

Clutching the child tightly to him the headwaiter jumped overboard. Around him the sea was filled with corpses and people clinging to debris. He started to swim steadily toward a lifeboat.

When the waves swept over the child's head he lifted her and told her to spit out the water, but after a while she swallowed a great deal of it. Wright listened to her heart but could hear nothing. "I carried the poor little tot on toward the boat because I didn't want to abandon her."

The lifeboat drifted off into the night, and Wright clung to the child for two more hours. Other passengers swam up, begging him to release the girl's body and to help the living. "It broke my heart," he said, "when I had to set her body adrift."

Charles and Selma Filster also managed to jump clear of the ship. They landed near Dr. Giro, who told them to "grab a body" and hold on to it. They swam for the shore. Soon the couple were tired; the water grew colder. A huge wave swamped them. When it passed, Charles Filster and the corpse he had been clinging to had disappeared.

Patrolman Price and his wife, Mary, stood on C deck. Both agreed the time had come to go over the side. They had watched others do it—and knew they must, even though Mary Price was crippled. Finally, with the assistance of a passenger, Patrolman Price got his wife's legs over the side, tied a life belt around her waist and around a hawser, and lowered her down toward a lifeboat. She hit the water, and the survivors in the lifeboat ignored her. Price kept shouting, "Pick her up! Pick her up!" But instead they shouted for him to jump.

One man on deck climbed to the top of the railing as though he was about to jump into a lifeboat. Price pulled his gun, saying, "If you do you are a dead man." He knew that the man would have gone through the bottom of the lifeboat. The man drew back.

Below, they started to pick up Mrs. Price from the water as William Price slid down a rope. When the policeman got into the boat he found his wife dead.

When Charles Menken and his wife jumped from C deck he had been stunned by a falling body and nearly drowned.

"When I regained my bearings my wife wasn't anywhere to be seen. I spent an hour looking for her, swimming from one corpse to another, from one swimmer to another. Then I found her, lying on her back, floating like she was in a pool. She just turned her head and looked at me and said 'Charley,' and I said 'Annie.' Then we just held hands, floating, as the waves kept smashing at us."

"Why don't you take an oar and row, instead of sitting there," a seaman shouted at Chief Engineer Abbott as the lifeboat bobbed helplessly in the sea.

"I can't. I cut my hand." Eban Abbott held up his left hand to the rest of the boat's passengers. There was no cut. He held up his right hand. Again, there was no mark.

"I can't row. I cut my hand," he repeated. "Nobody can row with a cut hand." He lapsed into moody silence.

A short distance away, Seaman Leroy Kelsey tried to steer his lifeboat toward the shore. He remembered the darkness and the "sullen" white-crested waves. "The girls were sick. One of them had gashed her forehead. The blood matted her hair. Then I heard the sound of water slopping under the floorboards. The plug was out—the boat was filling! One of the passengers sacrificed his shirt and shivered in the rain. The plug was jammed back in. Then, like a monstrous flaming torch, the burning ship, out of control, swung around. She bore straight down upon us. She was going to run us down! At the last moment she swung away, caught by the sea, a flaming nightmare."

On C deck half a dozen passengers were trapped by fire in a corridor space of only a few feet. Rescue was impossible; Father Egan had been called to give final absolution. He knelt at the edge of the fire. The heat burned the skin off his knees. Raising his hand, the priest spoke the words. Then he rose, clothes smoldering, and ran back onto the deck, tears streaming down his face.

"Father! You've got to jump. Everybody's going!"

It was true: crew and passengers were swarming over the side. Cruise Director Robert Smith grabbed a woman passenger and jumped overboard. He would support her for hours before both were rescued.

Rafael Mestre had been trying to get himself to jump overboard but his courage failed him. "Then I saw this woman," he recalled. "She was weeping because she had no preserver. I gave her one I found, strapped it on her and threw her as far out as possible from the side of the ship." Before he could reconsider, the young Cuban sprang over the side. He swam steadily for an hour before a rescue boat found him. In it was the body of the woman he had given the life jacket to. She had drowned.

Dr. Joe Bregstein still hesitated. The flames were a few feet away. Gladys and Ethel Knight of the Concordia Singing Society were beside him. The dentist looked at his son.

"He'll be all right with us," urged Ethel Knight. "We're good swimmers and we've got our preservers."

"And your little boy's got a life vest," added Gladys Knight. "Let him come with us. We'll swim with him to the boat."

Bregstein was close to tears. "I can't swim very well," he began.

"Then all the more reason we should take the boy," said Ethel. "We can make it; sure we can."

From down the deck came a dull roar as part of the superstructure caved in.

"Dr. Bregstein—"

"Okay, young ladies. Take good care of my boy." He bent and kissed Mervin on the cheek. "You'll be okay, son. They'll get you to the beach."

The child nodded. Supported by the girls, Mervin Bregstein plunged over the side.

Tears streaming down his face, Joe Bregstein reached the rail, the impulse to be with his son overcoming all else. He climbed over backward, hanging from deck level over the side. He felt a sudden tugging at his ankles from below, then strong hands swept him onto D deck. He rushed to the rail. A passenger restrained him. "The rescue boats are coming in. They'll get us off."

Dr. Bregstein looked across the water. Small boats were moving toward the *Morro Castle.* "They're bound to pick up Mervin and the girls," he shouted.

But the rescue flotilla missed the trio drifting toward shore. After hours of swimming the girls lapsed into a stupor. They were unaware when the sea snatched Mervin Bregstein away from them. His body was never found.

In spite of the sea's pounding, Dr. Giro had stubbornly clung to the corpse. Once a lifeboat came close. "It seemed to be manned by some of the ship's crew. There were people all around in the water, including some children. But the boat didn't stop to pick up anybody, and there seemed to be only a few people in the boat.

"Soon afterward another boat came by. That, too, seemed to be full of seamen and stewards. It was going quite fast toward the beach, and seemed to ignore anybody in the water."

On the forepeak of the liner Acting Captain Warms muttered, "They needn't have jumped. There's plenty of life gear for everybody." But panic and inefficiency had rendered much of the gear useless.

Seaman Leroy Kelsey peered intently through the pouring rain over the prow of his lifeboat. "Sea Girt!" he bellowed. "It's the light at Sea Girt! And look!"

A red star shot up into the sky. Somebody on shore was firing a rocket to guide them.

Kelsey looked around the boat. The sea was slopping over the side. He said, "Come on, let's break out the sail; we don't want to be out here forever." They rigged it and squared away toward the shore.

Then Kelsey started to sing, and a handful of people picked up the chant:

"Roll, Jordan, roll,
I want to go to heaven when I die,
To hear Jordan roll."

The *Morro Castle* was a faint glow far on the port side, and the lights from Sea Girt blinked more clearly through the murk. Then they heard the dull roar of the surf. The boat pitched skyward and dropped sickeningly in a smother of foam.

"Everybody get ready to jump!" Kelsey ordered.

Into the surf came a man from shore with a line in his hands. "Jump!" he yelled. "But watch the surf and undertow." The men tumbled into the sea, then helped the three girl passengers over the side. The lifeboat survivors were dragged ashore.

BETWEEN 3:00 a.m., when the fire alarm was sounded aboard the *Morro Castle,* and 3:25 a.m., when the SOS was sent, 14 separate Coast Guard stations received "positive calls" that a large ship was blazing a few miles out to sea. The Coast Guard lookouts saw nothing, so they decided to wait.

When the SOS signal was picked up by the navy and by civilian stations in New York, New Jersey and Long Island, a general alert went out along 300 miles of coast.

By 3:40 a.m. Coast Guard headquarters in Washington, D.C., was apprised of the disaster. At 7:00 a.m., when he awoke, President Franklin D. Roosevelt received the news.

On paper the Coast Guard commanded a small armada of ships in the disaster area. Twenty-five miles away from the burning *Morro Castle* the large patrol boat *Cahoone,* with only two inexperienced radio operators on board, did not pick up the repeated order to speed to the rescue until 4:00 a.m. The cutter *Tampa,* berthed at Staten Island, also missed the original order, and sailing was delayed until 5:39 a.m. The *Sebago,* her boilers stripped for overhaul, her radio shack deserted, did not sail for fifteen hours. The 75-foot patrol boats within the area lacked radio.

The Coast Guard air station at Cape May, 88 miles southwest of the *Morro Castle,* had seven aircraft, but only one considered "suitable for rescue or observation work offshore," and only two pilots. Hours passed before they became airborne.

Commercial ships reacted rather more practically to the crisis when the SOS was picked up. The freighter *Luckenbach* was picking up survivors by 4:00 a.m. The liner *Monarch of Bermuda* turned around and raced 20 miles to the *Morro Castle*. The *City of Savannah* and the *President Cleveland* also sped to assist.

A Coast Guard surfboat from Sea Girt had put to sea simply to investigate "the ball of flame" its captain had seen. Aboard was a crew of five, including the helmsman, Warren Moulton.

"We managed to get across the bar and for the next seven or eight miles we had an awful fight until we were within half a mile of the burning ship," Moulton recalled. "Then we ran into something I never want to see or hear again. The ocean was alive with screaming men and women, and so many grabbed the surfboat that it nearly capsized. I do not know how many times we stopped. The crew did all they could to keep others off and prevent our running over someone in the water.

"The water was so deep that my hands on the gas throttle were covered. All around were men and women, all excited, a few with their hands stretched out toward us, calling for help, and we, already overloaded, unable to help at all.

"As we reached the *Luckenbach* I looked at our cargo: women back in the stern piled three deep, men and women over the engine box, cordwood fashion, all alive. Just how many there were I didn't know, but we had our hands full to get them aboard the ship and keep our boat from being smashed alongside."

ON the forepeak of the *Morro Castle*, George White Rogers began flashing out a distress signal on the signal lamp. Watching him, Clarence Hackney later recalled an expression of "cold amusement" on the chief radio officer's face.

AT 4:00 a.m. radio stations on the East Coast broadcast news of the disaster. A New Jersey station announced that everybody on board had been rescued. So fishermen all along the coast decided to wait for daybreak before investigating the fire out at sea.

The news flash puzzled James Bogan, one of the youngest sea captains on the coast and skipper of the 30-ton *Paramount*. From the wharf at Manasquan Inlet he watched the fireball on the horizon and wondered how anyone could know for certain that everybody had been rescued. At 4:30 a.m. he telephoned the Coast Guard station and was urged to "go on out there as fast as you can."

Swiftly he mustered a crew made up entirely of fishing-boat captains, and at 4:40 a.m. the *Paramount* surged out to sea.

A fisherman alerted other boats. Soon a small armada of smacks chugged through the swell, following the *Paramount*. But that false radio announcement had cost nearly forty valuable minutes. Time enough for the sea and the *Morro Castle* to claim many more victims.

STEWARD Daniel Campbell jumped from B deck and found the water strewed with broken furniture, the sea coated with hot ash. Swimmers clung to anything buoyant. Several passengers recalled seeing two men tussling for possession of a deck chair. It ended with one of them kicking free and vanishing into the night.

Radioman Charles Maki, a powerful swimmer, was in the water an hour before he reached a lifeboat. At its helm was Seaman Joe Spilgins. With perhaps a dozen half-dressed passengers, helped by a couple of stewards and Assistant Engineer Antonio Bujia, Spilgins had maneuvered the boat down to the water level. His was the last lifeboat to leave the *Morro Castle*.

As it drifted clear of the burning hull another dozen swimmers scrambled aboard. Among them were Rafael Mestre, Charles and Annie Menken and Father Egan.

When radioman Maki arrived he picked up an oar and urged the other men to help row toward shore. Soon the lifeboat was slopping purposefully through the darkness.

After a while, at the suggestion of Father Egan, the others sang to encourage the oarsmen. Uneven voices blended into a chorus whose repertoire ranged from an Episcopalian hymn to "Tea for Two." They were still singing when the boat beached, hours later.

DR. EMILIO GIRO HAD managed to keep his wits and stamina, believing it would not be long before rescue came. The issue was whether he could stay alive until then. He knew how easily the icy water broke a man's resistance. He had seen it happen several times in the past few hours.

ALONE again on the dark swell, Headwaiter Carl Wright experienced a strange tranquillity. The *Morro Castle*, the inferno, the bodies—all were forgotten for the moment. He was still in that state of euphoria when the *Paramount* fished him aboard.

"Long before we reached the *Morro Castle* we were picking up survivors," said *Paramount* skipper Jimmy Bogan. "They were all over. If they had on life preservers we got them with grappling hooks." Bogan's foresight in picking an experienced crew paid off. "It was a ticklish business running the boat close enough to a man or a woman, or a group of three or four, in that rough water, without bumping one of them, and yet getting close enough for a crewman to throw a line with certainty, or even—in the case of the weaker swimmers—to reach out and seize them."

NOBODY really knew what happened to many of the people on the *Morro Castle*. Dr. Van Zile was the subject of a number of legends, all heroic, but none verified. One account placed him in the ship's surgery waiting for casualties that never came. Another

DR. CHARLES COCHRANE, Passenger

had him standing on the bridge, passing around a flask of rum before perishing in the flames. In a third version he went over the side, took off his life jacket in the water and strapped it on a child—an extraordinary feat for even the fittest man.

Incredible stories were told of others. The ship's manicurist, Ella Jacoby, died in the flames, witnesses swore, after freeing the liner's parrot from its cage in the veranda tearoom. A ship's musician would be immortalized for playing ragtime jazz through the corridor on B deck—long after the area was a solid mass of flame.

At daybreak Mrs. Hiram Hulse, wife of the missionary bishop of Cuba, struggled feebly in her life jacket and puzzled over a deep rumbling that seemed to come from beneath the waves. As she and her husband had jumped from the ship the impact of the water had knocked Mrs. Hulse unconscious; when she awoke there was no sign of the bishop. "He's drowned," she repeated. "He's drowned. It's the Lord's way. . . ."

Nearby, Cruise Director Smith identified the rumbling sound as the engines of a large ship. He shouted encouragement to Mrs. Hulse. She muttered, "My husband's dead. It's the Lord's way. . . ."

A few hundred yards from her the Right Reverend Hiram Hulse looked around him and mumbled, "Plucked from the valley of death into the arms of safety." He was the first passenger to be picked up by the *Monarch of Bermuda*.

LENA SCHWARZ,
Stewardess

ROBERT SMITH,
Cruise director

CHARLES WRIGHT,
Headwaiter

DR. JOSEPH BREGSTEIN,
Passenger

JOSEPH SPILGINS,
Seaman

Her captain, Albert R. Francis, had gently nudged the Furness Line cruise ship to within 200 feet of the *Morro Castle*. In the gray light of dawn the extent of the disaster silenced the passengers and crew lining the rails of the *Monarch of Bermuda.*

He recalled that the *Morro Castle* "was anchored, bow into the wind, keeping the flames from the forepeak, where a small group of people stood. The rest of the ship was in flames. You could still hear the screams and cries of the passengers. It was horrible."

When the duty operator had awakened Captain Francis with the distress message, he had bolted to the bridge in pajamas and worked out the fastest course to the *Morro Castle.*

While he plotted he fired off a volley of orders: the engine room was to cram on every ounce of steam; the first officer was to prepare lifeboats for lowering. The ship's doctor and nurse were ordered to set up a casualty clearing station in the first-class lounge; the purser and his stewards to man all gangways and channel survivors to the lounge for medical checks; the galley staffs to prepare urns of coffee, tea and soup; all passengers to provide spare clothes for the victims.

The *Monarch of Bermuda*'s crew responded swiftly, and the engine room put on enough speed to send the liner slicing through the water at 20 knots. At 7:00 a.m. they saw the glow. Twenty minutes later the Right Reverend Hiram Hulse was hauled aboard and wrapped in a blanket. He received a medical check, was put to bed and given coffee laced with rum.

On the *Morro Castle* Acting Captain Warms and the others with him watched the five lifeboats bobbing toward them from the *Monarch of Bermuda.* Second Officer Hackney and George Alagna both recalled the excellent seamanship of the lifeboat crews, who had a "calmness and control you only get in a good British ship."

Warms looked at Dr. and Mrs. Vosseler, the only passengers to have reached the forepeak. "Time for you to go," he said.

The couple nodded and shook the hands of those remaining on board. Then they made the difficult descent down a Jacob's ladder to a lifeboat.

"Anybody else?" called a voice from below.

"No. We are staying," said Warms steadily.

"We are all staying," echoed George White Rogers.

In the time the chief radio operator had been on the forepeak he had laid the foundation of a legend that would survive his lifetime. He had made two theatrical attempts to find a way through the wall of flame stretching back to the stern. The heat had beaten him back. Next he had attempted to rescue a woman passenger trapped in a porthole just forward of the bridge. First he had two seamen hold him over the side, where he dangled for a while like a monstrous jellyfish. He was hauled back aboard. Then he took off his shoes and prepared to swing on a rope, Tarzan fashion, down the side of the ship to rescue the woman. When it came to the final leap Rogers decided the rope was not strong enough to support his bulk.

While he thought out a new way to reach the screaming woman, she freed herself, fell into the sea and drowned.

Rogers busied himself with the signal lamp.

"He was so cool," First Officer Freeman remembered.

"He had a limitless supply of advice," Hackney recalled.

It seemed to Watchman Pender and Storekeeper O'Sullivan that the chief radio officer was "working at top speed and keeping up our spirits."

The *Monarch of Bermuda*'s lifeboats fanned out around the stern of the *Morro Castle.* Through a megaphone an officer urged those remaining on board to jump, adding, "We'll get to you. Have no fear."

Dentist Joe Bregstein, standing on D deck, felt reassured at the sound of that voice. "It was so English, so calm, so authoritative." Dropping over the side, he floundered in the water for moments until strong hands pulled him into a lifeboat.

Stewardess Lena Schwartz leaped over the side and surfaced beside another lifeboat. As soon as she was aboard she began to concern herself with the rescued passengers. When the officer in charge gently suggested she should rest, Mrs. Schwartz replied, almost fiercely, "I still have a job to do."

CHIEF ENGINEER ABBOTT spoke to no one; he seemed oblivious to the cold, the rain and the pounding of the seas. Around him the other occupants of the lifeboat shivered. There were now 29 people aboard. Only three of them were passengers.

The crew found the lifeboat difficult to handle. Waiter Milton Stevenson recalled, "Some of us were pretty yellow around the gills." Like the others, he eyed the chief engineer curiously. Abbott looked away.

Then suddenly the sound of breaking surf awoke new fears in Abbott. "Row away from here!" he cried. "It's too dark to go ashore! The shore's too rocky!"

Dr. Charles Cochrane, who was in the lifeboat, himself deeply shocked at the loss of his sister, felt sorry for the ship's officer. "I had heard him mutter that he would be arrested if he came ashore with so few passengers."

Abbott was still urging the oarsmen to put out to sea when the lifeboat was caught by the crest of a wave and sent scooting onto the beach. A group of fishermen pulled it up on the sand. Abbott was the first man ashore. He ignored the fishermen. Turning to the lifeboat's complement he said, "Remember. None of you should talk to newspapermen. They would never understand." Then he walked up the beach, tears streaming down his face.

ON the sun deck of the *Monarch of Bermuda* others wept that morning. By 8:00 a.m. the liner had picked up over 50 passengers—the final count was 71 rescued by the *Monarch.*

As boatload after boatload came alongside, the survivors already on board peered down, seeking familiar faces. For some the reunions were little short of miraculous.

Mrs. Hiram Hulse appeared to Stewardess Lena Schwartz to be "on the point of death when they got her on board," but she recovered quickly when she found her husband. She and the bishop wept openly. Cruise Director Smith and the woman passenger he had supported for hours in the water also burst into tears when they stepped onto the *Monarch of Bermuda.*

Otherwise there was virtual silence on board the rescue ship.

"The rescue operation performed by the Furness Line ship and its crew," a later commendation stated, "was in the highest traditions of the sea."

So, too, was the work of the crew of the *Andrea S. Luckenbach,* which had 26 survivors aboard, and of the liner *City of Savannah,* whose lifeboats rescued 65 people from the water.

The same could not be said for the Dollar Line's *President Cleveland.* An hour after hearing the SOS the ship was abeam of the *Morro Castle.* Forty more minutes passed before she lowered two lifeboats. Both made a brief circuit of the *Morro Castle*; the officers in charge concluded there was nobody on board, and they returned without a single survivor.

By breakfast-time thousands of people moved along the Jersey shore, keeping pace with the pall of smoke that drifted about five miles off the beach. There was an almost carnival atmosphere among the onlookers. Restaurants, cafés and coffee shops had an end-of-season boom.

After a slow start the rescue operation had become a massive and coordinated effort among Coast Guard, civilian and military spotter planes, police, fishermen, National Guard, local hospitals and mortuaries.

The Saturday editions of the newspapers were already printed when news of the disaster broke, giving radio a clear lead. All three radio networks had mobile units broadcasting on-the-scene accounts across America. At Sea Girt a CBS reporter described the scene: "Since daybreak, Coast Guard boats have pitched and tossed through the whitecaps, making tortuous progress toward that dreadful pall on the horizon. Sometimes you can see the flames, but generally they are shut out altogether by the squalls of rain that must be making it hell for everybody out there."

WCAP, a local station at Asbury Park, announced: "A call has gone out for all Coast Guard men to be rushed to the area by automobile and truck to man fishing and pleasure craft. First reports are coming in of survivors coming ashore at various points."

Scores of newspapermen were beginning to piece together

reports of the calamity. But it was radio's day. The airwaves were filled with accounts. CBS: "Nobody knows yet how many have lived—and how many have died. It will be some hours, perhaps even days, before the final toll becomes known."

NBC: "At nine o'clock this morning it was announced that a morgue will be established at Camp Moore, the New Jersey National Guard training quarters. Already the first bodies are being taken there."

THE open-cockpit military two-seater banked and skimmed over the sea. From the rear seat the fifty-five-year-old governor of New Jersey, A. Harry Moore, waved a red flag to guide rescue ships toward people in the water. It was a flight that Moore would never forget. "The waves were extremely high and the boats had difficulty in sighting those in the water. When I spotted a swimmer, the pilot would drop a smoke bomb nearby. I shall always recall one man. He was struggling feebly, partly submerged, when he heard our plane and looked up. I waved to him."

Dr. Emilio Giro did not even return the wave. He knew he could not afford such a simple gesture. He had spent many hours in the water, clinging to a corpse. But the will to stay alive had been steadily drained by the cold, the salt water and his constant seasickness. He sensed rather than heard the aircraft; moments later an acrid cloud drifted over him as a smoke bomb plopped into the sea.

Captain Bogan of the *Paramount* had been chasing from one bomb burst to another; frequently the result was a corpse to be hooked and dragged aboard. This time he was luckier. Dr. Giro was alive, though barely, when Bogan pulled him out of the water.

ON the promenade at Asbury Park a handful of the resort's officials peered out to sea. Far down the coast the pall of smoke was slowly moving closer; keeping pace with it on the shore were an estimated 50,000 people.

"Just supposing," one of the officials said, "they beached her here. She's worth a fortune to the town."

THE *Morro Castle* DRIFTED northward, dragging her anchor, her rudder inoperative. From time to time the hulk canted to port or starboard with sickening force.

The men on the forepeak had divided into two groups: Acting Captain Warms and the deck officers on one side, crewmen gathered around Storekeeper O'Sullivan on the other. Between the groups stood Rogers and Alagna.

Staring intently at the pall of smoke, Rogers asked, "How come it got a hold so quick?"

"It was set! I'm positive. It spread too fast," Hackney declared. His accusation got a chorus of agreement.

Arthur Pender thought it looked like a chemical fire because flames in the writing room were blue-white.

When Rogers was asked his opinion he shrugged. "Guess I was too busy getting out the SOS to notice the color of the flames."

Warms killed further speculation. "If it was set, I guess I know why." He glanced at Alagna. Then he peered out to port. The *City of Savannah* was a few cable lengths away.

"Rogers," said the acting captain, "use your lamp to ask her to contact the line as to what I should do."

Rogers blinked out the message. It was a strange request. Any orders Warms could give now were virtually meaningless: the *Morro Castle* answered only to the elements.

The command Warms had longed for had been the shortest in maritime history, barely seven hours. He reviewed every order, every course change, every step he had taken, "and I knew I had done everything correctly." Warms's seamanship had been technically excellent. His failure had been in not anticipating that the fire could spread so quickly; he should have ordered all fire doors closed and asked for outside help sooner.

Exhausted and acutely depressed, Warms turned to the Ward Line for his next orders.

They never came. The officers and crew on the *City of Savannah* were far too busy settling survivors to pay attention to Rogers' blinking lamp.

On the forepeak the group watched yet another boat approach.

A New York Harbor tug that had buffeted down the New Jersey coast jockeyed alongside the *Morro Castle*'s bow, and a man leaned out of the pilothouse with a megaphone. "My name's Swenson," he called up to the forepeak. "You wanna be taken off?"

"No!" Warms shouted down.

"Okay. You wanna tow? It won't cost you a thing."

"What kind of line you got?"

"Eight inch," said Swenson.

Hackney and Freeman shook their heads in disbelief. The idea that the tiny tug could tow the 12,000-ton liner was sheer nonsense. Before Warms could respond to the offer, the 1800-ton Coast Guard cutter *Tampa,* under the command of Lieutenant Commander Earl G. Rose, came up on the *Morro Castle*'s port side.

"Do you want a tow?" the magnified voice boomed out from the *Tampa.*

"Yes," bellowed Warms.

"All right. We will put a twelve-inch hawser on board you and tow you to New York."

The arrival of the cutter galvanized Rogers. As he watched the *Tampa* lower a surfboat he kept up an elated chant, "They're coming, they're coming, they're coming. . . ."

The surfboat, crewed by eight coastguardsmen, brought the tow hawser across to the *Morro Castle*'s bow. A heaving line was thrown down to haul up the hawser. Then the handful of men on the forepeak began a job usually performed by powerful winches.

They went at it like a tug-of-war team, with Rogers as the anchor man. Foot by foot, yard by yard, almost 50 fathoms of hawser was pulled up and made fast. It took two hours.

By then the weather had worsened. The rescue flotilla withdrew toward shore. Only the *Tampa* and the New York Harbor tug remained alongside the *Morro Castle.*

The *Morro Castle*'s dragging anchor was cut loose, and the *Tampa* moved ahead of the hulk, taking the strain on the hawser. Astern, the tugboat acted as a temporary rudder—keeping a line taut to the hull to provide some steerage.

Alongside the bow of the *Morro Castle,* one of the *Tampa*'s lifeboats lifted off the last of the liner's crew. One after the other the seamen scrambled over the side. When it was Rogers' turn he suddenly saw something that terrified him. The lifeboat had picked up three bodies. They lay, bloodied from being smashed against the side of the *Morro Castle*, in the bottom of the lifeboat.

"Jump! Damn you! Jump!" the lifeboat's officer commanded. Rogers lost his hold on the Jacob's ladder and sprawled into the boat, across the bodies. He shrieked and fainted.

Warms was the last man into the lifeboat.

AT 11:55 a.m. Commander Rose of the *Tampa* was satisfied. The *Morro Castle*'s captain and crew were safely below, wrapped in blankets, sipping coffee. The ship's pharmacist discovered that Rogers was suffering from acute nervous exhaustion and inhalation of smoke, and had him put to bed. Commander Rose ordered full speed and the Coast Guard cutter headed for New York.

IN Manhattan thousands of people lined the waterfront, looking expectantly to the mouth of the harbor. Ward Line offices on Wall Street were besieged by newsmen, relatives and friends.

At midday the first list of known dead was posted by the line—eight men and five women. Thirty minutes later the number of dead rose to 40 as reports came in. By nightfall the list would grow to 100—34 short of the final toll. In proportion to their numbers, twice as many passengers as crew died.

Afternoon headlines passed on accusations against the crew:

FIRE ALARM LATE SURVIVOR ASSERTS

FIREMAN HOLDS CREW IGNORANT OF FIRE FIGHTING

GIRL DECLARES OFFICER FIGHTING FLAMES
ASKED HER NOT TO AROUSE PASSENGERS

Late in the afternoon NBC broke the story that Martin Conboy, United States attorney for the southern district of New York, had announced that he would investigate to discover whether there was any criminal angle in the disaster.

The *Monarch of Bermuda* docked at West Fifty-fifth Street in Manhattan. Dentist Joe Bregstein, dodging reporters, was met by his fiancée, Muriel Rubine, with the news that there was no word of young Mervin. Cruise Director Robert Smith and Chief Stewardess Lena Schwartz managed to slip ashore quietly.

Some newspapers were not unduly concerned with accuracy. From Sea Girt a reporter filed a story of a body washed ashore with a bullet hole in its forehead. There is no official record of that body, but even today the story persists that a sailor was shot on board for looting when the fire broke out.

The feature writers began apportioning blame. The New York *World-Telegram* referred to the "failure" of the U.S. Coast Guard. A writer for the New York *Sun* criticized government economies that had "struck the Coast Guard a hard blow." In Washington the Secretary of Commerce stated that he believed it should be mandatory for all large liners to carry experienced fire fighters to train and direct the crew in emergencies.

During the afternoon William Warms, dressed in borrowed oilskins, spent most of the time alone at the *Tampa*'s stern, watching the burning *Morro Castle* being towed a few cable lengths behind. George White Rogers slept all afternoon. The other survivors sat silent, shrugging off questions from the curious coastguardsmen.

At 6:00 p.m. the *Tampa* and *Morro Castle* were abeam of Asbury Park. A few hundred yards away to the port side lay the resort's brightly lit Convention Hall and hotels. Car lights winked along Sunset Avenue.

At that moment the tugboat's hold on the liner's stern was suddenly severed, and the *Morro Castle* came around broadside to the gale, increasing the tension on the towing rope.

At 6:01 Commander Rose radioed Coast Guard headquarters in New York: "Derelict unmanageable in increasing gale."

For seven minutes the *Tampa* struggled to turn the *Morro Castle.* Suddenly there was a loud crack—and the *Tampa*'s engines died. The hawser had snapped and coiled around the cutter's propeller shaft. Commander Rose ordered anchor to be dropped and summoned urgent tow by radio. In the cutter's stern Acting Captain Warms watched the *Morro Castle* shudder at its newfound freedom. Then, trailing smoke and flame, it seemed to gather speed and head directly for Convention Hall at Asbury Park.

THE staff of radio station WCAP, which broadcast from Convention Hall, had an excellent view of the sea. At 7:30 p.m. announcer Tom Burley was about to give a station identification when he glanced out into the night. "She's here!" he shouted. "The *Morro Castle*'s coming right toward the studio!"

She actually ran aground less than 300 feet from where Burley sat. By then he had recovered enough to give listeners a graphic description of the burning ship.

City Manager Carl Bischoff, in the throng watching on the seafront at Asbury Park, stared in amazement. "Carl," someone said to him, "she's in our front yard. This is the biggest thing's ever happened to us. They're going to come from all over to see it. Raise a city flag on her to stake our claim!"

ON THE BEACH

BY midday Sunday, September 9, 1934, Asbury Park was experiencing an unprecedented boom. The mild sunny weather helped to draw an estimated 25,000 people to the resort. Roads were posted with signs reading TWO MILES TO THE MORRO CASTLE WRECK, COME AND SEE THE MORRO CASTLE and ASBURY PARK—THE HOME OF THE MORRO CASTLE. Concessionaires lined all approaches to Convention Hall with frozen-custard and hot-dog stands, children's rides and shooting galleries. Over Convention Hall a banner flapped:

22 CENTS TO SEE THE S.S. MORRO CASTLE
BENEFIT OF THE FAMILIES OF THE DEAD

By lunchtime 10,000 people had paid for a closer view of the liner. There was little to see besides the blackened hull and the burned-out superstructure: a mass of twisted steel, buckled plates and charred, rusted framework.

Newsmen paid $5 to board the ship by means of the breeches buoy rigged between the ship's stern and the ground floor of Convention Hall. A gas mask cost another $5; a flashlight, $1. The money went into a fund to buy liquor for the firemen on duty.

Although newsmen were supposed to remain in the stern area of B deck, David Garmey and a few other reporters slipped past Ward Line officials and policemen to go below. He described a "long dark passageway, clogged with ashes, broken bits of steel, the walls bent and the floor, ripples of warped steel," and told of "thousands of rivets" protruding from the decks, forced out by the heat. "Girders supporting the superstructure and the floor below sagged terribly." He descended a metal stairway and arrived on C

deck. "Once there were staterooms here. Piles of black ashes are all there is left; even the iron walls have melted." On the boat deck he found that "five lifeboats still hang from their davits, unused, unwanted now."

Sickened, the reporter left the ship.

After a two-day search a handful of bones were sifted from the ashes and declared to be those of the captain, Robert Wilmott.

WHEN the *Tampa* finally reached New York, George White Rogers, the last survivor to leave, was carried off the cutter on a stretcher to a waiting ambulance.

Newsmen demanded, "Who's he?"

"That's the hero of the day," replied Clarence Hackney.

In a convoy of cars the reporters chased after the ambulance. At the Marine Hospital, Rogers, installed in a private room with a nurse at his side, posed in bed for photographers and stated that he only "did what anyone else would have done."

Warms and other officers of the *Morro Castle* spent Sunday closeted with lawyers of the Ward Line. Company attorneys also

visited Rogers in the hospital and Abbott at his home. Later Abbott's widow, Ada, would report that the company ordered her husband to "button up," and presumably similar instructions were given to the others.

By early afternoon the lawyers had put together a series of statements to show that the fire had not been caused by any inefficiency on the part of the line or the crew, and that once the fire had been discovered every officer and crew member behaved in an exemplary manner.

Warms's statement contained the remarkable information that he "ordered" his chief engineer into a lifeboat when Abbott "collapsed from the effects of the smoke."

Ward Line officials visited the Seamen's Institute in downtown New York, where most of the crew were recuperating. There they offered free clothing and money to all crew members who signed statements confirming their good impression of the officers.

But running counter to almost everything in those sworn affidavits was an interview George Alagna gave to journalist Damon Runyon of the New York *American.* Alagna declared that the captain failed to command while panic ruled the liner. He also hinted that a firebug had been on the vessel. Understandably, the story produced consternation.

Attorneys for the Ward Line saw that Alagna's claims, apart from the harm they could do to the line's image, could invite countless damage suits. One course of action emerged clearly: the line would maintain that Alagna's allegations were totally untrue and they would be contested at any hearing.

That afternoon the Ward Line lawyers interviewed Warms, Rogers and Hackney again. By early evening they had a new picture of Alagna's behavior aboard the *Morro Castle.*

Rogers filled in the finer details. "Ever since he tried to call that strike, Alagna was looked upon as an agitator and a vengeful person." The words "radical," "troublemaker" and "difficult" appeared repeatedly in the chief radio officer's statement. On Sunday evening Rogers and Warms made statements to the district attorney. The move to discredit Alagna had begun.

THE OFFICIAL INVESTIGATION into the disaster by a board appointed by the U.S. Department of Commerce opened at the Custom House in New York on Monday, September 10, 1934.

Acting Captain Warms was the first witness. He told the board he believed "some unidentified person willfully started the fire that destroyed the ship and cost so many lives." Supporting evidence was provided by Clarence Hackney and Ivan Freeman. Then George White Rogers took the stand and presented a picture of George Alagna as a dangerous agitator.

Alagna was arrested next day as a material witness and lodged in the House of Detention in New York.

The hearings dragged on for weeks. Warms and Abbott, barred from going to sea until the investigations were concluded, received full salary from the Ward Line. The other deck officers received half salary. Some crew members whose testimony the Ward Line regarded as crucial also received payments.

By the end of September the New York *Herald Tribune* told its readers: "A clearer picture of what happened aboard the *Morro Castle* is beginning to emerge. Officers of the Ward Line felt for the first time the sting of official criticism and were subjected to a biting cross-examination."

A great deal came to light: the cargoes of arms; the lack of boat and fire drills; Warms's previous suspension; Abbott's removing his insignia.

When Spilgins mentioned the unseaworthiness of the lifeboats he was subjected to a barrage of questions. Doggedly, Spilgins stuck to his story that the tanks designed to keep the boats afloat were almost rusted through. However the board did not pursue this in the questioning of Warms and his fellow deck officers.

Rogers caused a sensation when he was reexamined and testified that the SOS "should have been ordered forty-five minutes earlier." What prompted this statement is not clear. However it was a perfect opportunity to attack Warms, who, Rogers believed, had been part of the "plot" to remove him from the ship. Rogers' testimony had one good effect, the release of George Alagna from custody. The chief radio officer now testified that his assistant had repeatedly gone to the bridge. "I want it to be known that the earlier testimony at this hearing was given with great reluctance on my part and had no bearing whatsoever upon George Alagna's conduct or his responsibility to me who was his direct superior on board." Rogers told the hearing that he had been proud to have Alagna as his first assistant and testified that while Alagna might not have been tactful in dealing with members and officers of the ship's crew, his character was irreproachable.

A reporter wrote, "It is good to know that America can still produce heroes like George White Rogers."

A WHOLE new life had opened up for the chief radio officer. The Radiomarine Corporation of America withdrew his dismissal notice, and the Veteran Wireless Operators Association gave him a medal for heroism. He politely declined a dozen offers of employment with shipping lines, and stated that his wife preferred to have him at home, in Bayonne, New Jersey. Yet most of his time was occupied with making public appearances.

At a lavish official reception given by the mayor of Bayonne, Rogers found himself surrounded by dignitaries from all walks of life. Among them was Bayonne Police Officer Vincent Doyle, a former ship's radio operator who had established an international reputation by designing and installing one of the first two-way radio systems for the Bayonne Police Department.

Doyle had a reputation for blunt speaking when aroused. He felt suspicious of Rogers—and he made it known. He later recalled that he had turned to Rogers and said, "I was invited here tonight to meet you and welcome you home as hero of the *Morro Castle*. I met you and I welcome you home, but you were quoted in the newspapers as saying that you were dragged out of the radio room aboard the *Morro Castle* when it was so hot in there that the solder melted out of the terminals of the panel of your transmitter. Was that statement of yours true?"

Doyle said later that Rogers did not answer, but just glared.

Doyle continued. "I am sure that, in your position as a radio operator, you have used a soldering iron many times. Do you know how hot your iron must be before solder will be melted by heat? Have you ever tried to hold an iron that hot in your bare hand?"

Still no answer.

"You have had a trying experience," he told Rogers. "My conscience, however, will not allow me to call you a hero. A hero should be modest and truthful. You are neither and I feel sorry for you. Good night."

He then apologized to the guests and left the reception.

A few days later, wearing a spanking-new white uniform, Rogers made his stage debut at the Rialto Theatre. He split his $1000-a-week salary with a theatrical agent. Posters announced: IN PERSON! RADIO HERO ROGERS TELLS INSIDE STORY OF MORRO CASTLE DISASTER.

After a week interest waned.

IN New York a federal grand jury spent months listening to testimony similar to that given before the U.S. Department of Commerce panel. On December 3, 1934, it indicted Acting Captain William Warms, Chief Engineer Eban Abbott and Henry E. Cabaud, Ward Line vice-president, for willful negligence. The line itself was also indicted.

Warms was accused specifically of failing to observe the law in ten matters:

To divide the sailors in equal watches.

To keep himself advised of the extent of the fire.

To maneuver, slow down or stop the vessel.

To have the passengers aroused.

To provide the passengers with life preservers.

To take steps for the protection of lives.

To organize the crew to fight the fire properly.

To send distress signals promptly.

To see that the passengers were put in lifeboats and that the lifeboats were lowered.

To control and direct the crew in the lifeboats after the lifeboats had been lowered.

Abbott was accused of:

Failure to assign members of his department to proper posts during the fire.

Failure to report to his own station in the engine room to give instructions to his men.

Failure to hold proper fire drills.

The chief engineer's decision to abandon ship was also attacked, as well as his escape in a lifeboat without attempting to rescue others.

Cabaud, the Ward Line vice-president, was charged with "willfully and knowingly causing and allowing the violations of the law" that Warms and Abbott were charged with.

At 4:30 the afternoon of December 4 Warms and Abbott were arrested by a deputy United States marshal. After being fingerprinted the two men were arraigned before Commissioner Garrett Cotter. By then both had learned they could face prison sentences of up to ten years, and fines totaling $10,000.

The prosecuting attorney, Francis W. H. Adams, told the court that both men were accused of "conduct which caused the loss of life of upward of fifty persons"—a curious figure in view of the final death toll of 134.

Ward Line lawyers posted bail bonds of $2500 for each man.

By Christmas 1934 over 300 claims totaling $1,250,000 had been filed against the Ward Line by survivors and relatives of the dead. Lawyers for the line asked the federal court to limit the total of any single claim to $20,000 and offered $250,000 as a full and final settlement. They based their case on the "limited liability" law that had been on the statute books since 1851, which provided that, in the event of disaster, only by proving the owners to have possessed knowledge of the unseaworthiness of the vessel or the inadequacy of the crew before sailing could passengers collect.

A game of legal bluff began. Lawyers for the survivors created the impression that they could positively prove unseaworthiness and inadequacy. The Ward Line made an offer of $500,000, which the survivors' lawyers rejected.

From London came another, more subtle, pressure. Lloyd's of

London, the principal underwriters of the *Morro Castle,* raised their eyebrows at reports of the Ward Line's attitude.

Seventy-one insurance companies, a third of them British, had insured the *Morro Castle* for $4,200,000. As the word spread that the Ward Line was in a protracted battle with survivors and relatives of the dead, more than one underwriter must have wondered whether there was something shady about the whole episode. Word reached the Ward Line that it could be assailed soon from all sides and that it might be years before the line could collect the $4,200,000 insurance.

It suddenly increased its offer to the claimants to $890,000. This was accepted. In the end the line collected $4,188,999 in insurance. It sold the *Morro Castle* to Union Shipbuilding of Baltimore for $33,605 as scrap iron.

On the day the hulk was towed away from Asbury Park, Rogers opened a radio-repair shop in Bayonne. Customers found him a bombastic shopkeeper, fond of telling them how lucky they were to have their sets mended by him. Business soon dropped off.

One day in February 1935 Rogers left the shop "to get a breath of air." Shortly afterward it caught fire. Bayonne police files reveal: "An inventory made by Rogers disclosed equipment had suffered damage to the extent of $1200. Arson was suspected. But no proof existed to warrant an arrest. He collected from the insurance company."

Early in 1936 Rogers reappeared in the headlines when he gave evidence at the trial of Warms, Abbott and Cabaud, which had been delayed until then by a series of legal moves. Warms was sentenced to two years' imprisonment; Abbott received four; Cabaud was fined $5000 and given one year's suspended sentence.

The Ward Line was assessed $10,000. The company filed an immediate appeal on behalf of Warms and Abbott.

Some time after the trial Rogers had a chance encounter with a Bayonne businessman who had been present at the reception at which Police Officer Vincent Doyle had publicly called Rogers a liar. The man told Rogers he thought Doyle's behavior had been uncalled for. He invited Rogers to dinner, and Rogers accepted.

The businessman offered to help Rogers get a new start in life—as a patrolman with the Bayonne Police Department. In June 1936 Rogers joined the Bayonne police force as assistant to Vincent Doyle in the radio department. How he came to be taken on is now impossible to ascertain. The likeliest explanation is that Rogers' businessman friend had sufficient influence to "bulldoze" him onto the force.

Rogers was not subjected to any physical examination, nor—and this is more incredible—was any account taken of his record. On more than one occasion he had come under grave suspicion as an arsonist. But all this seemed to have been forgotten.

Doyle was a warm, outgoing man, and he gradually established contact with his assistant. They found common ground in their seagoing experiences and an interest in things electrical. Their clash almost two years before might never have happened.

But as the barriers came down, Doyle became aware of Rogers' arrogance. "He just couldn't stop telling me how clever he was." And after some months Doyle detected Rogers' recurring preoccupation with exploding devices. Rogers explained how explosions could be triggered by timing devices to go off at an exact moment.

"George, is that how it was on the *Morro Castle?*" Doyle asked at the end of one lengthy explanation.

Rogers looked at Doyle and smiled.

In April 1937 the U.S. Circuit Court of Appeals, in a unanimous decision, set aside the conviction of Warms and Abbott. The court held that "Warms maintained the best tradition of the sea by remaining on his vessel," and that Abbott's behavior in leaving the ship was "caused by suffering from smoke, and therefore he was not responsible."

News of the verdicts brought a marked change in Rogers. He became almost obsessive in his desire to discuss the fire, and dwelt increasingly on how the blaze had been set. Doyle began to keep a record of his assistant's statements, noting finally, "George knows that I know he set fire to the *Morro Castle.*"

Doyle knew that what Rogers had told him was not strong enough to obtain a conviction. He told no one of his suspicions. But he continued to question Rogers on every aspect of the *Morro Castle* disaster, and began to form the picture of Rogers which was so remarkably in tune with later psychiatric reports.

Finally, on March 3, 1938, Doyle learned exactly how Rogers set the fire. "He told me how to construct an incendiary fountain pen; how it had been placed in the writing-room locker. . . ."

The next afternoon Doyle was still wondering how best to present his sensational evidence when he met Rogers outside the police radio department, looking pensive and withdrawn.

"There's a package for you," Rogers said.

Doyle nodded and went into the department. Rogers remained just outside the doorway. On the workbench was a package. Doyle unwrapped it and found a heater for a fish tank. There was nothing unusual in that; from time to time Doyle used the department's facilities to repair electrical equipment for his colleagues.

Attached to the heater was a typed label: "This is a fish-tank heater. Please install the switch in the line cord and see if the unit will work. It should get slightly warm."

Doyle was puzzled by the instructions. They carried no signature, but the label had been typed on the standard office machine of the radio department. He turned toward the door to ask Rogers for a comment, but Rogers had disappeared.

For a moment Doyle toyed with the heater, then plugged it in and flicked the switch.

The resulting explosion broke windows in the workshop and shook the main police headquarters building 200 feet away.

Doyle's left hand, left leg and right foot were smashed. His left eardrum was fractured. He was rushed to Bayonne Hospital, where he underwent emergency surgery.

The next day Rogers visited Doyle in the hospital and asked through his tears, "How can I get the guy who did this to you?"

Two weeks later Rogers was charged with the attempted murder of Doyle.

After eighteen weeks in the hospital Doyle began to assemble a formidable dossier. He declared that Rogers, while being questioned about the attempt on Doyle's life, admitted to Bayonne's chief of detectives, Tom Masterson, that the bomb on the *Morro Castle* had been a "simple" matter to arrange. The local district attorney's office decided that though the circumstantial evidence on the *Morro Castle* case was strong, it might not be enough to obtain a conviction and might tend to confuse the charge for which Rogers was then being tried. The prosecution decided to exclude the report and concentrate solely on the attempt on Doyle's life.

This curious decision caused considerable bitterness in Doyle and his colleagues. Equally unusual was the agreement between the prosecution and defense that the report of the psychiatrist appointed to examine Rogers should remain confidential. That document indicated that to some extent Rogers' repressed sexual wishes probably caused his criminal behavior.

The attitude toward the medical evidence is best summed up by a note attached to the bulky police files on the case: "Don't need a fancy doctor's report to tell us that R. is a nut." The note was unsigned. Since the defense was not entering a plea of insanity, it would not wish to complicate its case, either, by introducing as evidence the psychiatrist's report.

At the end of the trial the judge summoned Doyle to his chambers. "As the victim of the crime, he asked my opinion on a just punishment for Rogers," Doyle recalled. "I did not hesitate to suggest that he be given the maximum sentence allowed by law."

On December 15, 1938, the judge sentenced Rogers to serve from twelve to twenty years in the state prison at Trenton. "Your crime," he said, "is one of the most diabolical nature and it fell short of murder only by the intervention of Divine Providence."

Rogers lost an appeal before the New Jersey State Supreme Court, and another before the Court of Errors and Appeals.

The New Jersey State Court of Pardons granted Rogers parole to "join the armed services," and on November 24, 1942, he was released from prison after serving less than four years.

The U.S. Navy refused to accept him. But once again his friend who had helped get him on the Bayonne police force came to his aid. "He still believed in Rogers," Vincent Doyle stated. "Why, I don't know—nor will anybody else. But the day Rogers was released, this man took him to New York."

Next day the Federal Communications Commission gave him a ninety-day permit to operate as a radio officer at sea. The Radiomarine Corporation of America assigned him to a ship sailing from San Francisco to Australia.

The voyage ended with Rogers' arrest in Darwin, Australia. His exact crime was not made clear. There is a veiled reference to "enemy alien activity" in the files of Vincent Doyle. But the FBI, which would undoubtedly have been concerned in such a charge, emphatically denied any involvement.

Afterward Rogers worked in a war plant in Jersey City and was dismissed on suspicion of stealing. Later he was dismissed from a plant in Brooklyn when employees showed signs of poisoning after drinking from a water cooler near where Rogers worked.

With the last of his capital he again opened a radio-repair shop in Bayonne. In May 1952 he was finally discharged from parole. By then his business was in financial difficulties.

Soon afterward he formed a relationship with two elderly neighbors: William Hummel, an eighty-three-year-old retired printer, and his unmarried daughter, Edith. Rogers had sold them a secondhand television set. Hummel shared Rogers' interest in electrical gadgets, and Rogers became a regular caller at the Hummels'. He found William Hummel sympathetic to a new preoccupation Rogers had developed—that he had been framed by the Bayonne Police Department all those years before because they were jealous of having a genuine hero among them.

His delusions became more grandiose and paranoid: the police were hostile and vile, and the world full of dangerous pitfalls. In all probability the Hummels unwittingly encouraged Rogers in this fantasy. Certainly Rogers received not only emotional but also financial support from them. When he told them the police were "keeping customers away from the shop," Hummel offered to subsidize the loss. By June 1953 he had lent Rogers $7500.

Then the relationship between the two men underwent a

change. In his diary Hummel wrote, "It has been unwise on my part to continually advance Rogers money. He is very temperamental, and I am in constant fear he might renege, and I would lose everything."

In June 1953 William Hummel put his home up for sale. He planned to move with his daughter to Florida. In his diary he wrote, "Must collect loan from G." On July 1, 1953, acting on a tip-off, the police broke into Hummel's home. They found father and daughter savagely bludgeoned to death. After painstaking police investigation Rogers was arrested. The trial began on September 13, 1954. Days later the jury found Rogers guilty of murder in the first degree and recommended life imprisonment. Police Captain Vincent Doyle, still bearing the marks of Rogers' murder attempt, was in court to hear sentence passed.

On March 4, 1955—seventeen years to the day since he had tried to murder Vincent Doyle—Rogers appealed the sentence of life imprisonment. The appeal was swiftly denied.

At 6:00 a.m. on January 10, 1958, George White Rogers died in prison of a brain hemorrhage.

Gordon Thomas and Max Morgan Witts

Max Morgan Witts and Gordon Thomas launched their literary collaboration in 1965 with a documentary film for a British Broadcasting Corporation series about the world's most spectacular natural disasters. That inspired Morgan Witts and Thomas to write *The Day the World Ended* (Reader's Digest Condensed Books, Volume 4, 1969), about the eruption of Mount Pelée in Martinique. When the team published *The San Francisco Earthquake* (Condensed Books, Volume 4, 1971) they were established as disaster experts.

Mr. Thomas was born in the Welsh mining country. He left school abruptly, greatly influenced by the advice his cousin, poet Dylan Thomas, gave him: "Stop all this nonsense about schools and universities, boy. Go out and write." So Gordon Thomas wrote his first book at eighteen. Now in his late thirties, he has sixteen books, numerous screenplays and television scripts to his credit. Speaking of his literary partnership with Morgan Witts, he says, "We are the closest of friends professionally, but we have only visited each other's houses twice. We don't think work should infringe on our private lives."

Mr. Morgan Witts was born in Detroit in 1931. His father was an English financier, his mother an American theatrical producer. He was educated in Canada, and has now taken British nationality. After a start as a television actor in Toronto he went on to become a director and producer for the BBC. He lives with his wife and two children in London, within walking distance of the broadcasting studio.

ACKNOWLEDGMENTS

Page 2: *The Hudson Valley, Sunset,* oil painting on canvas by Thomas Chambers, is from the National Gallery of Art, Washington, D.C., gift of Edgar William and Bernice Chrysler Garbisch. Used by permission.

Page 468: portion of front page from *The New York Times,* copyright 1934 by The New York Times Company, is reprinted by permission.

Pages 482-483, 550 (boat): The Mariner's Museum. Pages 542-543, 550-551 (personalities), 562-563, 574: UPI.

Page 500: map by Paul Bacon.